CONTENTS

CONTENTS

HUMAN BEHAVIOUR
AND ADAPTATION

SYMPOSIA OF THE
SOCIETY FOR THE STUDY OF HUMAN BIOLOGY

Volume XVIII

HUMAN BEHAVIOUR AND ADAPTATION

Edited by
N. BLURTON JONES and V. REYNOLDS

TAYLOR & FRANCIS LTD

LONDON

1978

First published 1978 by Taylor & Francis Ltd, 10–14 Macklin Street,
London WC2B 5NF

© 1978 Taylor & Francis Ltd

Printed and bound in Great Britain by Taylor & Francis (Printers) Ltd,
Rankine Road, Basingstoke, Hampshire RG24 0PR.

ISBN 0 85066 137 4
ISSN 0081-153X

Distributed in the United States of America and its territories
by Halsted Press (a division of John Wiley & Sons Inc),
605 Third Avenue, New York, N.Y. 10016.

PREFACE

THIS volume contains the papers given at the Society's Symposium of 6–7 January 1977 at St. Antony's College, Oxford. This was the first meeting of the Society to deal specifically with human behaviour. We decided not to attempt to represent the whole spectrum of research on human behaviour, nor even the range of biology-based human ethology. Instead we concentrated on two areas which not only interested us very strongly but which overlapped with the interests and activities of members of the society – ecology and physiology. The work representing these two areas is linked around the theme of adaptation. However, they approach two different aspects of adaptation: in part one the long-term accommodation to the environment on an evolutionary time-scale and on the time-scale of culture change. In part two, the papers concern short-term reactions to the environment. One or two of these papers deal with mankind at the limits of his flexibility, when he creates a social and material environment which seems to stress people to the limits of their adaptability and the borders of pathology.

The meeting owes its success to the financial support of the Nuffield Foundation, and the Royal Society, which enabled us to gather so many distinguished speakers from overseas. We would also like to thank, on behalf of the symposium, the speakers, and the participating members of the society, the hard working and courteous local organizers, Robert Attenborough, Gillian Naish, Jane Sell, and Caroline Palmer who ensured that everyone had somewhere to sleep and plenty to eat and drink, that the slides got shown and that most people had somewhere to sit.

June 1978

N. BLURTON JONES
VERNON REYNOLDS

PART I

LONG-TERM ADAPTATION:

ECOLOGICAL ANTHROPOLOGY
AND
EVOLUTIONARY THEORY

INTRODUCTION

N. Blurton Jones

Institute of Child Health, University of London

When the Society asked Vernon Reynolds and myself to organize a two-day meeting on behaviour, we decided to try to concentrate on two areas which interested us, and which might appeal to the Society's traditional interests in normal physiology and in human evolution. Dr. Reynolds undertook to organize the day on behaviour and physiology, and particularly stress physiology, one theme of this day being perhaps the limits to adaptation, and whether or not they are exceeded in modern urban conditions. The day I organized was intended to examine the parallels between cultural and biological evolution. In composing this day's programme I aimed to achieve three things: (1) an airing for contemporary ecologically-minded anthropology in the U.K.; this is a school of anthropology most well represented in the U.S.A.; (2) an airing for the extremely exciting developments in evolutionary biology which are probably important whether you study behaviour or not and which Trivers and McFarland and others are building on to perhaps turn the study of animal behaviour to a hypothetico-deductive science for the first time; (3) most difficult, but correspondingly important, to achieve some exchange of views on the old issue of culture and biology in human behaviour. In particular I hoped that the exchange would take place around the concept of adaptation as it is used both in anthropology and in biology. I thought that the time was particularly ripe for this, firstly because the new evolutionary biology makes us see that there is an evolutionary advantage in individual, temporal, and situational variation in behaviour. One comes to expect behaviour to differ in different situations, and for individuals who find themselves in different situations to behave differently. One also expects individuals to behave differently at different stages of their life cycle. Secondly, the new evolutionary biology gives us clearer criteria for measuring adaptation and some tools for investigating the adaptiveness of behaviour.

Cultural ecology and its variants make it very clear that there is a sense in which cultural practices and ideologies are adaptive and ultimately somehow, and to some degree, help people get by in the material world. The ecologically-minded anthropologists and archaeologists are doing such a very good job that I sometimes wonder why biologists should get involved in the study of culture. The main reason why I think they should is that biologists have confronted some of the same criticisms of the concept of adaptation as anthropologists are confronting, namely—adapted for what? and how do you test whether it is adaptive?

Biologists have for very long claimed that culture and cultural transmission is man's greatest adaptation. But here they have always given up thinking and started writing purple passages, and at this point the ecological anthropologists are very much better scientists than the biologists. Biologists could instead attempt to follow their view that the propensity for culture evolved and is indeed adaptive (Durham, 1976; Alexander, 1974). It could only evolve if it increased the inclusive fitness of the individuals transmitting and receiving culturally influenced behaviour. This implies that there might be constraints in selectivity in cultural transmission. Just as with physiological adaptation, a change is only adaptive if it occurs in a correct direction. Variability in rates of sweat secretion is in itself quite unadaptive. What is adaptive is that you sweat more in a hot environment and less in a cold one.

Contemporary developments in evolutionary theory might impel biologists to ask anthropologists: (1) when you use the term "adaptation" are you talking about groups or individuals? (2) are you sure that communications and ideologies are about groups, and not about individuals influencing other individuals? (3) to biologists adaptation implies changes which maximize something, in biology changes that maximize inclusive fitness; what, if anything, do anthropologists envisage the culturally determined behaviour of people to be maximizing?

One cannot stress too strongly that biologists cannot, and

mostly do not, deny that human behaviour changes rapidly; nor that cultural influences on human behaviour are immense and interesting. So in return, anthropologists might well be asking biologists: when you think that evolution is relevant to human behaviour, which of the following possible processes do you have in mind: (1) deeply canalised epi-genetic mechanisms underlying behaviour; (2) constraints on the emission and reception of cultural influences and learning, such as to produce behaviour that maximizes inclusive fitness; (3) selection of culturally transmitted behaviour by differential mortality of (a) individuals and (b) groups (for instance when Marvin Harris (1971) says there were a lot of cultures that are not around any more); (4) does one have in mind an entirely different cultural evolution—the evolution of cultural instructions instead of genetic instructions, the *ideas* that are still around being the ones that are good at catching on. This theory has been proposed by Ruyle (1973) and by Dawkins (1976).

Perhaps I should run through some basic fallacies that arise in these kinds of discussions: (1) what is adaptive must be regarded as good—I don't know of any biologist who feels this is a logical statement, but many of their readers and critics have assumed biologists are saying this; (2) evolved behaviour must be innate in Lorenz's sense of being unchangeable or environment-resistant. I think every biologist now is quite ready to realise that an animal which behaves in mode A in situation A and mode B in situation B when these are different but more appropriate modes of behaving will be a more successful individual than one who performs the same behaviour in each situation; (3) there are often confusions of proximal and ultimate causation. This is a distinction that Tinbergen has worked particularly hard at making clear in animal behaviour. It is also a distinction with which ecological anthropologists such as Harris (1968) and Gross (1975) are perfectly familiar. Ethologists talk of proximal or short-term causation; Harris and Gross have used "motivation" for exactly the same thing. Ethologists talk about functions and survival value of behaviour, the consequences of behaviour which feed back over time to select out some behaviour and not others. Anthropologists such as Harris call this kind of causation "causes" rather than motivations; (4) it is sometimes assumed that cultural materialists and biologists are ignoring people's ideas and beliefs and regard these as not interesting. This doesn't follow either. Harris has quite clearly argued for some sort of balance between the study of ideas and belief and the study of measurable, observable behaviour in anthropology. Biologists who study behaviour may well on the whole be very sceptical of the methods used in studying ideas and beliefs and also very sceptical of some of the assumptions about ideas and beliefs being causal: they may as well be rationalizations or adaptive messages to give about your own behaviour, a topic discussed by Trivers (1971, 1974) and also by Wilson (1975) and Goffman (1959).

The first paper, not delivered at the meeting but invited to add balance to this section of the book, is by W. H. Durham. In it he introduces his arguments for regarding inclusive fitness as the criterion of adaptation for cultural evolution just as with organic evolution.

The second and third papers in this session concern respectively an anthropologist's and a biologist's reactions to the problem of how to demonstrate adaptiveness. Vayda argues for a close look at the response of individuals and cultures to sudden, clear, adverse events. McFarland argues for a more ambitious and highly quantified approach which follows from Tinbergen's emphasis on compromise in adaptation.

McFarland ends his paper with some speculations about the adaptiveness of cultural conformity. Starting from the argument that learning would evolve only if constrained to lead to *more* adaptive behaviour he argues that this will also apply to imitation and other means of cultural transmission. It also of course applies to "rational" capacities. Arguments about "rational economic man" have always confused the application of reason (thought) to problems, with the choice of the goals to be reached. The more "prosaic" the goal the more "rational" it is thought to be! Choice of goals must always depend on a value decision somewhere along the line.

McFarland then discusses a mechanism which might maintain a reciprocal altruism system based on individuals' recognizing fellow altruists by similarities in their behaviour, not by recognizing individuals. In this system, altruists would be under pressure to conform to recognizable and rapidly changeable behaviour.

Newcomers or would-be cheats will benefit if they can mimic this behaviour but may always be expected to fail to catch up with the changing fashions of the altruists. These speculations usefully draw attention to the conformity aspects of culture but it remains for the conditions to be defined under which the system McFarland proposes could exist and to see whether these are the conditions under which there is indeed strongest pressure to conform.

Rappaport's paper reminds us of the complexities of human ideologies and their role in culture, making an attempt to set these in the context of adaptation and communication, with special emphasis on the possibilities for lies in a language-using animal. Packer's paper deals, purely within a context of animal behaviour, with what probably should become a most important issue in the study of culture: the question of individual or group. In the study of animal behaviour this is really no longer a question. Social organization and group behaviour has to be interpreted as an outcome of the strategies of the individuals within the group. There seem to be few attempts to apply this kind of interpretation to the study of human society. Some stirrings of this kind of approach can be traced in the writings of Marx, whose affinities with Darwin seem to have been recognized by none except Marx himself. But even contemporary analysts of culture seem ready to overlook these aspects of the original theories of cultural materialism. From where I stand between biology and human sciences, this ready assumption that culturally determined behaviour is for the good of the group has much more dangerous undertones of panglossianism than any theories of adaptiveness in biology.

Sibly and Blurton-Jones present a partly worked out example of the approach that McFarland describes in his paper and that McFarland and Sibly are pursuing with field studies of animals. This paper provides a very simplified, down-to-earth example of the Oxford optimization approach.

David Harris's paper on the Aboriginal population of Northern Queensland is an exciting addition to the documentation of hunter–gatherer societies. The completeness of the description he is able to develop from early census materials and travellers' accounts and from careful consideration of the natural environment is as elegant as the best of modern archaeology. He has been courageous enough to set his conclusions on paper before seeing the results of current archaeological investigations of the same area.

I think that the parallels in methods and approaches in the study of behaviour and in the use of the concept of adaptation will be quite clear to readers of these papers. The only area of dispute that might remain concerns the criteria of adaptation: what measures of survival or well-being are we using and whose survival or well-being are we examining—individuals or groups? Underlying this of course is a much bigger question about the mechanisms of evolution that we assume to be working. Durham (1976) has convincingly argued that cultural evolution is complementary to organic evolution, and that cultural adaptations maximize inclusive fitness just like other adaptations. I find his theory attractive, if only because its heuristic value is as great as that of the theory of natural selection. However, it is not clear whether he is correct in his counter-argument against Ruyle and Dawkins, that natural selection would prevent the evolution of a transmission mechanism that permitted "meme" evolution to work against the inclusive fitness of individuals. It also seems clear that cultural transmission would not be subject to the same rules of kin selection as apply in genetic evolution. Natural selection would (if it were quick enough!) press for cultural mechanisms that compensated for this, that weighted costs and benefits according to the genetic relatedness of individuals and the actual costs and benefits to inclusive fitness of altruism and aggression toward them. This is perhaps implicit in Alexander's (1974) attempts to apply kin selection theory to human kinship systems. One would expect considerable difficulty in testing such propositions because the data are a confusion of emic and etic categories. The selective advantages that accrue from who someone actually has children with, which children's survival someone actually aids, will differ from the advantages that accrue from whom someone says one should have children with.

References

ALEXANDER, R. A. (1974) The evolution of social behaviour. *Annual Review of Ecology and Systematics*, **5**, 325–83.
DAWKINS, C. R. (1976) *The Selfish Gene*. The Clarendon Press, Oxford.

DURHAM, W. H. (1976) The adaptive significance of cultural behavior. *Human Ecology*, **4**, 89–121.
GOFFMAN, E. (1959) *The Presentation of Self in Everyday Life*. Doubleday Anchor, Garden City, New York.
GROSS, D. R. (1975) Protein capture and cultural development in the Amazon Basin. *American Anthropologist*, **77**, 526–40.
HARRIS, M. (1968) *The Rise of Anthropological Theory*. A history of theories of culture. Crowell, New York.
HARRIS, M. (1971) *Culture, People, Nature: an Introduction to General Anthropology*. Crowell, New York.
RUYLE, E. E. (1973) Genetic and cultural pools: some suggestions for a unified theory of biocultural evolution. *Human Ecology*, **1**, 201–15.
TRIVERS, R. L. (1971) The evolution of reciprocal altruism. *Quarterly Review of Biology*, **46**, 35–37.
TRIVERS, R. L. (1974) Parent–offspring conflict. *American Zoologist*, **14**, 249–64.
WILSON, E. O. (1975) *Sociobiology. The New Synthesis*. Belknap, Cambridge, Mass.

THE COEVOLUTION OF
HUMAN BIOLOGY AND CULTURE

WILLIAM H. DURHAM

Department of Anthropology and Program in Human Biology,
Stanford University

Introduction

AT the heart of the controversy over sociobiology and human social behaviour lies a distinction between two separate kinds of mechanisms by which human attributes may come to exist at high frequency in a population. One of the mechanisms, the favourite among biologists and sociobiologists in particular, is a *genetic* mechanism. An attribute, introduced to a human population's gene pool by mutation, migration or recombination, may spread by gene flow *if* it confers a reproductive advantage to its carriers *and if* that reproductive advantage results from genetic differences between carriers of the trait and non-carrier conspecifics. In this case, a trait is said to spread by 'natural selection': the differential reproduction of individuals because of genetic differences between them.

The other mechanism, usually the favourite among social and cultural anthropologists, is a *cultural* mechanism. An attribute may increase in frequency in a human population when it is spread by learning and maintained by tradition. Here the transmission of the attribute may be completely distinct from the biological processes of inheritance. Instead of differential reproduction, theories of cultural evolution propose that human attributes result from the differential replication by learning and imitation of variants introduced into a 'cultural pool' by innovation and diffusion. By contrast, this process might be called 'cultural selection' (see Durham, 1976a).

Because these models of inheritance may be readily distinguished on the basis of mechanism (essentially genes versus brains), a common assumption of both biologists and anthropologists has been that human biology and culture must therefore be studied in a mutually exclusive fashion. Scholars in both fields habitually ignore that other inheritance mechanism which is not conventionally a part of their own discipline, or at most assign to it some small, "modifying" influence. Most biologists and anthropologists have unfortunately overlooked a possible coevolutionary relationship between human biology and culture and continue to attempt the separation of their interwoven effects (Durham, 1976a, b).

Sociobiology, although widely touted as "the new synthesis", has proven to date to be no major exception to this rule. Defining the field as "the application of evolutionary biology to the social behaviour of animals, including *Homo sapiens*" (Barash, 1977:2; see also Wilson, 1975), sociobiologists have repeatedly analysed human social behaviours in terms of natural selection theory and the genetic inheritance mechanism. Prominent examples include Trivers's (1971) "model for the natural selection of reciprocally altruistic behaviour [which] can readily explain the function of human altruistic behaviour and the details of the psychological system underlying such behaviour' (p. 48), Wilson's discussion of "genes favouring homosexuality" in humans (p. 555) and "the genetic evolution of ethics" (p. 563), and Hartung's (1976) examination of "natural selection's influence in determining preferential treatment of males in the inheritance of wealth" (p. 613). Studies like these which analyse human behaviours in the terms of natural selection assume, *by the definition of natural selection*, the genetic inheritance mechanism for these behaviours. Without explicit incorporation of the alternative, cultural mechanism, sociobiological explanations of human social behaviour have automatically implied that observed behaviours are the end products of cumulative genetic change.

For at least two reasons, this implication has often been erroneous. First, correlations between theories from evolutionary biology and observed human behaviour in no way constitute evidence of causation. As I have argued elsewhere (Durham, 1976a) and continue to argue below, these correlations may equally result from the *cultural* inheritance mechanism and a complementary process of *cultural* evolution. Second, by singling out the genetic inheritance model, sociobiologists have over-looked the fact that culture is, as Simpson (1972) recently put it, "the more powerful means of human adaptation". The cultural mechanism provides a way to modify phenotypes that is (1) more rapid than changes resulting from natural selection, (2) better able to track environmental change or stability, and (3) sometimes even responsive to perceived human need as described below. Given that human beings do have *two* principal inheritance mechanisms, and that the cultural mechanism is surely *no less influential* than the biological one, a preoccupation with natural selection and genetic models is likely both to distort our under-standing of human social behaviour, and to prolong the unnecessary debate of biology versus culture. More progress is likely to be made by a theoretical perspective that includes *both* mechanisms of inheritance and makes no *a priori* assumptions about their relative importance in the evolutionary development of a given form of social behaviour. In the pages that follow, I would like to discuss some of the conceptual features that such a coevolutionary theory might have.

In fairness to a number of authors, I should point out that a few, very recent studies of human social behaviour make no unproven assumptions about the inheritance mechanism(s) behind the behaviours studied (see, e.g. Dyson-Hudson and Smith, in the press). Rather than "the application of evolutionary biology" to human behaviours, these studies focus instead on the adaptive significance of human attributes however evolved. While my own preference would be to call these human behavioural ecology or biocultural anthropology (cf. Greenwood and Stini, 1977), they are sometimes called sociobiology by their authors. This may partly reflect a changing definition of the field in the light of heavy criticism. If sociobiologists really are now interested in the biological *and cultural* bases of human social behaviour, then they should explicitly redefine the discipline. In the meantime, sociobiology may mean very different things to different people.

While critical of sociobiology on the one hand, I must also be critical of existing evolutionary theories of culture. It is commonly assumed, even by well known cultural ecologists, that because the cultural *mechanism* is independent of genetic transmission, the *spread and retention* of cultural attributes is somehow independent of human survival and reproduction (cf. Steward, 1955, p. 32). In contrast, I would like to propose that cultural attributes are often maintained and perpetuated *because of* their survival value for human beings. Logically speaking, cultural traits, unlike genetic traits, are not required to confer benefits in reproductive success in order to spread in a population. As one British anthropologist recently noted: "Since cultural traits are learned and not genetically transmitted, differential reproductive rates do not necessarily act as selective forces in the evolution of culture" (Burnham, 1973, p. 95). However, I would like to argue here that survival and reproduction benefits do contribute significantly to the spread and persistence of cultural traits.

It will be useful to begin with a few examples.

Adaptive Cultural Practices

In 1974, Solomon Katz and colleagues at the University of Pennsylvania published in *Science* their analysis of traditional maize-processing techniques in the New World (Katz, Hediger, and Valleroy, 1974). The paper focused on a widespread, indigenous cooking treatment which involves boiling corn for 30 to 50 minutes in water containing some form of alkali—either from dissolved lime, wood ashes, or lye—before its direct consumption or conversion to dough and *tortillas*. The report came to two major conclusions of importance for scholars concerned with the relationship between human biology and culture.

First, the alkali treatment process was shown to enhance the nutritional value of maize for human consumption. Indigenous strains of corn are particularly notorious for a low available lysine content, for example, because most of this essential amino acid occurs within corn as part of the indigestible protein called glutelin. Among other nutritional consequences, the alkali cooking treatment acts to break up the indigestible glutelin into usable forms and thereby increases the relative nutritional value of corn for human consumption. As the researchers put it, "unless corn is prepared by specific techniques, its nutritional value as a dietary source is at best marginal, and any human population that attempted to depend on it as a major staple would suffer some degree of malnutrition'' (p. 183). Here, then, is a cultural practice, discovered perhaps by accident but spread and maintained for generations by learning and socialization processes, which has direct nutritional and biological consequences for individual human beings.

Their second conclusion is equally important for this discussion. Drawing on a sample of 51 New World societies from the Human Relations Area Files, they showed that there has been a close relationship between the use of the alkali process and the extent to which societies cultivate and consume maize. For this analysis, societies in their sample from North, Central and South American areas suitable for corn cultivation, were rated (1) according to the extent to which they practise maize cultivation, (2) according to the relative percentage of maize in their diets, and (3) by whether or not they use alkali when preparing maize for their own consumption. Katz and co-workers used these indices to show that there exists a nearly one-to-one relationship between those societies that both cultivate and consume large amounts of maize and those that use an alkali treatment of some sort. At the same time, those societies where maize is not so important in cultivation and consumption almost without exception do not use alkali cooking techniques. These anthropologists then argued that their analysis explains the use of the traditional alkali process as a ''necessary concomitant'' of intensive maize agriculture and high maize consumption.

I mention this study in some detail here for several reasons. First, I think it constitutes a particularly good example of a cultural practice having a clean-cut adaptive value for its individual practitioners. In contrast to a common focus on group- or population-level adaptive values in most previous studies of cultural ecology and evolution (cf. Alland, 1970; Alland and McCay, 1973), the evidence presented by Katz and colleagues suggests that the nutritional benefits of this cultural practice contributes directly to the ability of individual human beings to survive and reproduce. Secondly, the authors call attention to the joint evolutionary implications of their findings:

> It is evident that in studies of human adaptability and evolution, the sciences of man must consider in greater detail the interacting relationships of human biology and culture.... In the case presented here, if the alkali cooking techniques used by societies consuming large amounts of maize are examined in the cultural context alone, then they would seem only to be innocuous methods for softening the outer kernel and would carry no adaptive or evolutionary significance. However the evidence presented here implies that without these cooking techniques a high degree of dependence on corn produces serious malnutrition (p. 773).

They conclude by saying that the study "suggests that it is increasingly difficult to accept evolutionary studies where biological and cultural adaptation are treated independently" (p. 773).

Unaware of this research at the time, I argued a similar point in a paper before a joint Smithsonian conference of biologists and anthropologists a few weeks earlier, but based on a different kind of analysis (Durham, 1976b). My interest then was the study of resource competition and human intergroup aggression with special reference to warfare in so-called "primitive" societies. Using a simple model derived from ecological principles and a careful scrutiny of some ethnographic literature on the subject, I argued that Mundurucú headhunts, for example, or Yąnomamö intervillage raids, or phases of war and peace among the Maring of New Guinea can be seen as adaptive social behaviours with various direct and indirect compensating benefits to the individual participants. The case is perhaps strongest for the Mundurucú, where several lines of evidence simultaneously point to this conclusion even though the original bias of the ethnographers, Robert and Yolanda Murphy, was for a safety valve interpretation (see for example, Murphy, 1957 and 1960).

According to the Mundurucú, the trophy heads captured in raids on enemy villages could produce an increase in the local abundance of game animals if certain rituals were also observed. To a human ecologist, this suggests that the Mundurucú were in competition with neighbouring rainforest groups for a limited supply of animal protein. Considering the relative scarcity and mobility of their prey (primarily peccaries and tapir), the elimination of competing consumers may have been the most direct means of increasing and maintaining their own harvest of game.

This interpretation is consistent with Mundurucú food preferences and hunting patterns, the central importance of game in their religion, the "mystical power" of the enemy trophy head to increase the game supply, and their common reference to enemy groups in the same terms as game, all of which are unaccounted for in the Murphys' argument. Although the Mundurucú may not have been conscious of these consequences, I think there is good evidence for arguing that head-hunting had net benefits, despite high apparent costs, for the survival and reproduction of adult Mundurucú through the increased supply of animal protein.

In short, I argued that this elaborate and ritualized cultural behaviour was highly adaptive for its participants and I felt that this was one example of a more common adaptive dimension in cultural practices. From the start, I have argued that there is no sense in presupposing some highly improbable genetic programming for this behaviour as some biologists have more recently been wont to argue. Rather I believe that this example and many others (suggested in sometimes very different terms by Cohen, 1974, Vayda, 1969, and Harris, 1974 for example) simply point to a complementary relationship between the biological processes of organic evolution and the invention, learning and diffusion processes of cultural evolution. Somehow, it escapes a number of sociobiologists that human behaviours can be highly adaptive for entirely cultural reasons.

Unfortunately, however, no coherent theory of cultural change has emerged to date which can adequately explain *how and why* we find cultural practices with the adaptive value suggested for corn processing techniques or for Mundurucú intertribal headhunting. In the absence of a cultural theory which can account for the adaptiveness of many cultural traditions, the sociobiology explanation of a biological basis for these traditions is a great temptation for scholars in both the biological and social sciences. An important first step toward a coevolutionary synthesis of biology and culture must therefore be the development of a theory of cultural evolution which is at once an outgrowth of earlier theories from cultural and ecological anthropology and also an adequate explanation of how and why adaptive cultural behaviours evolve when they do. For the remainder of this paper, I shall discuss some of the conceptual features for such a theory.

Conceptual Elements of Cultural Theory

In 1956, George Peter Murdock provided a useful conceptual starting point for the analysis of cultural evolution in his article, "How Culture Changes". Defining culture as the combined "habits of action" and "habits of thought" shared by members of a society, Murdock described a model for evolutionary change in culture in terms of the differential persistence of habitual forms. As he wrote,

> Every innovation that has been socially accepted enters, as it were, into a competition for survival. So long as it proves more rewarding than its alternatives a cultural habit will endure, but when it ceases to bring comparable satisfactions it dwindles and eventually disappears. The process superficially resembles that of natural selection in organic evolution. It should be noted, however, that cultural traits do not compete directly with one another but are competitively tested in the experience of those who practise them (Murdock, 1956, p. 330).

The central idea of this formulation, that more "rewarding" cultural variants will be selectively retained over less rewarding variants in time is a point further developed by Campbell (1965, 1975) and also by Ruyle (1973) to some extent. In all these approaches, the cultural practices that are eliminated through trial and error or "social competition" are, as Murdock says, by and large the less adaptive ones (p. 330).

These theories have a simple and nearly intuitive conceptual structure. They require that there be sources of variation, a selection or elimination process on the basis of a loosely defined "reward" of some sort, and effective mechanisms for the maintenance of positively selected variants. As Murdock says, "the net effect of the various processes of cultural change is to adapt the collective habits of human societies (i.e., their "pool" of cultural traits) progressively over time to the changing conditions of existence" (p. 332).

Each of the elements of this conceptual scheme have now been studied by a number of anthropologists and other social scientists. H. H. Barnett (1953), Allen Johnson (1972) and Leslie Spier (1971) among others have studied the sources of cultural variation—primarily accident, invention, and diffusion. Allan Tindall (1976) has recently reviewed some of the theory in the study of element three of this scheme, mechanisms of retention, which he calls "cultural transmission". Although Tindall concludes that theories of transmission are still at an early stage of development (but see also Cavalli-Sforza and Feldman, 1973: Feldman and Cavalli-Sforza, 1975), it appears that the *major* stumbling-block for understanding culture change on the whole remains element two: the criterion of selective retention. To date there remains little agreement over the nature of the "reward" so carefully unspecified by Murdock.

According to one leading theory, for example, the effective selection criterion is the amount of free energy obtained from a cultural practice. Proponents of this view, including Leslie White and Yehudi Cohen, suggest that culture change results from the "improvement of the mechanical means with which energy is harnessed and put to work as well as by increasing the amounts of energy employed" (White, 1949, p. 375; see also Cohen, 1974). While there is little doubt that energy utilization does increase with some kinds of cultural change, this theory does not well explain traditions remotely related to energy procurement *per se* (consider incest avoidance, or again maize processing and Mundurucú headhunting). Another recent view sees cultural behaviours as contributing to the homeostatic regulation of human ecosystems. It is implied that traditions develop over time to buffer human populations from environmental changes and degradation (e.g. Rappaport, 1968 and 1975). While useful for understanding many human ecological relations, as an evolutionary theory this view encounters the difficulty of trying to explain how things *change* with a model for why they remain the *same*. A third theory asserts that all cultural characteristics have some practical, generally material, value for their practitioners (e.g., Harris, 1974). This view too has given insights into some of the more obvious "riddles of culture" as Harris calls them, but it has been criticized roundly (cf. Hallpike, 1973) for failing to identify in a consistent fashion just who benefits from a cultural practice (individuals, social groups, or regional populations, for example) and in what terms they do benefit. Leaving these parameters imprecise, this view amounts to saying only that if you look hard enough you will find some benefit for somebody somewhere for any given cultural practice.

These and other theories, of course, have had some success in particular case studies, and it is clear that they have provided a good deal of insight into the workings of human social systems. But again, not one of these is adequate for explaining *how*, by cultural means, people evolve social customs that contribute to their ability to survive and reproduce in their natural and social environments.

In the interest of explaining the existence and persistence of adaptive cultural traditions, I would therefore like to suggest that human survival and reproduction (as measured by "inclusive fitness" after Hamilton, 1964) is an important and underestimated general criterion behind the selective retention of cultural evolution. In other words, I would like to propose that to an important and generally unrecognized extent, culture evolves by the selective retention of non-genetic traits that enhance the ability of human beings to survive and reproduce in a given environment. Such a notion is important because it would imply that biological and cultural evolution may be complementary to a large extent. If this were the case, it would make no sense *either* to view biological and cultural adaptations as independent phenomena (consistent with the argument of Katz *et al.*), *or* to argue that human behavioural adaptations can be adequately explained in terms of natural selection (as sociobiology often implies). A possible coevolutionary relationship between biology and culture therefore has important implications for understanding why people do what they do (cf. Durham, 1976a, b).

A reasonable question to ask at this juncture is, what rationale is there for proposing such a coevolutionary theory? Why would one expect survival and reproduction to enter into cultural theory?

Rationale

There are actually a number of good reasons for proposing a coevolutionary view of human biology and culture. Consider first an argument based on the organic evolution of the *capacity* for culture. Many scholars have failed to appreciate that the organic evolution of the capacity for culture had, at least at one time, important implications for the actual *process* of cultural evolution. What was presumably genetically "selected for" in our ancestors was an increasing ability to modify their phenotypes through learning and experience, true enough, but only because those ancestors persistently used that ability to enhance their relative survival and reproduction. The capacity for culture, one could say, continued to evolve not merely because it *enabled* superior adaptations, but also because it was used to *produce* superior adaptations. Our hominid ancestors must therefore have had ways of keeping culture "on track" of the adaptive optima as those optima varied from place to place and changed from time to time. The conclusion is important: as the capacity for culture evolved, *the developing culture characterizing a group of people must have been adaptive for them in the survival and reproduction sense whatever else it may have been.*

It is important to note that this conclusion does *not* require that the cultural meaning of things was consciously or unconsciously related to their survival and reproduction consequences. It means only that, *however* culture changed and evolved, and *whatever* meaning was given by people to their cultural attributes, the *net effect* of those attributes was to enhance human survival and reproduction. Symbolic anthropologists will be interested in a major deduction from this argument. A coevolutionary theory *can* contribute to an understanding of the adaptive significance of cultural attributes, but it is not necessarily the key to understanding the meaning and symbolic significance that people may give to those attributes.

Obviously things have changed since the days when the capacity for culture was evolving because it was used by proto-hominids to produce superior adaptations. It is then appropriate to ask, is culture still used by human beings as a way to enhance their survival and reproduction, or have we lost the ability to keep culture "on track"? Has cultural evolution by one of these other principles of optimization, for example, more recently run counter to human survival and reproduction, and has culture therefore lost much of its original adaptive significance for human existence?

It is, of course, impossible to give the definitive answer at this time, but for a number of reasons I am inclined to think that there remains an important adaptive dimension to human cultural attributes. These reasons can be divided into two categories: those related to the action of cultural selection *within* groups and those related to cultural selection *between* groups. In this paper, I would like to focus on the first of these because the importance of cultural selection within groups has been generally underestimated in culture theory. Elsewhere (Durham, in the press), I have described in greater detail the consequences of group-level cultural selection for coevolutionary theory.

Cultural Selection within Groups

For convenience, in the description of levels of cultural selection I will define *social group* to be any subset of a human breeding population containing individuals whose survival and reproduction are directly and substantially interdependent because of interactions among them. It can be thought of as a collection of individuals whose behaviour creates at least a given arbitrary amount of interdependence so that the collection is bounded by frontiers of far less interdependence. It may be helpful here to think of the breeding population as some entire ethnolinguistic population or "culture" and to think of social groups as smaller, more interdependent bands, camps or villages within that population.

Basic to any theory of cultural change and adaptation, of course, is the way in which distinct human social groups acquire their cultural attributes. In this section, I propose the hypotheses (*a*) that the cultural characteristics of human social groups result to a large extent from internal, individual-level selective retention, and more importantly, (*b*) that this process generally selects for cultural attributes that enhance the ability of their carriers to survive and reproduce.

My reasons are these. First, I believe that there is ample evidence that some process of selective retention continues to operate on the accumulation and modification of cultural attributes within human social groups. People remain somehow selective in their receptivity to cultural innovation, for we know that many more innovations are introduced by invention and diffusion than are retained at length within any given society. Second, this continuing selective retention appears to be influenced by a number of human biases described in the literature which, I propose, tend to keep people from selectively retaining cultural attributes that counter their individual survival and reproduction provided they have a choice (see also Durham, 1977 and in the press). Of these, perhaps the most important are learned biases. Robert LeVine (1973) has argued that the process of socialization teaches children from an early age not only adherence to social norms and traditional patterns of behaviour, but also selectivity in the adoption of new forms on the basis of what is held to be adaptive and "for their own good".

A second sort of bias might be called the bias of satisfaction (see Ruyle, 1973 and 1977). Presumably throughout the organic evolution of hominids there was a persistent (genetic) selective advantage for a neurophysiology that rewarded with sensory reinforcements and a feeling of "satisfaction" those acts likely to enhance survival and reproduction and which produced unpleasant, distressing, or painful feedback in response to potentially dangerous behaviours. Eugene Ruyle, among others, has argued that the selective retention of cultural habits has continued to be influenced by the general sense of satisfaction that they do or do not bring to their bearer. While we disagree over the definition and relative utility of the concept of satisfaction, I concur that "square wheels, crooked spears, and sickly children are unlikely to provide much satisfaction" (Ruyle, 1977) but I feel that this is *because* they are unlikely to do much for survival and reproduction.

There is evidence for a third source of bias within the learning structures and function of the human brain. Recent research by Seligman and others (e.g., Seligman and Hager, 1972; Hinde and Stevenson-Hinde, 1973) suggests that the learning process may be "canalized" in a way that would influence cultural evolution. I am not persuaded by hard-core genetic structuralists (see Laughlin and d'Aquili, 1974) that there is a determinism rather than a bias to be found therein. However, to the extent that there is a bias on culture imposed by the biochemistry and physiology of the brain, the evolution of that organ would also mean a bias in favour of the selective retention of more versus less adaptive cultural traits.

The biases resulting from socialization, satisfaction, and cognition suggested by these authors (and probably others unrecognized and undiscovered) taken together represent a reasonably strong probabilistic "force" tending to keep culture on track of the adaptive optima. This "force" would operate at the level of individual human beings and bias them as culture carriers. As a result, individuals would tend to select and retain from competing variants, consciously or not, those cultural practices whose net effect best enhances their individual ability to survive and reproduce (Durham, 1976a, b). Hypothetically, this process of cultural selection would result in the spread and maintenance of cultural attributes that are adaptive in the general sense of contributing to their bearer's reproductive success.

To summarize up to this point, I propose that human beings are not just passively receptive to cultural innovation but that we have and develop a number of selective biases which, in turn, result in a tendency to acquire those cultural attributes that past experience and some degree of prediction suggest to be most advantageous for survival and reproduction. To the extent that these propositions are valid, cultural evolution would remain functionally complementary to natural selection even though there need be *no* genetic basis to the selected attributes. Operationally, culture change may also be independent of organic evolution rendering it thus more rapid, better able to track environmental change or stability, and sometimes even a response to perceived human need. At the same time, cultural attributes which evolved in this way can have the interesting property of reducing or eliminating organic selection pressures. Similar phenotypic traits acquired by different genotypes in this fashion may make the genotypes equally or more nearly equally "fit" (Durham, 1976a). As population geneticist Theodosius Dobzhansky (1951) once put it, "the transmission of culture short-circuits biological heredity". On the other hand, cultural change in this perspective has the opposite potential of creating new and different organic selection pressures (cf. Washburn, 1959 and 1960; Geertz, 1973; Kretchmer, 1972).

The combination of these features gives reason to believe that cultural selection may account for the origin and maintenance of more forms of human social behaviour than do mutation and transgenerational changes in the frequency of any presumed behaviour genes. It will be seen that a theory of cultural evolution with these properties shifts the burden of proof for any explicitly *biological* basis for adaptive human behaviours over to the sociobiologists. Until we have direct and compelling evidence that a given human behaviour has a discrete genetic basis, the demonstration that such behaviour has adaptive functions does not *by any means* prove it to be the product of natural selection. There is very possibly a *cultural* explanation. My insistence on this point, however, is not meant to prolong the debate of biology *versus* culture in our understanding of human behaviour. Rather, it is intended to emphasize that cultural processes are likely to be at least as important as organic ones in the evolution of human adaptations. It is intended to persuade biologists that theories of human behavioural adaptation must make *explicit allowance* for non-genetic mechanisms behind the transmission of traits in a population. It is also intended to persuade anthropologists that human survival and reproduction remains an important influence behind the ongoing evolution of cultural practices.

While distinguishable on the basis of their means of transmission, biological and cultural inheritance by this argument would be functionally complementary. Indeed, the biological and cultural influences would often be confounded in human phenotypes (cf. Cavalli-Sforza and Feldman, 1973).

Although the hypothetical process of cultural selection described here would normally result in adaptive phenotypic attributes, it is frankly easier to conceive of cultural influences getting "off track" in the evolution of a phenotype than it is for the more biological influences. Maladaptive cultural practices *can* be maintained at substantial frequency in a social group, particularly when the biases previously mentioned are overridden or prevented from functioning by force, threat, misinformation, or the abolition of alternatives. As I have argued elsewhere (Durham, in the press), this may create traditions which *appear* to be exceptions to the rule I propose, namely that cultural behaviours are generally adaptive for their practitioners. However, my arguments should not be seen as necessarily implying that cultural selection by individuals leads to some sort of universal adaptive optimization for the group. One reason for this is that individuals need not all be interdependent in the same way or by the same amount within a social group. Evolving asymmetries in dependence relations between individuals and between "interest sub-groups" (which might be called elements of social *structure*) can give rise to a degree of manipulative control by some over the behaviour of others (Durham, 1976a). In extreme cases, these structural constraints on the adaptations of individuals within society can result in behaviours which appear to require altruistic sacrifice. I should point out that to those in control, manipulated behaviours may accrue handsome survival and reproduction benefits. For those being manipulated, on the other hand, I would suggest that the behaviour may actually be seen as a *relatively adaptive compromise* given powerful structural constraints. (For an elaboration of this point, see Durham, in the press.)

Maladaptive behaviours can also recur through the conscious or deliberate choice of individuals to behave counter to their reproductive interests for whatever reason, but I am suggesting that his behaviour is not likely to become a long-lasting tradition.

Where circumstances do permit the preceding biases to operate, however, a culture would hypothetically evolve to enhance the ability of human beings to survive and reproduce in their particular habitats. In principle, this cultural selection between alternative variants may proceed consciously *or* unconsciously, and it may also proceed according to any number of other proximate or "cognized" criteria (again like energy, homeostasis, etc.) *that are closely correlated with* reproductive success of human beings in the environment concerned. A correlation with reproductive success, I would argue, is actually the reason that these other criteria have been partly successful in the first place. But while I am accepting their validity in part, I am proposing that any selective retention by these other criteria does not generally oppose the ability of human beings to survive and reproduce. I believe that the arguments here should prove more widely applicable than theories based on any of the other criteria, and that this theory can be used to predict limits to their utility. Unlike the energy formulation, for example, this argument suggests that people are not likely to harvest energy either in a way or in an amount that would cause them reduced survival and reproduction.

One final qualification must be included in the argument. A large number, perhaps even a majority, of the identifiable cultural aspects of human phenotypes involve extremely low costs and/or benefits to the survival and reproduction of their carriers. Cultural traits in some cases may be virtually inconsequential to reproductive success and there may be essentially no relative reproductive advantage among alternative forms. With little basis for discriminating between survival and reproduction consequences, the hypothesized process of cultural selection would not be very effective for these traits. The spread and perpetuation of recognizably low-cost attributes are then likely to be better explained in other ways (like momentary phenotypic reward, or arbitrary symbolic value). As I have argued elsewhere (Durham, 1976a), the importance of survival and reproduction to our understanding of human cultural attributes is therefore expected to be conditionally dependent upon the degree to which an attribute taxes the highly variable amounts of time, energy, and resources available to individuals. If customary "high-cost" behaviours (like Mundurucú head-hunting) are seen to persist in a culture, they are expected to be fitness-enhancing almost without exception. Some "low-cost" behaviours on the other hand may very well have no important relation to fitness. My prediction, therefore, is that there are few, if any, cultural practices that are maintained in the absence of force or threat and persist even though individual parents would achieve substantially higher reproductive success without them or by available alternative practices.

Summary and Conclusion

In conclusion, let me summarize briefly both the traditional "separationist" theories of biology and anthropology, and the "coevolutionary" perspective suggested here. Underlying this discussion has been an assumption that the attributes shared by members of a human society could in theory be located along a spectrum running from purely genetic to purely cultural. To date, there has been a tendency for anthropologists and biologists to deny, discredit, or ignore one end of the spectrum or the other in favour of traditional disciplinary biases of interpretation. Sociobiology is a recent example of this tendency. Without explicit inclusion of any extragenetic inheritance mechanism, the explanations of human social behaviour in terms of neo-Darwinian theory imply (or at the very least seem to imply) that specific behaviour genes direct the development of specific and often complex social traditions.

At the other extreme are various theories of cultural evolution reviewed in Service (1971) and Kaplan and Manners (1972) for example. Although considerable insight has been gained by the analysis of cultural attributes in terms of energy, homeostasis, or material benefit, for example, not one of these criteria can both stand for the general case and explain how adaptive cultural habits evolve when they do. Hence, despite some analogies between the processes of organic and cultural evolution by these theories, the selective retention of human attributes is thought to proceed by different, sometimes antagonistic, criteria.

In contrast, I have argued that for those of us interested in interpreting the variation in cultural behaviour exhibited within and between human societies, the task is instead one of synthesis. The existence of a wide variety of adaptive cultural practices ranging from traditional maize processing techniques to Mundurucú head-hunting forays implies that there is often a common criterion behind the selection processes of biology and culture whose mechanisms remain separable in principle. Simply stated, my hypothesis is that the selective retention in biological *and* cultural evolution generally favours those attributes which increase, or at least do not decrease, the ability of human beings to survive and reproduce in their natural and social environments. This perspective has the advantage of explaining both how human biology and culture can often be adaptive in the same sense, and how they may interact, as suggested by Katz *et al.* (1974), Kretchmer (1972), and others in the evolution of human attributes. This theory, moreover, contains an important irony. *If* cultural differences between human societies are largely the result of individual-level cultural selection for more-versus-less adaptive traits as proposed here, then our capacity for culture has meant a capacity to reduce or even eliminate many of the organic selection pressures that would have favoured the very refinements of genetic control required by theories which rely solely on the mechanism of natural selection.

In short, the advantage of this theory is its ability to explain the evolution of adaptive human attributes without presuming a genetic basis or predisposition for everything we do. This formulation may also have a number of practical uses in human behavioural research. It suggests, for example, a renewed emphasis on individuals and their problems of survival and reproduction within society. This may lead to new interpretations of ethnographic behaviours which have commonly focused on group-level behaviours. It also suggests new directions for future research. Measures of reproductive success (operationally defined as S_{ij}, the number of descendants of an individual i alive j generations later, and extended where appropriate to include "offspring equivalents" from the reproduction of relatives, see West Eberhard, 1975) may prove useful as analytic tools for understanding specific cultural practices and as modelling devices for formulating future research questions. This kind of approach should be most helpful when the "costs" of a given practice can be factored out in terms of time, energy and resources and where it is possible to detect associated differentials in reproductive benefit. Thus I suggest that coevolutionary analysis is most appropriate in studies of human nutrition, subsistence, food taboos, human intergroup aggression, population regulation and demography, migration, and other "high-cost" practices. I believe that the theory is also adequate for predicting its own limitations as I have suggested. Considering the abundance of day-to-day cultural practices which involve little time, energy, or resource use, I re-emphasize that this argument does not say that everything we do is best explained in terms of reproductive success. For reasons given above, the adaptive consequences of human cultural attributes are not their sole significance. A perfectly valid endeavour for anthropologists and human ecologists remains the understanding of the meaning that cultural traits may have for their bearers. In the eyes of the natives, this meaning may or may not be related to adaptation. There can always be pigs, or even *tortillas*, for the ancestors.

Acknowledgments

I wish to thank Kathleen Durham, Frank Livingston, Howard Norman, Elizabeth Perry, Roy A. Rappaport, Alfred S. Sussman, and Jim Woods for useful discussion and criticism of this paper. I gratefully acknowledge the support and encouragement of the Michigan Society of Fellows during the preparation of this manuscript.

References

ALLAND, A. (1970 *Adaptation in Cultural Evolution*. Columbia University Press, New York.

ALLAND, A. and McCAY, B. (1973) The concept of adaptation in biological and cultural evolution. In *Handbook of Social and Cultural Anthropology* (ed. J. J. Honigmann). Rand McNally, Chicago.

BARASH, D. P. (1977) *Sociobiology and Behaviour*. Elsevier, New York.

BARNETT, H. G. (1953) *Innovation: The Basis of Cultural Change*. McGraw-Hill, New York.

BURNHAM, P. (1973) The explanatory value of the concept of adaptation in studies of culture change. In *Explanations of Culture Change: Models in Prehistory* (ed. C. Renfrew). University of Pittsburgh, Pittsburgh.

CAMPBELL, D. T. (1965) Variation and selective retention in sociocultural evolution. In *Social Change in Developing Areas: A Re-interpretation of Evolutionary Theory* (ed. H. R. Barringer, G. I. Blankstein, and R. W. Mack). Schenckman, Cambridge, Massachusetts.

CAMPBELL, D. T. (1975) On the conflicts between biological and social evolution and between psychology and moral tradition. *American Psychologist*, **30**, 1103–26.

CAVALLI-SFORZA, L. and FELDMAN, M. W. (1973) Models for cultural inheritance. I. Group Mean and within group variation. *Journal of Theoretical Population Biology*, **4**, 42–55.

COHEN, Y. A. (1974) *Man in Adaptation: The Cultural Present*. Aldine, Chicago.

DOBZHANSKY, T. (1951) Human diversity and adaptation. *Cold Spring Harbor Symposium on Quantitative Biology*, **15**, 385–400.

DURHAM, W. H. (1976a) The adaptive significance of cultural behaviour. *Human Ecology*, **4**, 89–121.

DURHAM, W. H. (1976b) Resource competition and human aggression, Part I: A review of primitive war. *Quarterly Review of Biology*, **51**, 385–415.

DURHAM, W. H. (1977) Reply to comments on "The adaptive significance of cultural behaviour". *Human Ecology*, **5**, 59–68.

DURHAM, W. H. (in the press) Toward a coevolutionary theory of human biology and culture. In *Evolutionary Biology and Human Social Behavior* (ed. W. Irons and N. Chagnon). Duxbury, North Scituate, Massachusetts.

DYSON-HUDSON, R. and SMITH, E. A. (in the press) Human territoriality: an ecological reassessment. In *Evolutionary Biology and Human Social Behavior* (ed. W. Irons and N. Changon). Duxbury, North Scituate, Massachusetts.

FELDMAN, M. W. and CAVALLI-SFORZA, L. L. (1975) Models for cultural inheritance: a general linear model. *Annals of Human Biology*, **3**, 215–26.
GEERTZ, C. (1973) *The Interpretation of Cultures*. Basic Books, New York.
GREENWOOD, D. and STINI, W. (1977) *Nature, Culture and Human History: A Biocultural Introduction to Anthropology*. Harper and Row, New York.
HALLPIKE, C. R. (1973) Functionalist interpretations of primitive war. *Man*, **8**, 451–70.
HARRIS, M. (1974) *Cows, Pigs, Wars and Witches: The Riddles of Culture*. Random House, New York.
HARTUNG, J. (1976) On natural selection and the inheritance of wealth. *Current Anthropology*, **17**, 607–22.
HINDE, R. A. and STEVENSON-HINDE, Y. (1973) *Constraints on Learning: Limitations and Predispositions*. Academic Press, New York.
JOHNSON, A. W. (1972) Individuality and experimentation in traditional agriculture. *Human Ecology*, **1**, 149–59.
KAPLAN, D. and MANNERS, R. A. (1972) *Culture Theory*. Prentice-Hall, Englewood Cliffs, New Jersey.
KATZ, S. H., HEDIGER, M. L. and VALLEROY, L. A. (1974) Traditional maize processing techniques in the New World. *Science*, **184**, 765–73.
KRETCHMER, N. (1972) Lactose and lactase. In *Biological Anthropology* (ed. S. H. Katz). Freeman, San Francisco.
LAUGHLIN, C. D. and D'AQUILI, E. G. (1974) *Biogenetic Structuralism*. Columbia University Press, New York.
LEVINE, R. A. (1973) *Culture, Behavior, and Personality*. Aldine, Chicago.
MURDOCK, G. P. (1956) How culture changes. In *Man, Culture and Society* (ed. H. L. Shapiro). Oxford, London and New York.
MURPHY, R. F. (1957) Intergroup hostility and social cohesion. *American Anthropologist*, **59**, 1018–35.
MURPHY, R. F. (1960) *Headhunter's Heritage*. University of California Press, Berkeley.
RAPPAPORT, R. A. (1968) *Pigs for the Ancestors*. Yale University Press, New Haven.
RAPPAPORT, R. A. (1975) Commentary on adaptation and adaptability. *Biological Anthropology* (ed. S. H. Katz). Freeman, San Francisco.
RUYLE, E. E. (1973) Genetic and cultural pools: some suggestions for a unified theory of biocultural evolution. *Human Ecology*, **1**, 201–215.
RUYLE, E. E. (1977) Comment on "The adaptive significance of cultural behaviour". *Human Ecology*, **5**, 53–55.
SELIGMAN, M. E. P. and HAGER, J. L. (1972) *Biological Boundaries of Learning*. Appleton-Century-Crofts, New York.
SERVICE, E. R. (1971) *Cultural Evolutionism*. Holt, Rinehart and Winston, New York.
SIMPSON, G. G. (1972) The evolutionary concept of man. In *Sexual Selection and the Descent of Man* (ed. B. Campbell) Aldine, Chicago.
SPIER, L. (1971) Inventions and human society. In *Man, Culture and Society* (ed. H. L. Shapiro). Oxford University Press, London and New York.
STEWARD, J. (1955) *Theory of Culture Change*. University of Illinois Press, Urbana.
TINDALL, B. A. (1976) Theory in the study of cultural transmission. *Annual Review of Anthropology*, **5**, 195–208.
TRIVERS, R. L. (1971) The evolution of reciprocal altruism. *Quarterly Review of Biology*, **46**, 35–57.

VAYDA, A. P. (1969) *Environment and Cultural Behavior*. Natural History Press, Garden City, New York.

WASHBURN, S. L. (1959) Speculations on the interrelations of tools and biological evolution. In *The Evolution of Man's Capacity for Culture* (ed. J. M. Spuhler). Wayne State University Press, Detroit, Michigan.

WASHBURN, S. L. (1960) Tools and human evolution. *Scientific American*, **203**, 63–75.

WEST EBERHARD, M. J. (1975) The evolution of social behaviour by kin selection. *Quarterly Review of Biology*, **50**, 1–33.

WHITE, L. A. (1959) *The Evolution of Culture*. McGraw-Hill, New York.

WILSON, E. O. (1975) *Sociobiology: The New Synthesis*. Harvard University Press, Cambridge, Massachusetts.

NEW DIRECTIONS IN ECOLOGY
AND ECOLOGICAL ANTHROPOLOGY*

ANDREW P. VAYDA and BONNIE J. McCAY
Department of Human Ecology and Social Sciences, Cook College,
Rutgers University, New Brunswick, New Jersey

IN this essay we consider four criticisms of ecological anthropology: its over-emphasis on energy, its inability to *explain* cultural phenomena, its preoccupation with static equilibria, and its lack of clarity about the appropriate units of analysis. Recognizing that some of these criticisms may not be justified, we nevertheless point to parallel concerns in ecology. Further, we ask whether new directions indicated by some ecologists might be appropriate paths for future work in ecological anthropology. A central theme is the desirability of focusing on environmental problems and how people respond to them.

The kind of environmental problems we are especially concerned with here are those constituting hazards to the lives of the organisms experiencing them. In other words, we are particularly concerned with problems that carry the risk of morbidity or mortality, the risk of losing an "existential game" in which success consists simply in staying in the game [82, 85; cf 80, cited in 78].

Our focus upon hazards and responses to them emerges partly from consideration of neo-Darwinian selection theory. As Colinvaux [22, p. 499] notes: "Selection . . . chooses from among individuals those which are best adapted to avoid the hazards of life at that time and place". Our focus reflects also the new concern of biologists such as Slobodkin [81, 82, 85] with the actual

---

* Adapted, with permission, from *Annual Review of Anthropology*, Volume 4.
Copyright © 1975 by Annual Reviews Inc. All rights reserved.

processes of responding to hazards or environmental perturbations rather than with formal alterations in hypothetical genetic systems. Related also is the emerging view among medical scientists that health is a "continuing property, potentially measurable by the individual's ability to rally from insults, whether chemical, physical, infectious, psychological, or social" [7, 8; cf 78]. At least some and perhaps all of the insults referred to in the preceding quotation can be subsumed in our category of hazards; even social and psychological insults may evoke physiological "stress" and disease [60, 79] as well as psychological and behavioural adaptive strategies [99].

A further influence on us has been the recent proliferation of research and thinking on problems of human response to "natural hazards" in geography [19, 20, 64, 98]. However, unlike many of the geographers, we do not restrict our notion of "hazards" to extreme geophysical events such as floods, frosts, droughts, hurricanes, and tornadoes. Burton and Hewitt [19] have already warned against classifying geophysical hazards according to their climatic, meteorological, geological, or geomorphic origin rather than in terms of magnitude, extent, frequency, and other "hazard characteristics". In line with this, we would also warn against classifying separately such nongeophysical events as predation by warfare, plundering or raiding [21, 55, 56], exactions of tribute and taxes [38, 48], or acts of religious persecution [27]. These also constitute hazards for some people and are comparable, as Barton's work [10] suggests, to natural hazards in terms of hazard characteristics and people's responses to them.

The nature of environmental problems and hazards and the responses to them will be discussed further as part of our attempt to clarify what some limitations of ecological anthropology have been and in what directions they might be overcome. Suffice it to say that any event or property of the environment which poses a threat to the health and ultimately the survival of organisms, including people, may be regarded as a hazard for them, and that responding adaptively to such hazards involves in our view—as in Bateson's [11, 12] and Slobodkin's [82]—not only deploying resources to cope with the immediate problem but also leaving reserves for future contingencies.

A convenient framework for indicating promising new directions in ecological inquiry and how these relate to a focus upon hazards and responses is provided by consideration of criticisms that have been or can be made of past work in ecological anthropology. We will consider particularly the approaches set forth in articles by Rappaport and Vayda [74, 91a, 95]. These are the approaches that critics have labelled "new ecology" [66], "newer ecology" [59], and "new functionalism", "neo-functionalism", or "neo-functional ecology" [2, 3, 33]. The label of "cultural ecology" is also sometimes applied [e.g. 5, 27], but Vayda and Rappaport [95] and Flannery [31] have rejected this as a designation for their chosen areas of inquiry and have applied it to other approaches (including Steward's [88] and Harris's [43]) which they have criticized. To facilitate exposition, we will forgo these scholastic distinctions and speak simply of "ecological anthropology" in the pages to follow. (For a survey and assessment of the various ecological approaches in anthropology, consult Anderson's recent article [6]).

Four main criticisms of ecological anthropology may be usefully considered here. One is that its point of view has been equilibrium centred—that its focus has been upon the discovery and elucidation of self-regulating, homeostatic, or "negative feedback" processes by which some kind of balance between human populations and their environments is maintained and that it has thereby ignored nonhomeostatic changes, system disruptions, and "unbalanced" relations between people and their environments [1, 5, 27, 40]. A second criticism is that showing how traits or institutions like potlatching or warfare work in relation to environmental problems does not constitute an acceptable explanation of those traits or institutions [33, 40]. A third criticism is that ecological anthropologists tend to concentrate their inquiries upon the production and consumption of food energy to a degree that amounts to a "calorific obsession" [18, p. 46] and the sin of "nutritional reductionism" [26, p. 45].

A fourth criticism is that the units analysed are either ill chosen or ill defined. This important criticism has not been made very explicit in appraisals of ecological anthropology, but it is implied by Friedman's strictures against making *a priori* reductions of "relatively autonomous phenomena" such as populations to a single phenomenon like a "homeostatic eco-system" [33, p. 466].

More explicit criticisms along similar lines have been made by non-anthropologists [e.g. 28, 86] about the way in which some sociologists and political scientists use constructs like "social system" and "political system".

Questions can be raised about the extent to which these four criticisms are justified. Several recent analyses in ecological anthropology have been explicitly concerned with disruptions of systems and with positive as well as negative feedback processes [e.g. 31, 58, 75, 92, 93]. Moreover, the ecological anthropologists have said clearly that they are not trying to explain traits or institutions but are trying simply to show how they work [24, 91, 95]. And they themselves [e.g. 31, 95] have criticized Steward [88] and his followers for neglecting environmental phenomena other than food resources. The fact that the criticisms persist in spite of this might be regarded as reason enough for considering them again here. Better reasons, however, are that similar criticisms are being voiced about work in biological ecology and that new developments in ecology in response to these criticisms may suggest possible parallel developments in ecological anthropology.

It will be convenient to consider first the criticism related to the "calorific obsession" and then to consider the remaining criticisms. Something like the calorific obsession has been operating among biologists too. Making the basic assumptions that all living organisms compete ultimately for energy and therefore that adapted organisms will be energetically efficient ones, biologists have spent much time, effort, and money in studying the transformation of energy by plants and animals and in measuring and simulating flows of energy through ecosystems (see 68, part 1; attempts to include man in the study of these systems are presented in 25, 51, 67, 69, 73, 89). Some biologists, however, are now questioning the assumptions underlying much of this work, Slobodkin, for example, distinguishes effectiveness from energetic efficiency:

> . . . an animal may be effective at hiding or effective at searching for food in the sense that it does these acts well and in the way that is appropriate to whatever environmental problems it may face. The energetic cost or lack of energetic cost associated with these acts may prove of interest if energy is, as

a matter of fact, limiting. The conditions under which energy is limiting can also be specified, but there is not any formal necessity for a connection between effectiveness and efficiency. Effectiveness may or may not involve optimization or maximization of some function relating to energy [83, p. 294].

Similar points are made repeatedly by Colinvaux in his introductory textbook, as, for example, on p. 233:

It is a mistake to believe that animals and plants have all evolved primarily as efficient converters of energy. The pressures of natural selection are pressures for survival, and survival may sometimes be more concerned with the efficient use of nutrients, ensuring that individuals mate, safe overwintering, or swift growth and dispersal, than with the efficient use, or even collection, of energy [22].

The implication of this for research is that studying the efficiency of energy capture and use by an individual organism or population can be valuable for understanding the strategies employed by that unit if, as Slobodkin says, energy is limiting. If it is not, and if other problems such as floods or water shortages or predation are threats to the survival of an organism, then the effectiveness of the organism's response to those problems and not the energy expended in making the responses is the important subject matter.

These implications have as much pertinence in ecological anthropology as in biology. In the case of people for whom energy and its translation into food and fuel calories do appear to be major limiting factors, energy flow studies can be expected to contribute significantly to our understanding of how the existential game is played. A careful study by Thomas [89] among the Quechua Indians of the Nuñoa District of the high puna of the southern Peruvian Andes provides confirmation of this, for Thomas found among the people a variety of tactics and strategies contributing to efficient use of the limited energy available. Among the sociotechnological adaptations here are: (1) exploiting a spatially dispersed, multiple resource base of energetically efficient crops and domestic animals; (2) interzonal trading whereby surplus resources produced in Nuñoa are exchanged for high energy foods from lower regions; (3) assigning much of the labour of herding to children, for whom it is energetically less expensive than it is for adults; and (4) restricting daily activities to sedentary tasks as much as possible. The Quechua Indians also make energetically efficient use of sheep, llama, and cattle dung for fuel and fertilizer [103].

Other studies of responses to shortages of calories have been made by anthropologists among such people as sisal workers in northeastern Brazil [38] and Quechuan migrants to low-altitude Peruvian towns where, because of poverty and the impossibility of continuing with adjustments practicable in the puna, the people became perhaps even more subject to the hazards of limited energy availability than they formerly were in their high-altitude homelands [35]. If ecological anthropologists want to make their energy-flow studies relevant to our questions about playing the existential game, the research opportunities certainly exist: shortages of calories, sometimes escalating to widespread famines (as happened recently in Ethiopia, Bangladesh, Afghanistan, and the Sahel), are major hazards for many people in the modern world. (For examples of studies of responses to famines in recent years and in the nineteenth century, see 13, 61, 63, 71, 105).

But what about cases in which the energy available is not a limiting factor for the people? The !Kung Bushmen studied by Lee [57] and the Tsembaga Marings studied by Rappaport [72, 73] might be examples, and so might members of the upper classes of many modern nations. Research on energetic efficiency among such people can provide answers to some questions but not to those that are most critical for assessing their health or adaptedness. It cannot, in other words, answer questions about how effectively the hazards actually confronting people in their environments—for example, water shortages in the case of the Bushmen and malaria-transmitting anopheles mosquitoes in the case of the Marings—are dealt with.

To consider the parallels between ecology and ecological anthropology in the other criticisms and in their implications for new directions, we may note first that in ecology, as in ecological anthropology, the tools of systems analysis have generated much enthusiasm and led to sophisticated models of the structure, function, and dynamics of natural communities and ecosystems [62, 96a, 97a]. However, some ecologists have come to the conclusion that these mathematical models cannot account for certain biological processes, the specificity of which places their description and predictability beyond the capacity of models that derive from classical physics and are now used in ecology. Because of the *specificity* and *opportunism* of evolution, such models cannot, for example, predict what new "trick" will be produced by an organism in response to an environmental problem. Thus Slobodkin [81], giving the example of a species of rotifer that has developed the "trick" of making itself inedible by enlarging its spines in the presence of a certain predator, notes that no mathematical theory could be expected to have predicted anything like that.

Similar conclusions can be reached with respect to the analysis of feedback systems and processes in ecological anthropology. Such analysis may show how a trait functions under some conditions for a particular group of people [23, 24, 95]—for example, shoulder-blade divination when game is becoming scarce among the Naskapi Indians [65]. But the analysis cannot be expected to predict the specific tricks, traits, processes, or institutions—like shoulder-blade divination—that people will evolve in coping with social or environmental problems [94, Chap. 1].

These considerations do not necessarily mean, however, that no predictive generalizations about responses to hazards can be developed in ecology and ecological anthropology. As one of us has suggested elsewhere, it still should be possible to elucidate general features of hazards and responses and to develop generalizations in terms of such variables as the magnitude, duration, and novelty of hazards, the magnitude and reversibility of responses to them, the temporal order in which responses of different magnitudes occur, and the persistence or nonpersistence of response processes [93, 94].

A framework for attempting this has been provided by Barton [10, Chap. 2], who presents a "typology of collective stress situations", based upon the criteria of magnitude, speed of onset, duration, and relative novelty. A good example of the kinds of studies needed for developing generalizations about the temporal properties of responses in relation to the temporal properties of hazards is Waddell's analysis of how the Fringe Enga people of the New Guinea highlands cope with recurrent, and sometimes severe, plant-killing frosts [96]. Waddell is explicitly concerned with the temporal ordering of responses and their articulation with the timing, recurrence, and severity of frosts. He posits the existence of a series of interrelated responses, ranging from the agricultural practice of "mounding" to migrations of varying degrees of permanence. Thus, whereas some observers have viewed massive migrations here as a "disorganized fleeing of starving victims", Waddell's focus upon how people actually cope with hazards leads to the conclusion that such migrations are the culmination of a structured set of responses to severe frost [96].

For criticism of equilibrium concepts in ecology, we may turn to a recent article by Holling:

An equilibrium centered view is essentially static and provides little insight into the transient behavior of systems that are not near the equilibrium. Natural, undisturbed systems are likely to be continually in a transient state; they will be equally so under the influence of man. As man's numbers and economic demands increase, his use of resources shifts equilibrium states and moves populations away from equilibria. The present concerns for pollution and endangered species are specific signals that the well-being of the world is not adequately described by concentrating on equilibria and conditions near them [46, p. 2].

We regard as cogent some parallel criticisms that anthropologists are beginning to make about an equilibrium centred view—for example, with respect to the size of primitive, prehistoric, or "pre-modern" human populations, which has often been thought [e.g. 14–16, 44] to have been maintained in finely adjusted equilibrium. Arguments and evidence are now emerging in support of an alternative view whereby the size of these populations is regarded as having fluctuated widely in most cases and the members of the populations are seen as having had to cope recurrently with the ups and downs of fertility and mortality [4, 30, 54].

Rejection of an equilibrium centred view does not, however, imply abandoning the study of the processes by which some properties of systems or organisms are kept unchanged even as other properties are changing. Thus, Holling and Goldberg [47], who say that the "key insight" of the ecological approach is that ecological systems are not in a delicately balanced state and that "natural systems were subjected to traumas and shocks imposed by climatic changes and other geophysical processes" long before man appeared on the scene, also say that the ecological systems that have survived are "those that have evolved tactics to keep the domain of stability, or resilience, broad enough to absorb the consequences of change". In other words, resilience itself may be a system property that as a result of evolutionary selection is maintained by various processes. Holling's examples [46] of forest insect and other animal populations that fluctuate widely and are able to survive periodic climatic extremes that would be fatal to a population in a finely adjusted equilibrium underscore the need to keep distinct the notion of equilibrium and the notion of the maintenance of system properties like resilience.

The maintenance of such properties has been described as "homeostasis" by Slobodkin [82, 84], Vayda [93], Bateson [11], and others. We regard this term as appropriate and will continue to use it here, although we recognize that there is a tendency among some anthropologists [e.g. 1, 27] to confuse it with concepts of static equilibria and unchanging systems—concepts inconsistent with the new directions indicated in the arguments of Holling and Slobodkin. Slobodkin in particular emphasizes that some properties of homeostatic systems must at times change so as to maintain other properties that are important for staying in the existential game—properties such as what Holling calls resilience and what might be described as remaining flexible enough to change in response to whatever hazards or perturbations come along [cf 12, 82. 84, 85]. The Quechua Indians of the Peruvian altiplano can be referred to again in this context. They appear to employ a wide variety of adaptations to hazards of their high-altitude environment—hazards such as energy scarcity, cold, and low oxygen tension. Some of the adaptations were summarised earlier. In addition, the people use other behavioural responses such as coca-chewing [e.g. 42] and various physiological responses, including changes in the respiratory and cardiovascular systems in response to hypoxia [17b, 34]. Bateson [11] and Slobodkin [82, 85] have suggested that certain interrelations of behavioural, physiological, and genetic means of responding to such hazards as confront the Quechua Indians may be important for homeostasis. More specifically, they suggest that the development of mechanisms at one level in response to persistent environmental problems frees mechanisms at another level to deal with other possibly more transitory hazards. This warrants more investigation and can be regarded as indicating further directions in which predictive generalizations can be sought. (For another discussion of interrelations of behavioural, physiological, and genetic adaptations, see 50).

Before we can give any other example of changes that might contribute to homeostasis, we must deal with the question of what units or systems are to be looked at as undergoing change and/or maintaining their properties. Some of the quotations that we have given from Holling's articles suggest that ecological systems are natural entities, units of adaptation with survival strategies like those of their component living organisms. This reflects a fairly common view among ecologists. Even before the advent of systems analysis in ecology, some natural historians were inclined to see natural communities as engaged in lawful processes directed towards achieving a "climax" community with superior social organization. With systems analysis the focus was shifted to ecosystems as the appropriate units of analysis. Ecosystems came to be viewed as self-regulating and self-determining systems with goals such as maximizing energetic efficiency or productivity, the efficiency of nutrient cycling, biomass, or, through an increase in species diversity and food web complexity, maximizing organization ("information" content) and stability.

Some ecologists now reject such ideas; the reader is referred to Colinvaux [22, pp. 549–72] for specific empirical and theoretical objections to each of the goals mentioned above. The important general objection stated by him is that "nowhere can we find discrete ecosystems let alone ecosystems with the self-organizing properties implied by the concept of the climax society" [22, p. 549]. The ecosystem is an analytic, not a biological, entity. Natural selection acts not upon it but rather upon individual living things. Interactions observed in complex ecosystems need not be regarded as expressing self-organizing properties of the systems themselves; instead they can be understood as the consequences of the various and variable adaptive strategies of individual organisms living together in restricted spaces.

In biology there has been controversy not only about whether natural selection can choose between ecosystems but also about whether it can choose between populations. The emerging resolution, based upon both theory and empirical observations, seems to be that selection works primarily and most importantly upon individual organisms or closely related genetic kin [3, 41, 87, 100, 101].

This resolution still leaves the question of accounting for the properties of the larger units—populations, communities, and ecosystems. Indeed, according to Orians [70], "perhaps the greatest challenge" for ecologists is the "development of theories about the properties of communities on the basis of selection for the attributes of their component individuals" [70, p. 1239]. By focusing on how individual organisms respond to hazards and problems, biologists can hope to come closer toward meeting this challenge, insofar as the attributes of individuals favoured by selection must include the ability to survive the hazards of particular times and places (for recent attempts to respond to the challenge see Force [32] and Barash [9]).

If we focus on how individual human beings respond to hazards and problems and on the ways in which the nature of their responses (including any patterns of aggregation and disaggregation that these may produce) are related to characteristics of the hazards and problems they face, we may move closer towards answering similar questions in social science. For, as Boissevain [17, p. 549] notes for ego-centred networks, forms of social organization are often used by people to solve problems, just as according to some sociobiologists [52, 53] social systems of interaction among nonhuman organisms are used by them to cope with their problems. Important here is the notion of *processes* of response, including processes whereby the unit of action may shift from individuals to various forms (and degrees of inclusiveness) of groups and perhaps back to individuals, in accord with the magnitude, persistence, and other characteristics of the hazards in question. We are suggesting, in other words, that processes of group formation and dissolution, as well as the processes whereby, for example, quasi-groups or coalitions become structured groups over time [17, p. 551; cf 17a] may be important as responses to environmental problems. Thus, the transience of organized group activity and composition among hunters and gatherers can be seen in relation not only to interpersonal difficulties but also to temporal properties of environmental problems [57a, 104]. Similarly, the formation, persistence, and dissolution of a large extended family among some Navahos studied by Downs [29] can be seen as responses to the changing nature of water supplies; a persistent drought finally resulted in the dissolution of the extended family into nuclear families, and even the breakdown of some nuclear families. Variations in the scope, content, and persistence of networks of neighbours in British rural communities may be related to the mobility of families, the size of the parish, and whether alternative sources of casual labour and occasional aid exist for coping with their problems [102]. Some kinds of social organization, such as segmentary lineage systems [48, 77], appear to be effective in coordinating the size of the responding unit with the dimensions of the problems the people face. The rapidity with which guerilla and underground activist groups dissolve and reappear may represent effective strategies within the environments of concentrated and coordinated state power [37, 38]. Rapidly forming, transient, and problem-specific groups characterized as a new "adhocracy" [12a; 90, Chap. 7] may represent especially effective strategies in the modern world insofar as the number, novelty, complexity, and unpredictability of the problems faced by individuals and by the business and political organizations to which they belong may be greater than ever before and may preclude effective collective responses by members of permanent social units.

The above examples give only glimpses of possible relationships between processes of group formation and dissolution and environmental problems or hazards. Much finer and more specific analysis is of course necessary for any given case.

An approach focusing on how individuals respond to hazards may also lead us to note instances where cultural loss may be individual gain. For example, consider a recent study by Diener [27]. The main question that he tries to answer is why Hutterite culture has persisted for four centuries despite the periodic loss of much of the Hutterite population through death from acts of persecution or through conversion to other beliefs. We would, however, ask also how individual Hutterites survived persecution, and we would then see (from Diener's own description) that (*a*) some did not survive; (*b*) some responded by moving to the economic and political frontiers of Europe and later North America; but (*c*) many others responded by giving up their Hutterite culture—they "despaired and abandoned their faith" [27, p. 613]. This may be coping in what some would regard a minimal and perhaps ignoble sense, but it does bring to our attention all those people who remain in the existential game because they give up their participation in particular cultures. Their actions are, in other words, homeostatic insofar as they constitute changes in some properties of a responding unit so as to maintain the unit itself.

One other reason for focusing on how individuals respond to hazards and problems may be noted: the fact that the hazardousness of particular events may vary significantly for different individuals in a population. For example, frequent cyclone-induced coastal flooding in Bangladesh is hazardous for migrant labourers who, being landless and poor, have few alternatives to working as hired fishermen or farming the extensive "char" fields made fertile by deposition from flooding. Mortality is, in fact, higher for them when floods occur than it is for local villagers, since the latter can more readily escape to high points in the villages or market places and can climb the trees near their homes. At the same time, the flooding appears to be a benefit rather than a problem for large landowners who can use their resources and influence to circumvent government regulations and can thus annex newly formed "char" lands [49]. Similarly, plant-killing frosts may be beneficial for Florida citrus growers who profit from the increased prices available for the surviving crops, given market scarcity, as well as from shorter harvest times and consequently lower labour expenditures [97]; migrant farmworkers, however, suffer because of the reduced wages and unemployment that the frosts bring.

We do not wish to belabour this topic. The important point is that in studying the responses of people to hazards or other problems, we begin to ask who is affected by the hazards and who is responding; whether individuals respond by cooperating in groups of various kinds or by leaving groups; whether enduring, widespread, and/or severe environmental hazards result in the transformation of the responding units; and perhaps whether such features of human social life as loyalty, solidarity, friendliness, and sanctity may sometimes be important either as incentives for group action that may be advantageous for members of the group or as inhibitors of ill-timed individual responses (e.g. premature withdrawal from the group) [cf 45; 76, p. 204].

In the context of our discussion of criticisms of ecological anthropology, we have made various suggestions about research and theory. In conclusion, it may be noted that our focus on environmental problems and on how people respond to them calls for the following:

(1) Paying attention to many possible hazards or problems in addition to those related to energy utilization.

(2) Investigating possible relationships between such characteristics of hazards as their magnitude, duration, and novelty, and the temporal and other properties of people's responses.

(3) Abandoning an equilibrium centred view and asking instead about change in relation to homeostasis.

(4) Studying how hazards are responded to not only by groups but also by individuals.

(5) Changing our primary research goals from the anthropologists' objective of understanding or explaining culture and the sociologists' objective of explaining groups to attempting to understand what is involved in successful or adaptive responses to environmental problems.

Acknowledgments

We thank Susan Lees for her work on earlier drafts of this paper. If it were not for the constraints of time, she would have been a co-author of the final version. We also thank Carmel Schrire, Charles Leck, and Herbert Price for their helpful comments and Suhasini Sankaran and Steve Czaczkes for their bibliographic assistance.

References

[1] ABERLE, D. F. (1968) General discussion. In *War: The Anthropology of Armed Conflict and Aggression* (ed. M. Fried and R. Murphy), pp. 97–100. Natural History Press, Garden City.

[2] ALLAND, A. (1972) Cultural evolution: the Darwinian model. *Social Biology*, **19**, 227–39.

[3] ALLAND, A. and MCCAY, B. (1974) The concept of adaptation in biological and cultural evolution. In *Handbook of Social and Cultural Anthropology* (ed. J. J. Honigmann), pp. 143–78. Rand McNally, Chicago.

[4] AMMERMAN, A. J. (1975) Late Pleistocene population dynamics: an alternative view. *Human Ecology*, **3**, 219–33.

[5] ANDERSON, E. N. (1972) The life and culture of ecotopia. In *Reinventing Anthropology* (ed. D. Hymes), pp. 264–83. Random House, New York.

[6] ANDERSON, J. N. (1974) Ecological anthropology and anthropological ecology. In *Handbook of Social and Cultural Anthropology* (see ref. 3), pp. 477–97.

[7] AUDY, J. R. (1971) Measurement and diagnosis of health. In Environ/Mental: Essays on the Planet as a Home (ed. P. Shepard and D. McKinley), pp. 140–62. Houghton Mifflin, Boston.

[8] AUDY, J. R. and DUNN, F. L. (1974) Health and disease. In *Human Ecology* (ed. F. Sargent), pp. 325–43. North Holland, Amsterdam.

[9] BARASH, D. P. (1974) The evolution of marmot societies: a general theory. *Science*, **185**, 415–20.

[10] BARTON, A. H. (1969) *Communities in Disaster: A Sociological Analysis of Collective Stress Situations*. Doubleday, New York.

[11] BATESON, G. (1963) The role of somatic change in evolution. *Evolution*, **17**, 529–39.

[12] BATESON, G. (1972) Ecology and flexibility in urban civilization. *Steps to an Ecology of Mind*, pp. 494–505. Ballantine, New York.

[12a] BENNIS, W. G. (1966) *Changing Organizations*. McGraw-Hill, New York.

[13] BHATIA, B. M. (1963) *Famines in India: A Study in some Aspects of the Economic History of India 1860–1945)*. Asia Publ. House, New Delhi.

[14] BIRDSELL, J. B. (1953) Some environmental and cultural factors influencing the structure of Australian aboriginal populations. *American Naturalist*, **87**, 169–207.

[15] BIRDSELL, J. B. (1968) Some predictions for the Pleistocene based on equilibrium systems among recent hunter-gatherers. In *Man the Hunter* (ed. R. B. Lee and I. DeVore), pp. 229–40. Aldine, Chicago.

[16] BIRDSELL, J. B. (1972) The problems of the evolution of human races: classification or clines? *Social Biology*, **19**, 136–62.

[17] BOISSEVAIN, J. (1968) The place of non-groups in the social sciences. *Man*, **3**, 542–56.

[17a] BOISSEVAIN, J. (1971) Second thoughts on quasi-groups, categories and coalitions. *Man*, **6**, 468–72.

[17b] BOYCE, A. J., HAIGHT, J. S. J., RIMMER, D. B. and HARRISON, G. A. (1974) Respiratory function in Peruvian Quechua Indians. *Annals of Human Biology*, **1**, 137–48.

[18] BROOKFIELD, H. C. (1972) Intensification and disintensification in Pacific agriculture: a theoretical approach. *Pacific Viewpoint*, **13**, 30–48.

[19] BURTON, I. and HEWITT, K. (1974) Ecological dimensions of environmental hazards. In *Human Ecology* (ed. F. Sargent), pp. 253–83.

[20] BURTON, I., KATES, R. W. and WHITE, G. F. (1968) The human ecology of extreme geophysical events. *Natural Hazards Research Working Paper 1*, Department of Geography, University of Toronto.

[21] CHAGNON, N. A. (1967) Yanomamö social organization and warfare. In *War: The Anthropology of Armed Conflict and Aggression* (ed. M. Fried and R. Murphy), pp. 109–59.

[22] COLINVAUX, P. A. (1973) *Introduction to Ecology*. John Wiley, New York.

[23] COLLINS, P. W. (1965) Functional analyses in the symposium 'Man, Culture and Animals'. In *Man, Culture and Animals: The Role of Animals in Human Ecological Adjustments* (ed. A. Leeds and A. P. Vayda), pp. 271–82. American Association for the Advancement of Science, Washington D.C.

[24] COLLINS, P. W. and VAYDA, A. P. (1969) Functional analysis and its aims. *Australian and New Zealand Journal of Sociology*, **5**, 153–56.

[25] COOK, E. (1971) The flow of energy in an industrial society. *Scientific American*, **225** (3), 134–47.

[26] COOK, S. (1973) Production, ecology and economic anthropology: notes toward an integrated frame of reference. *Social Science Information*, **12**, 25–52.

[27] DIENER, P. (1974) Ecology or evolution? the Hutterite case. *American Ethnologist*, **1**, 601–18.

[28] DORE, R. (1961) Function and cause. *American Sociological Review*, **26**, 843–53.

[29] DOWNS, J. R. (1965) The social consequences of a dry well. *American Anthropologist*, **67**, 1388–1416.

[30] DUMOND, D. E. (1975) The limitation of human population: a natural history. *Science*, **187**, 713–21.

[31] FLANNERY, K. V. (1971) The cultural evolution of civilizations. *Annual Review of Ecology and Systematics*, **3**, 399–425.

[32] FORCE, D. C. (1974) Ecology of insect host–parasitoid communities. *Science*, **184**, 624–32.

[33] FRIEDMAN, J. (1974) Marxism, structuralism, and vulgar materialism. *Man*, **9**, 444–69.

[34] FRISANCHO, A. R. (1975) Functional adaptation to high altitude hypoxia. *Science*, **187**, 313–19.

[35] FRISANCHO, A. R. *et al.* (1973) Adaptive significance of small body size under poor socio-economic conditions in southern Peru. *American Journal of Physical Anthropology*, **39**, 255–60.

[36] GERLACH, L. P. (1971) Movements of revolutionary change: some structural characteristics. *American Behavioral Scientist*, **14**, 812–36.

[37] GERLACH, L. P. and HINE, V. H. (1973) *Lifeway Leap: The Dynamics of Change in America*. University of Minnesota Press, Minneapolis.

[38] GREENWOOD, D. J. (1974) Political economy and adaptive processes: a framework for the study of peasant-states. *Peasant Studies Newsletter*, **3**, 1–10.

[39] GROSS, D. R. and UNDERWOOD, B. (1971) Technological change and caloric costs: sisal agriculture in northeastern Brazil. *American Anthropologist*, **73**, 725–40.

[40] HALLPIKE, C. R. (1973) Functionalist interpretations of primitive warfare. *Man*, **8**, 451–70.

[41] HAMILTON, W. D. (1964) The genetical evolution of social behavior. I–II. *Journal of Theoretical Biology*. **7**, 1–16, 17–51.

[42] HANNA, J. M. (1974) Coca leaf use in southern Peru. *American Anthropologist*, **76**, 281–96.

[43] HARRIS, M. (1968) *The Rise of Anthropological Theory*. Crowell, New York.

[44] HAYDEN, B. (1972) Population control among hunter/gatherers. *World Archaeology*, **4**, 205–21.

[45] HIRSCHMANN, A. O. (1970) Exit, Voice and Loyalty: Responses to Decline in Firms, Organizations and States. Harvard University Press, Cambridge.

[46] HOLLING, C. S. (1973) Resilience and stability of ecological systems. *Annual Review of Ecology and Systematics*, **4**, 1–23.

[47] HOLLING, C. S. and GOLDBERG, M. A. (1971) Ecology and planning. *Journal of the American Institute of Planners*, **37**, 221–30.

[48] IRONS, W. (1974) Nomadism as a political adaptation: the case of the Yomut Turkmen. *American Ethnologist*, **1**, 635–58.

[49] ISLAM, M. A. (1974) Tropical cyclones: coastal Bangladesh. See Ref. 98, pp. 19–24.

[50] KATZ, S. H. and FOULKS, E. F. (1970) Mineral metabolism and behavior: abnormalities of calcium homeostasis. *American Journal of Physical Anthropology*, **32**, 299–304.

[51] KEMP, W. B. (1971) The flow of energy in a hunting society. *Scientific American*, **255** (3), 105–15.

[52] KOLATA, G. B. (1975) Sociobiology (I): models of social behavior. *Science*, **187**, 50–51.

[53] KOLATA, G. B. (1975) Sociobiology (II): the evolution of social systems. *Science*, **187**, 156–57.

[54] KUNSTADTER, P. (1972) Demography, ecology, social structure and settlement patterns. In *The Structure of Human Populations* (ed. G. A. Harrison and A. J. Boyce), pp. 313–51. Clarendon, Oxford.

[55] LAUGHLIN, C. D. Jr. (1974) Maximization, marriage and residence among the So. *American Ethnologist*, **1**, 129–41.

[56] LAUGHLIN, C. D. Jr. (1974) Deprivation and reciprocity. *Man*, **9**, 380–89.

[57] LEE, R. B. (1969) !Kung Bushman subsistence: an input–output analysis. In *Environment and Cultural Behavior* (ed. A. P. Vayda), pp. 47–79. Natural History Press, Garden City.

[57a] LEE, R. B. (1972) !Kung spatial organization: an ecological and historical perspective. *Human Ecology*, **1**, 125–48.

[58] LEES, S. H. (1974) Hydraulic development as a process of response. *Human Ecology*, **2**, 159–75.

[59] LESSER, A. (1968) War and the state. In *War: The Anthropology of Armed Conflict and Aggression* (ed. M. Fried and R. Murphy), pp. 92–96. Natural History Press, Garden City.

[60] LEVI, L. (1974) Psychosocial stress and disease: a conceptual model. In *Life Stress and Illness* (ed. E. K. Gunderson and R. H. Rahe), pp. 8–33. Thomas, Springfield.

[61] MASON, J. B., HAY, R. W., HOLT, J., SEAMAN, J. and BOWDEN, M. R. (1974). Nutritional lessons from the Ethopian drought. *Nature*, **248**, 646–50.

[62] MAY, R. (1973) *Stability and Complexity in Model Ecosystems*. Princeton University Press, Princeton.

[63] MAYER, J. (1974) Coping with famine. *Foreign Affairs*, **53**, 98–120.

[64] MITCHELL, J. K. (1974) Natural hazards research. In *Persectives on Environment* (ed. I. R. Manners and M. W. Mikesell), pp. 311–41. Washington. D.C., Association of American Geographers.

[65] MOORE, O. K. (1957) Divination—a new perspective. *American Anthropologist*, **59**, 69–74.

[66] MURPHY, R. F. (1970) Basin ethnography and ecological theory. In *Languages and Cultures of Western North America* (ed. E. H. Swanson Jr.), pp. 152–71.

Idaho State University Press, Pocatello.

[67] ODEND'HAL, S. (1972) Energetics of Indian cattle in their environment. *Human Ecology*, **1**, 3–22.

[68] ODUM, E. P. (1971) *Fundamentals of Ecology*, 3rd ed. Saunders, Philadelphia.

[69] ODUM, H. (1971) *Environment, Power and Society*. Wiley, New York.

[70] ORIANS, G. (1973) A diversity of textbooks: ecology comes of age. *Science*, **181**, 1238–39.

[71] PARKHURST, R. (1966) The Great Ethopian famine of 1888–1892, a new assessment. *Journal of the History of Medicine and Allied Sciences*, **21**, 95–125, 272–94.

[72] RAPPAPORT, R. A. (1968) *Pigs for the Ancestors*. Yale University Press, New Haven.

[73] RAPPAPORT, R. A. (1971) The flow of energy in an agricultural society. *Scientific American*, **225** (3), 116–32.

[74] RAPPAPORT, R. A. (1971) Nature, culture, and ecological anthropology. In *Man, Culture and Society* (ed. H. L. Shapiro), pp. 237–67. Oxford University Press, New York. Rev. ed.

[75] RAPPAPORT, R. A. (1974) Energy and the structure of adaptation. Presented at 140th Annual Meeting of The American Association for the Advancement of Science, San Francisco.

[76] RUYLE, E. E. (1973) Genetic and cultural pools: some suggestions for a unified theory of biocultural evolution. *Human Ecology*, **1**, 201–15.

[77] SAHLINS, M. D. (1961) The segmentary lineage: an organization of predatory expansion. *American Anthropologist*, **63**, 322–45.

[78] SARGENT, F. H. (1966) Ecological implications of individuality in the context of the concept of adaptive strategy. *International Journal of Biometeorology*, **10**, 305–22.

[79] SELYE, H. (1971) The evolution of the stress concept—stress and cardiovascular disease. In *Society, Stress and Disease: The Psychosocial Diseases* (ed. L. Levi), pp. 299–311. Oxford University Press, New York.

[80] SHIMKIN, D. B. (1966) Adaptive strategies: a basic problem in human ecology. In *Three Papers on Human Ecology*. Mills Coll. Assem. Ser., Oakland, Calif., pp. 37–52.

[81] SLOBODKIN, L. B. (1965) On the present incompleteness of mathematical ecology. *American Scientist*, **53**, 347–57.

[82] SLOBODKIN, L. B. (1968) Toward a predictive theory of evolution. In *Population Biology and Evolution* (ed. R. C. Lewontin), pp. 187–205. Syracuse University Press, Syracuse.

[83] SLOBODKIN, L. B. (1972) On the inconstancy of ecological efficiency and the form of ecological theories. In *Growth by Intussusception: Ecological Essays in Honor of G. Evelyn Hutchinson. Transactions of the Connecticut Academy of Arts and Sciences*, **44**, 293–305.

[84] SLOBODKIN, L. B. (1974) Mind, mind and ecology: a review of Gregory Bateson's collected essays. *Human Ecology*, **2**, 67–74.

[85] SLOBODKIN, L. B. and RAPOPORT, A. (1974) An optimal strategy of evolution. *Quarterly Review of Biology*, **49**, 181–200.

[86] SPROUT, H. and SPROUT, M. (1968) *An Ecological Paradigm for the Study of International Politics*. Woodrow Wilson School of Public and International Affairs, Princeton University Center of International Studies. Research Monograph, 30.

[87] STERN, J. J. (1970) The meaning of 'adaptation' and its relation to the phenomenon of natural selection. In *Evolutionary Biology* (ed. T. H. Dobzhansky), vol. 4, pp. 39–66. Appleton-Century-Crofts, New York.

[88] STEWARD, J. (1955) *Theory of Culture Change: The Methodology of Multilinear Evolution.* University of Illinois Press, Urbana.

[89] THOMAS, R. B. (1973) *Human Adaptation to a High Andean Energy Flow System.* Occasional Papers in Anthropology, No. 7. University Park: Pennsylvania State University, Department of Anthropology.

[90] TOFFLER, A. (1970) *Future Shock.* Random House, New York.

[91] VAYDA, A. P. (1968) Foreword to *Pigs for the Ancestors* by R. A. Rappaport. Yale University Press, New Haven.

[91a] VAYDA, A. P. (1969) An ecological approach in cultural anthropology. *Bucknell Review,* **17** (1), 112–19.

[92] VAYDA, A. P. (1970) Maoris and muskets in New Zealand: disruption of a war system. *Political Science Quarterly,* **85,** 560–84.

[93] VAYDA, A. P. (1974) Warfare in ecological perspective. *Annual Review of Ecology and Systematics,* **5,** 183–93.

[94] VAYDA, A. P. (1976) *War in Ecological Perspective: Persistence, Change and Adaptive Processes in Three Oceanian Societies.* Plenum, New York.

[95] VAYDA, A. P. and RAPPAPORT, R. A. (1968) Ecology, cultural and non-cultural. In *Introduction to Cultural Anthropology* (ed. J. A. Clifton), pp. 477–97. Houghton Mifflin, Boston.

[96] WADDELL, E. (1975) How the Enga cope with frost: responses to climatic perturbations in the Central Highlands of New Guinea. *Human Ecology,* **3,** 249–73.

[96a] WALTERS, C. J. (1971) Systems ecology: the systems approach and mathematical models in ecology. In *Fundamental of Ecology,* 3rd ed. pp. 276–92. Saunders, Philadelphia.

[97] WARD, R. M. (1972) Models of weather hazard perception and decision making in Florida agriculture. Presented to Commission on Man and Environment, International Geographical Union, Calgary, Alberta (cited in Ref. 64).

[97a] WATT, K. E. F., Ed. (1966) Systems Analysis in Ecology. Academic Press, New York.

[98] WHITE, G. F., Ed. (1974) *Natural Hazards: Local, National, Global.* Oxford University Press, New York.

[99] WHITE, R. W. (1974) Strategies of adaptation: an attempt at systematic description. In *Coping and Adaptation* (ed. G. V. Coelho, D. A. Hamburg and J. E. Adams), pp. 47–68. Basic Books, New York.

[100] WILLIAMS, G. C. (1966) *Adaptation and Natural Selection: A Critique of Some Current Evolutionary Thought.* Princeton University Press, Princeton.

[101] WILLIAMS, G. C., Ed. (1971) *Group Selection.* Aldine-Atherton, Chicago.

[102] WILLIAMS, W. M. (1963) *A West Country Village: Ashworthy.* Routledge & Kegan Paul, London.

[103] WINTERHALDER, B., LARSEN, R., and THOMAS, R. B. (1974) Dung as an essential resource in a highland Peruvian community. *Human Ecology,* **2,** 89–104.

[104] WOODBURN, J. (1968) Stability and flexibility in Hadza residential groupings. In *Man the Hunter* (ed. R. B. Lee and I. DeVore), pp. 103–10. Aldine, Chicago.

[105] WOODHAM-SMITH, C. (1962) *The Great Hunger.* Harper & Row, New York.

OPTIMALITY CONSIDERATIONS IN ANIMAL BEHAVIOUR

D. J. McFarland

Department of Zoology, University of Oxford

BEHAVIOUR patterns are subject to natural selection in the same manner as the morphological characteristics of animals. We can therefore regard animals as being designed by natural selection to make the best use of their time. In other words, the behaviour patterns observed in the natural environment are the result of some optimization process. As biologists, we must assume that the optimality criterion is closely related to Darwinian fitness—measured in terms of the individual's genetic contribution to future generations. However, this does not mean that the mechanisms involved in the optimizing process are necessarily solely genetic. Animals may be innately predisposed towards particular behaviour patterns, but they may also learn new patterns, and such knowledge may pass from one individual to another. In this paper I attempt to show how optimization processes can be investigated in a rigorous and empirically testable manner.

There are two distinct lines of argument for the introduction of optimality principles into the analysis of behaviour patterns in animals. One argument derives from decision theory, a discipline developed by economists and psychologists. The other argument arises from Darwin's theory of natural selection.

The Argument from Decision Theory

There is widespread agreement that an understanding of decision-making can be gained from (1) the formulation of a maximizing principle, (2) the recognition that there will inevitably be some trade-off among various aspects of the problem, which will necessitate (3) the formulation of an optimality criterion. As an example, let us consider a university committee set up to review applications for a lecturership. Their maximizing principle is to choose the best candidate, but the requirements of the post are such that there will inevitably be a trade-off between the teaching ability T and the research ability R of any given applicant. Suppose that the committee arrives at an agreed short list of two applicants A and B, and that they are able to score these for teaching and research, so that for applicant A, $T = 9$ and $R = 1$; while for applicant B, $T = 2$ and $R = 7$. Any assessment of an applicant's overall strength of candidature must rest upon the optimality criterion used to evaluate teaching ability in relation to research ability. For example, if the criterion implies that strength of candidature $C = T + R$, then applicant A would score $C = 9 + 1 = 10$, while for applicant B, $C = 2 + 7 = 9$. On the other hand, if we let $C = T \times R$, then A scores $C = 9 \times 1 = 9$, while B scores $C = 2 \times 7 = 14$. Clearly, by altering the optimality criterion, without changing the scores, it is possible to come to a different conclusion as to which is the best applicant.

We now have to ask what factors influence the optimality criterion. In the university context, factors such as government attitude, financial pressures, and so forth, are likely to determine policy concerning the balance between teaching and research. These are analogous to ecological factors. An overriding influence will be the climate of ideas concerning the maximizing principle. While in some universities the best candidate is seen in academic terms, in others it may seem better to appoint the youngest candidate, the most politically conformist, etc.

Translation of this example into terminology relevant to animal behaviour is not difficult at a superficial level. For example, let us suppose that there are two main factors contributing to feeding tendency: (1) degree of hunger, in terms of physiological requirement for food, and (2) strength of food cues, in terms of the animal's estimate of the availability of food. There will be an optimality criterion combining these into an overall feeding tendency, similar to those combining teaching and research abilities into an overall strength of candidature. Any tendency to feed has to be weighed against tendencies for other types of behaviour, because it is important that the criterion determining the feeding tendency be related to the animal's needs as a whole. Therefore we would expect the decision criterion for feeding to be shaped by natural selection in accordance with the animal's ecological circumstances. For instance, when food availability is erratic, more weight should be given to cue strength, while the weight attached to hunger should be related to the animal's physiological tolerance.

In modelling the processes involved in decision-making it is convenient to think in terms of some "common currency", by means of which the alternative courses of action may be compared along a single scale or index. For example, in deciding between different routes up a hill, it might be useful to think of height gained per unit time as a measure of progress common to all possible routes.

In applying these ideas to decision-making in animals, we have to take into account the internal state of the animal, and the likely consequences of each possible course of action. The consequences must be evaluated in two different ways. Firstly, it is obvious that all activities have consequences which change the state of the animal. Secondly, every activity has consequences that have to be judged against the maximizing principle. Thus in climbing a hill, an animal's state of hunger, or energy reserves may be an important factor in the decision as to which route to take. A consequence of taking any particular route will be some alteration of the hunger state, depending upon the amount of energy used in the climb. At the same time, each particular route will have consequences in terms of the maximizing principle—some measure of gain in height. Thus if the aim is to climb the hill as quickly as possible, i.e. to maximize the speed of ascent, then one route will be better than another. One route may be short, but involve a high energy expenditure, while another may be long, but less expensive in energy. Depending upon the exact optimality criterion, there may be some trade-off between time and energy. For example, one route may be very short but expensive on energy, so that an animal with a low initial hunger may be able to attempt it, but an animal with a high initial hunger may not have sufficient energy to complete the course at the required speed, and may actually take longer than if another route had been chosen. In any real-life situation, there are many such factors complicating the decision-making process.

In recent years it has become possible to handle this type of problem in mathematical terms. One formulation, which has proved to be particularly useful, states that an animal is designed to deploy its behavioural options in a manner which continuously maximizes a mathematical function called a Hamiltonian, after the nineteenth-century mathematician W. R. Hamilton. Expressed in words, the Hamiltonian contains two terms, called plant equations and objective function. The term "plant equations" is borrowed from the field of process control. It has become thoroughly incorporated into the vocabulary of systems theory, and is particularly appropriate in behaviour studies, because it makes intuitive sense to distinguish between the bodily processes (plant) and their control by the brain. The plant equations describe the ways in which the state of the system changes as a consequence of environmental factors and of the behaviour of the animal. An indication of the ways in which plant equations may be obtained is given by McFarland (1976). The objective function describes the relationship between the state and the behaviour of the animal, and their associated costs and benefits. We can imagine that nature has carried out a costing on each possible state, and each possible activity, that is within the animal's repertoire. (The objective function is sometimes called a costing function). The objective function is envisaged as a property of the individual animal, presumably genetically determined, and possibly modifiable by learning. Thus objective functions can be expected to differ from one individual to another, although they might be expected to be similar in related individuals, and in individuals living in similar environments. A more detailed account of the concept of the objective function is given by McFarland (1977).

Insight into the workings of the Hamiltonian formulation can be gained by considering it as a hill-climbing problem. Sibly and McFarland (1976) show how lines (called isoclines) joining points of equal Hamiltonian-value can be represented as concentric circles, and viewed as contours (lines joining points of equal height) on a symmetrical hill. A point on the hill represents the state of the animal at a particular time, and a triangular area represents the states that the animal can attain in a given period of time, as illustrated in Figure 1.

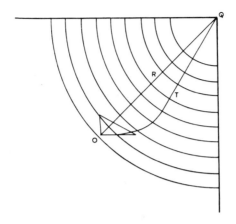

FIG. 1.   Hill-climbing model, with contours of equal Hamiltonian-value. Q is the top of the hill, O is the starting-point of the animal, R is the best possible route, T is the constrained trajectory. The small triangle represents the constraints upon the behaviour of the animal.

The maximizing principle is to gain as much height as possible per unit time. Thus the best possible route cuts all contours at right angles, as illustrated in the figure. However, circumstances may be such that the best possible route may not be attainable. In such cases, the animal should take the optimum route under the prevailing circumstances.

The circumstances that prevent an animal from taking the best possible route usually take the form of constraints upon its behaviour. The problem for the animal is to change its state in the optimal manner by deploying the appropriate behaviour. However, the consequences of behaviour may be such that the animal cannot attain a particular state (Sibly and McFarland, 1972). For example, if a desired nutritional state involves a particular balance of protein and fat, an animal may not be able to attain that balance, if it has access to only one type of food, which contains a different mixture of protein and fat. Some of the constraints upon behaviour may appear to be biologically obvious, but it may nevertheless be mathematically important to mention them explicitly. In particular, an animal can often indulge in only one activity at a time, it is not capable of negative behaviour (i.e. what

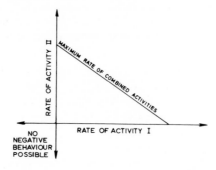

FIG. 2. Constraints upon behaviour represented in a two-dimensional activity space.

is done cannot be undone), and there are always constraints upon the rate at which an animal can change its state by means of a particular activity. These constraints are summarized in Figure 2. From this it can be seen that the constraints combine in such a way that movement from a given initial point is restricted to a triangle. As the animal changes its behaviour, the triangle moves up the hill, and traces a trajectory, as illustrated in Figure 1. Notice that the trajectory does not take the direct, best possible route up the hill, but follows another route, which is optimal under the prevailing constraints. The reason for this can be seen

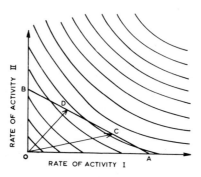

FIG. 3. Constraint triangle superimposed on contour map, showing optimal route OC, and most direct route OD.

by looking closely at the way in which the triangle lies in relation to the isoclines (Figure 3). If the animal were to spend all its time in behaviour I, its trajectory would be along OA, cutting through 4·7 isoclines. This means that behaviour I has a relative advantage of 4·7. If the animal spent all its time in behaviour II, 3·4 isoclines would be cut, and the relative advantage would be 3·4.

The greatest progress up the hill can be made by combining activities I and II, so that the resulting trajectory lies along OC, which cuts through 5·2 isoclines. Thus OC is the direction that should be taken. However, the most direct route up the hill would appear to be OD since this is the route which cuts the isoclines at right angles. Thus, while OC actually takes the animal higher up the hill, OD is the most direct overall route. This disparity is due to the way in which the isoclines cut through the triangle. The situation would be different if the triangle were in a different orientation with respect to the isoclines, or if the triangle were a different shape. In other words, the constraints on the animal's behaviour (the shape of the triangle) affect the relative advantages of the different possible courses of action in a given situation. The rule that the Hamiltonian should be continuously maximized simply means that the animal should choose the activity with the greatest relative advantage at the time. As a consequence of the behaviour of the animal, the triangle moves up the hill, and the balance of relative advantage shifts from one activity to another.

The application of this type of optimality theory in animal behaviour leads to a particular form of hypothesis-testing procedure, which has so far been used in only a few studies (Dempster, 1977; Houston, 1977; McFarland, 1977). In this approach, a maximization principle is assumed, and a particular form of the objective function is postulated, and formulated in mathematical terms. The Hamiltonian method is then used to generate predictions, which take the form of specific behaviour sequences. The hypothesis is then tested in laboratory experiments designed to reproduce the conditions assumed in the model, or against the sequence as it is observed in nature. Ability to reproduce the behaviour of the animal is then taken as evidence in favour of the postulated objective function for that particular individual animal.

The Argument from Natural Selection

As biologists, we can expect natural selection to shape the decision-making processes of animals in such a way that the resultant behaviour sequences tend to be optimally adapted to the current environmental circumstances. In other words, we can regard natural selection as a designing agent tending to produce the optimal design for any given set of conditions. Such consider-ations of optimal design apply just as much to the temporal organisation of behaviour as they do to the anatomical properties of animals. However, we cannot expect an individual animal always to behave optimally in its natural environment. Genetic variation between individuals, competition between individuals, the patchy nature of the environment, and changes in the nature of the environment, all combine to make it very unlikely that an individual animal can ever be perfectly adapted to its niche.

We can imagine, however, a hypothetical "ideal" animal that is perfectly adapted to its natural environment. The objective function of such an animal will be identical to a *cost function* which is characteristic of the environment, in the sense that it reflects the selective pressures that moulded the objective func-tion during the course of evolution. The cost function, therefore, specifies the instantaneous level of risk incurred by (and repro-ductive benefit available to) an animal in a particular internal state, engaged in a particular activity in a particular environment. Such an animal, if perfectly adapted to its environment, will deploy its behavioural options so as to maximize the Hamilto-nian, and thereby achieve that behaviour sequence which max-imizes its inclusive fitness in the prevailing circumstances.

In practice, we can distinguish two basic procedures by which behaviour sequences can be investigated from the optimality point of view. In the first, a maximization principle is assumed, and a particular form of the objective function postulated. As mentioned in the previous section, this hypothesis is then tested in laboratory experiments. Ability to reproduce the behaviour of the animal is then taken as evidence in favour of the postulated objective function.

In the second approach, an attempt is made to measure the components of the cost function empirically, by means of observations and experiments made in the field. The aim in this type of study is to determine whether animals in a particular natural environment are deploying their behavioural options in the optimal manner. The Hamiltonian formulation can be used to generate behaviour sequences, or strategies, for a given environment, provided that sufficient is known about the cost function characteristic of the environment, and the plant equations characteristic of the animal.

As an example, let us consider the herring gull incubating its eggs. This situation is being studied in detail by members of the Oxford Animal Behaviour Research Group, notably R. McCleery and R. Sibly, supported by the Natural Environment Research Council. The animals are studied intensively during the four-week incubation period, particular attention being given to three main problems:

(1) The *plant equations* are made up of factors influencing the internal state of the incubating bird, of which the most important is hunger; plus factors affecting the animal's estimate of the environmental situation, of which the weather and food supply are of prime importance. The problem is to measure these variables under field conditions.

(2) The *behaviour* of individual birds is monitored continuously, both on the territory, and at the various possible feeding sites. To obtain the type of data that is required for optimality calculations, the behaviour is monitored round the clock.

(3) The *cost function* is a function both of the internal state of the animal, and of its behaviour. The function is characteristic of the environment. Obviously, for an incubating bird there is a risk attached to being in a particular state of hunger, which depends upon the environment. If the animal had a reliable food supply it could afford to risk a higher level of hunger, than if its foraging fortunes were uncertain. Similarly, when a bird leaves the nest, as a result of disturbance, or when pressed by hunger, there is a chance that its eggs will be eaten by a neighbour. To evaluate the cost function it is necessary to obtain estimates of such risks, by conducting appropriate field experiments.

An indication of the methods used to make the measurements necessary to provide answers to these problems is given by McFarland (1977). In practice, such an ambitious study is only possible in situations about which a great deal is known as a result of previous ecological and behavioural study. In the case of Walney Island, we benefit from the many years of research by Tinbergen and his students. In some cases, however, it is possible to use the optimality approach to ask more restricted questions, which may then be used as a basis for further study. The project outlined in the paper by Blurton Jones and Sibly (p. 135) is an example of this approach.

Normally an incubating gull will sit tight until relieved by its mate. Both parents incubate the eggs, and a nest left unattended is soon subject to predation by neighbours. It is important, therefore, that the sitting bird should not leave the nest before being relieved by its partner. This rarely happens under normal circumstances, unless the bird is flushed from the nest by a predator, such as a fox, or a human. Field studies have shown that the non-sitting member of a pair is often foraging for food, or resting on the beach. It normally returns to the territory within three to twelve hours of leaving. Sometimes, however, the return may be delayed as a result of some mishap or injury. The sitting bird, with increasing hunger, should eventually decide to desert the nest, because Herring gulls breed in many successive seasons and it is not in the genetic interests of the individual to endanger its life for a single clutch of eggs. The basic dilemma for the incubating gull lies between the possibility that its partner may return at any time, and the increasing necessity to obtain food. The situation is complicated by the fact that the gull must ideally assess the returns on time invested in foraging, which vary considerably with the weather, the state of the tide, and the time of day. Moreover, individual gulls tend to specialize in particular types of foraging, so that the sitting gull should take account of its own foraging skills in assessing the likely returns from time spent foraging in different places. Every aspect of the behaviour has risks and benefits attached to it. Thus a bird foraging on the refuse tip may be poisoned, a gull on the shore line may get oil on its feathers. There is also the energetic cost of each activity to be taken into account. By systematically evaluating the cost and benefits involved in the behavioural routines of both members of mated pairs of gulls we can aim to arrive at a mathematical formulation of the cost function.

In real life, an animal has to decide whether to sleep, feed, groom, etc., at any particular time. In addition to its motivational state and the strengths of its various behavioural tendencies, the decisions reached will be heavily influenced by the decision criteria embodied in the objective function. If I believe that animal behaviour is subject to natural selection, I must conclude that the objective function is shaped by natural selection, because the decision criteria strongly influence the order in which animals go about their daily tasks.

The animal can be studied as if it carried out a cost–benefit analysis in making its decisions. If the animal is not highly adapted to its environment, it may not make the analysis correctly; i.e. its objective function may not match up to the cost function characteristic of the current environment. Nevertheless, the animal is still an optimizing agent with respect to its own objective function.

There is no suggestion intended that the individual animal necessarily carries out the cost–benefit analysis in a cognitive fashion, although this may occur to some extent in intelligent animals. The form and pattern of the behaviour is the outcome of a design operation which aims at the optimal compromise between the competing selective pressures characteristic of the environment. Obviously, in a non-stationary environment, there will be an advantage in organizing the decision-making processes in a flexible manner. Thus we can expect the laws governing learning to be designed in such a way that they tend to shape the objective function of the individual, and make it more like the cost function of the current environment. To study such phenomena we have to know something about the make-up of the individual animal, and something about its ability to shape up to the environment. This is where the Herring gull study is so instructive. There is no question that individuals differ greatly. Some specialize in foraging for mussels, others for crabs, a quite different technique. Some specialize in stealing eggs or chicks from neighbours, and others have apprenticed themselves at the local corporation refuse tip.

However, while recognizing that learning is of great importance in enabling individual animals to adapt closely to their niche, we are not yet in a position to incorporate learning into the mathematical framework of optimal decision theory. Such a step is crucial for understanding the biological bases of cultural change, and for this reason I devote the remainder of this chapter to a general discussion of this topic.

Learning

An animal living in an unvarying environment can rely on equally invariant patterns of behaviour to ensure survival and reproduction. For such animals the same stimulus always elicits the same response, and the theory of natural selection leads us to expect that the response will be adaptive. Biologists are not surprised to find that the invariant features of the environment, such as the properties of gravity, are responded to in a stereotyped manner by all members of a species. Thus the anti-gravity and postural reflexes of dogs are consistent and stereotyped. If we believe that natural selection tends to make animals optimally adapted to their environment, we should expect this to be especially true of responses to invariant environmental features, because the genetic underpinning of the optimal behaviour will have had plenty of time to spread through the population.

Not all aspects of all environments, however, are stable. If the environment changes in some crucial respect, persistence in a fixed pattern of behaviour may be maladaptive. The ability to adapt to *unpredictable* changes in the environment is due to learning. Adaptation to predictable changes, such as diurnal or seasonal cycles or changes in the social environment of an individual due to ageing, may be the result of motivational or maturational changes within the animal. Changes of this kind can be handled by the type of optimality theory outlined above, by embodying pre-programmed elements into the structure of the model. As yet, the unpredictable variation, which necessitates learning, does not come within the scope of the general theory, although some progress can be made in this respect.

When an animal learns to respond to an environmental stimulus in a new way, its behavioural repertoire undergoes a permanent alteration. Learning is an irreversible process, and although an animal may appear to forget, or to extinguish learned behaviour, the internal changes brought about by learning are irreversibly altered (McFarland, 1971), and the learned behaviour can be

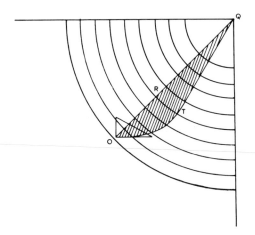

FIG. 4.   Hill-climbing model showing room for improvement by learning (shaded area). Other conventions as in Figure 1.

inhibited only by further learning (Mackintosh, 1974).

Any change in the animal's make-up will either be beneficial, in terms of increasing its inclusive fitness, or it will be deleterious. Obviously, we would expect learning to bring about beneficial changes on average, because the learning processes themselves have been subject to natural selection. The idea that learning must be adaptive has long been recognized by the more biologically minded students of behaviour (e.g. Thorndike, 1911; Tinbergen, 1951; Lorenz, 1965), but only recently has the force of this argument been fully recognized by learning theorists (Seligman, 1970; Hinde and Stevenson-Hinde, 1973). In terms of optimality theory, the argument leads to an interesting conclusion, which can be illustrated by reference to the type of model portrayed in Figure 4.

This model represents the simple hill-climbing situation outlined earlier. For an animal starting at position O, the optimal trajectory T is the optimal route when the animal is operating under the constraints represented by the triangle (Figure 3). The best possible route R is the one that would be taken were there no such constraints upon the behaviour of the animal. Therefore, any trajectory that falls between T and R will be better than the trajectory T. In other words the space between T and R (the shaded area in Figure 4) represents room for improvement.

One obvious way in which an animal could improve upon the trajectory T is to learn to alter the constraints upon its behaviour. This will have the effect of permitting a more direct route up the hill. For example, let us suppose that activity II, in Figure 3, is feeding behaviour, the effective rate of which can be improved by the animal learning to recognise a particular new kind of food. Instead of the maximum feeding rate being at B, it might now be at B¹ (Figure 5). The triangle is now a different shape, and the

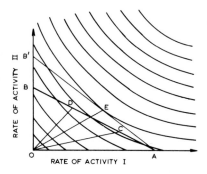

FIG. 5. Constraint map showing how improved performance OE can result from learned modification of the constraint on activity II. B′ is the new constraint; other conventions as Figure 3.

optimal trajectory is now OE rather than OC. Clearly, this represents an improvement, since OE is much nearer the direct route OD than is OC. It is also obvious that the learning process itself is constrained, since it is unlikely that the animal will learn to take a new food that decreases its feeding rate. In other words the learning process is designed in such a way that learning tends to increase fitness.

As a similar example, we might consider the possibility that the incompatibility constraint be relaxed. Normally, activity I is completely incompatible with activity II, so that they cannot occur simultaneously. However, it is possible for the animal to learn to combine two activities. For instance, en route to a possible feeding site, a fox may mark its territory. Such a combination

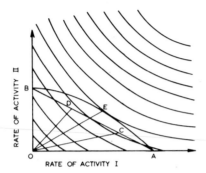

Fig. 6.   Constraint map showing how improved performance OE can result from learned modification of the incompatibility constraint. Conventions as in Figure 3.

of activities will have the effect of distorting the constraint triangle, as illustrated in Figure 6.

However, alteration of behavioural constraints is not the only way that learning can affect behaviour. From the theory of natural selection, we would expect learning to improve the adaptedness of the individual animal in relation to its niche (McFarland, 1977). In practice, there are two different ways in which we can characterize the niche: firstly, as mentioned earlier in this chapter, we can identify the objective function that is characteristic of the individual animal. This tells us the relationship between the state and behaviour of the animal, and the costs and benefits associated with these variables. From the objective function we can get a good idea of the niche to which this particular individual animal is best adapted. Secondly, the components of the cost function can be measured empirically, in the field, so that an optimal behaviour sequence or strategy can be predicted on the basis of a cost function appropriate to a particular environment. In comparing such predictions with the behaviour observed in that environment, the extent to which the animal is behaving optimally is being tested. Thus in the first case the question is whether a particular property of the individual animal (i.e. the objective function) is optimally related to the environment. In the second case the question is whether the animals in a particular natural environment are deploying their behavioural options in the optimal manner. In the case of the "ideal" animal, both methods of investigation should yield the same result, in the sense that the objective function characteristic of the individual should be the same as the cost function characteristic of the environment, and the animal will (by definition) be behaving optimally in its natural environment.

At this point it may be useful to outline a simple hypothetical example. Let us suppose that there is a species of bird that can be divided into a number of varieties on the basis of feeding habits. Some are specialized, by virtue of their morphological and behavioural features, to take larger prey than others. Although their specializations form a continuum, ranging along the gradient from large to small prey, we suppose that the different varieties can be indexed by beak length. That is, a bird with a particular beak length is specialized to take a particular type of prey, and to have a behavioural repertoire and objective function, which is characteristic of the specialization. For the purposes of this example, beak length has become a synonym for objective function, although in reality the former is a scalar quantity and the latter a vector function.

Let a bird with beak size α (bird α) be best suited to take prey size A, while a bird with beak size β (bird β) is best adapted to prey size B. On a graph of prey size plotted against fitness (Figure 7), we can see that bird α does best with prey size A, and less well with prey larger or smaller than A. Bird β fares likewise with respect to prey size B. Suppose, however, that bird β is obliged to

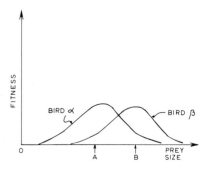

FIG. 7.   Graph of prey size against fitness for two types of bird, α and β.   is adapted to prey size A and β is adapted to prey size B.

take prey size A due to a scarcity of prey size B in the environment in which the bird finds itself. Clearly bird β will have reduced fitness, unless it can learn to adapt to the situation. There are two possible ways in which this could be done. Firstly, the bird could learn the whereabouts of habitats in which prey of size B were more plentiful (thus moving from position A in Figure 8).

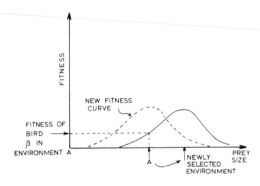

FIG. 8.   Bird β in environment A may increase fitness by moving to a new environment, or by modifying its object function to suit environment A (dotted curve).

Secondly, it may be that the bird could modify its objective function so that it becomes better suited to its current habitat. (It could not, of course, alter its beak size, but in this example we are taking beak size as synonymous with objective function.) This would have the effect of altering the fitness curve in Figure 8.

In general terms, the animal that is not optimally adapted to its current environment can either choose a new environment, or it can learn to adapt better to its current environment. In the first case, the animal is altering the cost function (a characteristic of the environment); in the second case it is altering the objective function (a property of the animal); in both cases the cost function and the objective function become more similar.

In terms of our hill-climbing example, we have to imagine two sets of contours, somewhat displaced with respect to each other, as illustrated in Figure 9. One set represents optimization with respect to the cost function, and the other represents optimization with respect to the objective function. An animal mis-

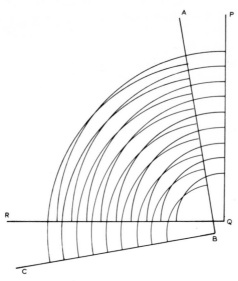

FIG. 9.   Contour map showing how the objective function PQR and cost function
ABC may be displaced with respect to each other.

matched with its environment will optimize with respect to its
objective function, but the resulting trajectory is evaluated (by
natural selection) with respect to the cost function. If the animal
is able to alter its objective function in an advantageous manner,
one set of contours will shift towards the other. Viewed from the
local perspective (Figure 10), the constraint triangle will appear to
rotate with respect to the cost function contours, thus enabling
the animal to take a more direct route up the hill. In other words,
by changing its objective function, the animal changes the relationship between its behavioural possibilities and the Hamiltonian isoclines (contours), thus increasing its overall fitness.

Cultural Adaptation

In this paper I have argued, by analogy, that, since animals are
survival machines (Dawkins, 1976), they must be designed to
optimize their use of time. The analogy is that animals are
designed as hill-climbing machines, whose evolutionary progress
is to be measured in terms of height gained per unit time. Each
individual has a set of criteria (embodied in the objective func-

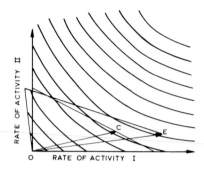

FIG. 10. Constraint map showing how improved performance OE can result from learned modification of the objective function to match with cost function.

tion), against which it can measure its progress. Nature also has a set of criteria (embodied in the cost function), against which she can measure the progress of a particular individual. The progress made by an animal, with respect to its own criteria, depends largely upon its freedom of action (the constraints upon its behaviour). The progress made by an animal, with respect to Nature's criteria, depends largely upon the extent to which the individual's criteria are matched to those of Nature. This, in turn, depends upon the particulars of the environment in which the individual finds itself. In other words, when the two sets of criteria are closely matched, we say that the individual is well adapted to its environment.

By formulating the problem in this way it is possible to test the extent to which the behaviour of an individual is well adapted to the environment. In principle, there are two ways of doing this. One way is to calculate the individual's criteria (objective function) from observation of its behaviour, and to try to relate this to the environment in which the animal is thought to operate. The other way is to attempt to measure Nature's criteria (the cost function) by directly estimating the risks, costs and benefits that ensue from the behaviour of animals in their natural environment. Both these approaches are, as yet, in an early stage of development (McFarland, 1977).

An animal that is unable to modify its criteria or its freedom of action, can do little to improve its characteristic progress up the hill. We would expect such animals to survive only in stable environments where they have achieved optimal performance through a long course of evolution. In inherently unpredictable environments we would expect animals to be able to learn to modify thier optimality criteria, and the constraints upon their behaviour. Such modification must not be mere tinkering, but must lead to improvement. The idea, once so favoured amongst psychologists, that learning is a form of blind experimentation, analogous to natural selection, is not consistent with the views expressed here. The learning process must be so biased as to lead to improved progress. Since Nature is the ultimate arbiter, the ultimate measure of progress must be the cost function. So the genes controlling the learning process will survive in accordance with their ability to pre-adapt the individual for the environment that it is to inhabit. In social animals such genes may include some which promote reciprocal altruism, in the sense that the action of one individual (the donor) may benefit another individual, at some cost to the donor, provided that there is a likelihood that the donor will be the recipient on a future occasion (Trivers, 1971; Dawkins, 1976). Reciprocal altruism appears to lead to the development of behaviour patterns which are for the "common good". It implies that the optimality criterion of the donor contains elements of that of the recipient. In other words, part of the objective function of one individual is embedded within that of the other, and vice versa (Becker, 1976). I believe that this (embedding) condition is an essential ingredient of a species capable of cultural adaptation.

There are three features of cultural adaptation that are relevant to the present argument. Firstly, the cultural element of the behaviour of an individual is learned, primarily under the influence of the behaviour of other individuals. Secondly, cultural adaptation involves a degree of conformity in the behaviour of different individuals. Thirdly, cultural traits are adaptive by virtue of the benefit they confer upon the individuals in the group. Some group structure is a prerequisite of cultural adaptedness, but this does not mean that it has evolved as a result of group selection (Dawkins, 1976). I am suggesting that the complex learned social conformity that characterizes cultural phenomena is based upon reciprocal altruism.

Imagine a gene that promotes conformity, perhaps by means of constraints upon imitative learning as suggested by Blurton Jones and Sibly on p. 154. An individual bearing this gene will be disadvantaged in terms of freedom of action or flexibility of learning. Natural selection will act against such individuals, unless they find themselves in a social environment in which the gene confers a counter-balancing advantage by helping to promote or maintain a particular cultural trait. The social behaviour of the individual is altruistic in the sense that it is of benefit to other individuals, while being a disadvantage to the donor unless he in turn is the recipient of similar behaviour from other individuals. The altruism is, therefore, reciprocal in the sense of Trivers (1971), and it is possible for all individuals to gain in such a situation (Becker, 1976).

A difficulty with this suggestion has been recognized by Hamilton (1975): "Whether reciprocation involves altruism or not, we see that insofar as it involves repeated acts between the same two individuals this useful and immensely variegating type of interaction can spread genetically, given only an ability to remember individual faces of those who have helped and those who have cheated in the past. Unfortunately, by the very aid it gives to the growth and diversification of social systems, reciprocation tends to undermine the basis of its success. Situations demanding reciprocation just once between individuals destined never to meet again naturally become more common and it becomes easier for cheaters to specialize in these and to hide from retribution. Cheating can also become more subtle, especially along lines which make it hard for victims to be sure just who has cheated them (p. 151)". Hamilton's conclusions are relevant to situations in which the reciprocation is entirely genetically based. However, if we allow that these genetically based traits may be maintained by learning, then individual recognition need not be a prerequisite of reciprocal altruism. For example, suppose that a particular gene G predisposes the individual to learn a particular behaviour pattern B, provided that the individual is raised in environment E. For instance a bird might be genetically predisposed to learn to imitate its neighbours' songs. Suppose also that the behaviour B contributes to the environment E, and it therefore influences other individuals that are raised in environment E. Suppose, also, that individuals showing behaviour B benefit from being in environment E to an extent that outweighs the cost of behaviour B. Individuals with behaviour B, therefore, derive a net benefit from being in environment E, but individuals not showing behaviour B may derive an even greater benefit, because they do not bear the cost of behaviour B. Since environment E is maintained by behaviour B, contributed by a number of individuals, it is important that such individuals should discriminate against any other individuals not showing behaviour B. Provided the cost of being discriminated against is sufficiently high, individuals not showing behaviour B will not be able to establish themselves in environment E, and gene G will be maintained in the population inhabiting environment E.

Since each individual inhabiting environment E benefits to a greater extent than the cost of his contribution to it, the extra benefit must derive from the contribution of others, so that a multiple reciprocal situation exists—the mutual cooperation is to the benefit of all the members of the group. Those who contribute are recognized by their behaviour while those who do not contribute are discriminated against. On the face of it, this situation would appear to be open to cheating, either by mutants G', who innately mimic that part of behaviour B which is recognized by other individuals, without performing that part of behaviour B which contributes to environment E, or by mutants G'', who learn some similar strategy. Such cheaters would be at an advantage in that they would not bear the contribution cost of behaviour B. In the case of the genetic cheaters, the fact that behaviour B is learned in environment E is likely to result in a change in the characteristics of behaviour B from one generation to the next, much as dialects develop in bird song and in human language. This change will be rapid compared with evolutionary time, so that any mutant G' will always be out of date. In other words, the acquisition of behaviour patterns by learning may lead to changes in fashion, which serve to protect the reciprocal social arrangements against cheaters.

In the case of cheaters with the mutant gene G'', it is difficult to see how they could invade the population from outside, because the gene G'' merely gives a predisposition to learn to cheat, while learning behaviour B. This behaviour would still have to be learned in the environment E, and the carriers of G'' would have to be juveniles, to avoid being discriminated against as soon as they appear in the population. A would-be cheater, raised in environment E, would have to successfully resist indoctrination, social pressure, etc., and would also have to escape detection in exercising the cheating behaviour. I have no doubt that the ability to develop such sophisticated skills could evolve under appropriate circumstances, but my point is that individual recognition of *bona fide* members of the group would not be necessary. While it may be true that individual recognition may be necessary for the detection and elimination of cads from a society, the major part of the cheating can be eliminated by educational methods applied to the population of juveniles as a whole.

I am suggesting that cultural adaptation may consist, in part, in groups of individuals in which each is predisposed to take account of the welfare of the other members of the group—in the sense that the objective function includes elements of the objective function of other individuals. During juvenile life, the individual learns, from other members of the group, to conform to group norms, especially with respect to social behaviour, language, etc. In this way the objective function is moulded into a form that differs from group to group, and from generation to generation, in accordance with changes in "fashion".

To be adaptive in the biological sense, such changes in the objective function would have to bring the cost and objective functions closer (Figure 9). Learned modification of the objective function cannot, of course, be based upon information about the nature of the cost function, unless we are prepared to allow that the individual understands the function of its own behaviour. It seems more likely that the learning is preprogrammed, in the sense that the juvenile is predisposed to learn certain types of things, such as the nature of its habitat, of its parents, and of food sources. It is also possible that individuals can learn to coordinate with others and modify the environment in such a way that the cost function is brought closer to the objective function.

The fact that cultural adaptations are learned has sometimes been seen as a stumbling-block for any cultural adaptation theory. This view probably stems from an unfortunate tendency to oppose learned and innate explanations of behavioural development. This is no longer a view that is acceptable to biologists (Hinde, 1974), since it has become obvious that the processes responsible for learning are themselves subject to natural selection and may differ considerably from one species to another. If we are prepared to regard cultural development as similarly constrained, we may be able to make some progress in our efforts to account for cultural adaptation.

References

BECKER, G. S. (1976) Altruism, egoism, and genetic fitness: economics and sociobiology. *Journal of Economic Literature*, **XIV**, 817–26.

DAWKINS, R. (1976) *The Selfish Gene*. Oxford University Press.

DEMPSTER, M. A. H. (1977) Optimal temporal organisation of behaviour. In Dempster, M. A. H. and McFarland, D. J. (eds.) *Animal Economics*. Academic Press, New York (in the press).

HAMILTON, W. D. (1975) Innate social aptitudes of man: an approach from evolutionary genetics. In *Biosocial Anthropology* (ed. Fox, R.). Malaby Press, London.

HINDE, R. A. and STEVENSON-HINDE, J. (1973) *Constraints on Learning*. Academic Press, New York.

HINDE, R. A. (1974) *Biological Bases of Human Social Behaviour*. McGraw-Hill, New York.

HOUSTON, A. I. (1977) Cost-benefit analysis of animal behaviour: a worked example of the Hamiltonian hypothesis. *Animal Behaviour* (in the press).

LORENZ, K. (1965) *Evolution and Modification of Behaviour*. Methuen, London.

McFARLAND, D. J. (1971) *Feedback Mechanisms in Animal Behaviour*. Academic Press, New York.

McFARLAND, D. J. (1976) Form and function in the temporal organisation of behaviour. In *Growing Points in Ethology* (ed. Bateson, P. P. G. and Hinde, R. A.). Cambridge University Press.

McFARLAND, D. J. (1977) Decision-making in animals. *Nature*, **269**, 15–21.

McFARLAND, D. and SIBLY, R. (1972) "Unitary Drives" revisited. *Animal Behaviour*, **20**, 548–63.

MACKINTOSH, N. J. (1974) *The Psychology of Animal Learning*. Academic Press, London.

SELIGMAN, M. E. P. (1970) On the generality of the laws of learning. *Psychology Reviews*, **77**, 406–18.

SIBLY, R. and McFARLAND, D. (1976) On the fitness of behaviour sequences. *American Naturalist*, **110**, 601–17.

THORNDIKE E. L. (1911) *Animal Intelligence*. Macmillan, New York.

TINBERGEN, N. (1951) *The Study of Instinct*. Clarendon Press, Oxford.

TRIVERS, R. L. (1971) The evolution of reciprocal altruism. *Quarterly Review of Biology*, **46**, 35–57.

ADAPTATION AND THE
STRUCTURE OF RITUAL

Roy A. Rappaport

Department of Anthropology, University of Michigan, Ann Arbor, Michigan

I SHALL be concerned with the place of ritual and certain of its products in human adaptation and in the adaptations of humans. This expression is not redundant—I mean by it to indicate that ritual enters into the adaptive processes of humanity both at the level of the species and at that of the more or less discrete social and cultural units into which the species is organized. I shall be more concerned with the relationship of ritual's general form to the adaptive properties of the species generally than with the place of particular rituals in the adaptations of particular societies.

Popular usage renders terms like "ritual" and "adaptation" vague; it is therefore necessary to make clear what is meant whenever they are used. Inasmuch as it refers to a wider range of phenomena and because it designates larger processes within which ritual's place is to be considered, I turn first to adaptation, which I take to be characteristic of, or perhaps even definitive of, living systems. Living systems are what Slobodkin and Rapoport have called, in a discussion of the difficulties of applying game theory to evolution (1974), "players of the existential game", the game in which the only reward for successful play is to be allowed to continue to play. The proper goal of the player of the existential game is so low in specificity as to appear to be a virtual non-goal: it is merely to persist. Because persistence is continuously threatened by disturbance I take the term "adaptation" to refer to the processes through which living systems—organisms and associations of organisms (e.g., clans, societies, populations, and even ecosystems)—maintain homeostasis in the face of perturbation (Rappaport, 1976a, 1977). It is obvious that resilience and its maintenance are crucial to players of the existential game, and in a world in which non-reversing changes in the composition and structure of environments, as well as fluctuations in environmental states, are continuous, resilience supposes that repertoires of responses include those effecting orderly transformations of the structures of adaptive systems. Adaptive processes, therefore, include evolutionary or self-organizing changes as well as those which are simply "functional" or self-regulating. In fact, evolutionary changes in subsystems can be viewed as functional with respect to the larger systems in which they occur. The connecting generalization is sometimes called "Romer's Rule" after Alfred Romer, the zoologist who first proposed it in a discussion of the emergence of the amphibia from the lobe-finned fish (1954). He proposed that those creatures did not come onto dry land to take advantage of the delights and opportunities of the terrestrial habitat. Indeed, dry land must have been extremely unpleasant for them. Rather, during periods of drought, which were presumably common during the Devonian, they must have frequently found themselves stranded as the shallow pools and streams in which these air-breathing bottom feeders lived dried up. Relatively minor modification of their limb structure—from bony fin to leg—greatly facilitated locomotion across dry land to other streams and ponds in which water remained, and therefore must have been selected for very strongly. Thus, the initial modifications which are associated with terrestrial adaptation made it possible to continue an aquatic way of life. This may be a zoological myth, but like all good myths it has a message: the most important question to be asked concerning an evolutionary change is: What does it maintain unchanged?

It is surely possible to distinguish on formal grounds those responses which entail no more than changes of state from structural or evolutionary change. But it is mistaken to separate them analytically because they are joined in nature. Both Bateson (1972, pp. 348ff.) and Slobodkin (1968) tell us that in organisms responses to perturbation which are instances of the two classes ("functional" and "evolutionary") seem to be organized into orderly sequences, commencing with those which are energetically or behaviourally expensive but easily reversible, proceeding finally to responses which are more efficient but irreversible. Genetic change is ultimate. Both Slobodkin and Bateson would advise evolving organisms to change no more than necessary, for irreversible changes are likely to decrease systemic flexibility, that is, the ability of the system to respond homeostatically in the future to stresses which may be unpredictable and are often novel. With some modification this model applies, I think, to social systems as well as to organisms, and so does the advice.

Resilience or flexibility is, then, not simply a matter of response, but of the organization of responses into orderly sequences. The maintenance of orderly adaptive response sequences may well require adaptive systems to embody certain structural features. Piaget (1972) and Simon (1968), among recent writers, propose that such systems can be conceived as hierarchically organized sets of regulators and subsystems: the subsystems having more or less specific goals, the most inclusive systems having, as I have already suggested, as proper or adaptive goals nothing more specific than their own persistence. Implicit in this view is that certain relations of specificity, speed, duration, reversibility, contingency and—in human social systems, sanctity—must characterize relations between the levels of such hierarchies if they are to persist—that is, if they are to continue to be able to respond homeostatically to perturbation (Rappaport 1976 b, 1978).

Flexibility is central to adaptive processes, and the enormous flexibility of the human species rests, of course, largely upon language. Whereas the capacity for language must have a genetic basis, there seems to be no genetic specification for any particular language nor for what can be said in any language. Their possession of language not only permits but requires human groups to stipulate linguistically the rules and most of the understandings in accordance with which they live. The rules and understandings of human groups are not genetically but only conventionally specified, and can thus be modified or even changed relatively quickly and easily. Language has thus conferred upon humanity the ability to devise a great range of organizations and techniques and to process and conserve enormous quantities of information. These gifts of language have made it possible for the species to invade and dominate virtually all of the world's regions. There are, however, problems intrinsic to the very virtues of language which will become apparent as I proceed. For now I shall only propose that the very features of language which confer flexibility upon the *species* threaten with chaos the *groups* into which the species is organized, and it is this threat that the ritual form ameliorates. This is to make a universal adaptive generalization about ritual. To argue it I am required to leave the matter of adaptation *per se* for a while so that I may deal with ritual in what I take to be its own formal terms. During the course of my discussion I shall, however, relate aspects of ritual to aspects of adaptive process, and will make a more general statement at the end.

I shall define ritual in terms of its most obvious aspects, those leading us to recognize particular events as rituals. I take ritual to be a structure or form, defining it as the performance of more or less invariant sequences of formal acts and utterances not encoded by the performers. I shall be concerned to unpack some of the implications and entailments of this definition, attempting to derive from it social contract, morality, a paradigm of creation, the idea of the sacred, the sense of the numinous and the notion of the divine. But first, I would call your attention to certain of its features.

First, it may seem banal to insist upon it, but ritual must be performed. No performance, no ritual. This is not simply to say that a ritual is not a book or a TV set. It is to say that the performance itself is an aspect of what is being performed. The medium, as they say, is part of the message. It is, in fact, a meta-message about whatever is encoded in the ritual. Second, invariance is a feature of my definition, and it may seem on the face of it paradoxical to assert that that which is characterized by rigidity preserves flexibility. I shall discuss this in some detail later, but now I call your attention to my characterization of rituals as only more or less invariant.

The phrase "more or less" recognizes imperfections in performance, of course, but it aims to do more than that. It also recognizes that within any liturgical order, regardless of how highly specified it may be, there is some room for variation. In the Mass one may take communion or not. In a Melanesian feast one may give away 20 pigs or 30. A visiting contingent at festivals of the Maring, a group with whom I have worked in the New Guinea Highlands (Rappaport, 1968) may include 20 dancers or 50. Most important, for the individual there is always a choice, at least logically possible, to participate in a ritual or not to participate in it.

The variant and invariant components of ritual are each associated with rather different classes of messages. Those encoded in the invariant order of the canon specify enduring or even putatively eternal aspects of the social and cosmological order. The invariance of the liturgical order is, perhaps, a metaphor for, or an icon of, the abiding nature of that which it encodes. In contrast, the messages carried by whatever variation the ritual allows or requires—taking the Eucharist or not, giving away 20 pigs or 30—indicate the current states of the performers, expressing, by association, the relationship of the performers to the invariant order encoded in the canon.

Two points need to be made concerning these two strands of messages. First, the relationship of sign to signified in each of them may be different. That which is signified in the canon is not confined to the here and now, may not be material, and might not even be considered to exist within the space-time continuum. I am thinking of gods and the like. Since these referents are not in their entirety present, reference to them requires the use of symbols. I use the term "symbol" in the very simple sense of Charles Peirce. A symbol is a sign related "only by law" (convention) to that to which it refers (Peirce, 1960, pp. 143ff.). Words are symbols in this sense. (Entailed by the conventional relationship of sign to signified is, or course, concept. The word "dog" refers not only to a particular sentence, it also signifies the concept "dog").

In contrast, the states of the performers signaled by variations in performance *are* in the here and now and as such the relationship of the signal to its referent need not be merely symbolic, and it often, if not always, is not. It may be indexical. An index is a sign which is, to use Peirce's phrase, "really affected by" its referent. For instance, a dark cloud is an index of rain. That the relationship of ritual signs to their referents is indexical is in some cases patent. A prestation of 30 pigs does not symbolize the donor's worth or influence. It indicates it. Some instances are not as patent but are more interesting. Among the Maring of New Guinea a man signals his pledge to help another group in warfare by dancing at their festival. I would claim that this act does not merely symbolize a man's pledge to fight, but is rather an index of that pledge, or something like it, because dancing is, in J. L. Austin's (1970) sense, performative. That is, the dancing brings into being the pledging. To dance is to pledge.

The indexical nature of the signs referring to current states of transmitters seems to me to be of considerable importance. I have just used the phrases "merely symbolic" and "merely symbolize". Because the use of the symbol is taken by some to be the crowning glory of our species, and because one anthropologist, at least, has taken the emergence of the symbol to have been an evolutionary development second in importance only to the emergence of life itself, these phrases may sound strange. I would simply note a vice intrinsic to the very virtues of the symbol. When a sign is freed from its referent, its referent can occur without it being signaled, and a signal can be transmitted without its reference being the case. This is to say that lying, if not made for the first time possible by the symbol, is enormously facilitated by it. Other animals may use symbols in some degree, but man's reliance upon the symbol is massive. Thus, if man is not the world's only liar, he is surely the world's foremost liar. This sets serious problems for him. If a social order depends upon communication but the system of communication accommodates falsehood, how may the recipients of information be assured that the messages they receive are sufficiently reliable to act upon?

It is much more difficult to lie indexically, and one of the ways to overcome the subversions of order threatened by falsehood and lack of credibility is to signal indexically. It is interesting to note that when he wishes to make himself more than ordinarily credible, man may leave the subtleties of language behind and attempt to communicate in a manner resembling that of the innocent and speechless beasts.

This is not to deny the continuing possibility of deceitfulness. I would not assert that a Maring dancer will necessarily honour his pledge to fight, or even that he was sincere when he made it. I simply assert that because the pledge was made indexically he did not lie about making it. What leads hosts to feel confident—to the extent that they do—that visiting dancers will honour their pledges is in part the association of their pledges with canonical messages, a matter which will be considered later.

We are led here to a second general point concerning the two strands of messages—let us call them the canonical and the self-referential. The self-referential rely for their significance and, in some cases their acceptability, upon the canonical. It is also the case, for reasons that should become apparent, that the canonical also depends upon the self-referential. Indeed, there is an indexical, self-referential message present in all ritual without which the canon would be devoid of force or significance. For now I only wish to make the point that ritual is not simply a congeries of messages or even meta-messages, but a very complex form of communication in which the two sorts of messages are mutually dependent.

It is unfortunate that there is no time to take up the indexical self-referential messages of ritual more than briefly because there is much that is interesting both about them and about how they are communicated. They can be communicated by variations in what occurs within rituals—variations in numbers of performers, in numbers of things given away, in the order in which people are called upon and so on. Also important are variations in when non-calendrical rituals occur because their occurrence must signal some contemporary condition. I would only note in this regard that the occurrence of non-calendrical rituals may summarize a great mass of complex more-less information and transform it into a simple yes–no signal, which is in its nature free of ambiguity (Rappaport, 1968). The occurrence of such rituals thus imposes a clarity upon situations which are in their nature ambiguous, and imposes sharp discontinuity upon what is naturally continuous. Similar observations have been made of animal rituals (e.g., Cullen, 1966).

As I noted earlier, liturgical orders—rituals—must be performed. If there is no performance there is no liturgical order. We have available to us in books accounts of liturgical orders performed in ancient Egypt, but they are dead, for they are no longer given breath by human voices or energy by human bodies. A liturgical order is an order of *acts* and *utterances*, and as such is enlivened or realized only when those acts are performed and those utterances voiced. Performance, this is to say, brings into being, realizes or makes real what is being performed. The act of performance, moreover, cannot help but also specify the relationship of the performer to what he is performing. He is not merely transmitting messages he finds encoded in the canon. He is participating in—that is, becoming part of—the order to which his own body and breath give life.

To *perform* a liturgical order, which is by definition a relatively invariant sequence of acts and utterances encoded by someone other than the performer himself, is perforce to *conform* to that order. As such, authority or directive is intrinsic to liturgical order. But participation suggests something more binding than whatever is connoted by terms like "authority" and "conformity". The notion of communication implies, minimally, transmitters, receivers and messages. Elsewhere I have argued that in ritual the transmitter is always among the most important receivers of his own messages; that is, there is a partial fusion of transmitter and receiver in ritual. This will be important shortly. Here I would note a further fusion. In ritual the transmitter–receiver becomes one with the message he is transmitting and receiving. In conforming to the order which comes alive in his performance he becomes a part of it for the time being. Because this is the case, for a performer to reject whatever is encoded in the canon that he is performing while he is performing it seems to me to be a contradiction in terms, and thus impossible. Thus, *by performing a liturgical order the performer accepts, and indicates to himself as well as to others that he accepts whatever is encoded in the canons of the liturgical order in which he is participating*, that is, of which he has become a part. This message of acceptance is the indexical message—or meta-message—that is intrinsic to all ritual, the self-referential message without which canonical messages are devoid of force, mere theological or philosophical speculation or opinion. The message of acceptance is not a trivial message because men are not bound by their genotypes to the acceptance of any particular order and have the choice, at least logically, of participating or not.

The assertion that acceptance is intrinsic to performance is on the face of it either dubious or indubitable, and thus requires some comment.

First, "acceptance" is not synonymous with "belief". Belief I take to be an inward state knowable subjectively if at all. (For an extended discussion, see Needham, 1972). Acceptance, in contrast, is not an inward state but a *public act* visible to both witnesses and the performer himself. Acceptance is, thus, a fundamental social act forming the basis, as unknowable and volatile belief cannot, for public social orders. Acceptance not only is not belief, it does not even imply belief. While the private processes of individuals may be persuaded by their participation to come into conformity with their public acts this is not always the case. Men may have their doubts. But doubt does not vitiate acceptance. Indeed, a number of theologians have told us that acceptance may be more profound than uncritical belief, for in his participation the performer may transcend his own doubts by accepting in defiance of them (O'Doherty, 1973, pp. 8ff.; Tillich, 1957, pp. 16ff.).

But what of insincerity and violation? To say that acceptance is intrinsic to performance is not to assert that the performer will abide by whatever rules or norms he has accepted. A man may, let us say, pilfer from the poor box on his way out of church to keep an assignation with his neighbour's wife after participating in a liturgy in which the Ten Commandments were recited by, among others, himself, without making his acceptance less real. Liturgical performance establishes conventions—understandings, rules, norms—in accordance with which behaviour is *supposed* to proceed. It does not *regulate* behaviour directly. Participation in a ritual in which a prohibition against adultery is enunciated might not keep a man from adultery, but it *does establish* for him a rule that he has accepted. Acceptance entails obligation, and whether or not a man abides by what he has accepted, he has obligated himself to do so.

We touch upon something of considerable importance here. It may be that some conventions are simply the products of usage. Linguistic conventions in non-literate societies are possibly examples. However, in other cases, particularly those concerning social relations, usage is full of vagary and violation and as such is not by itself capable of establishing convention. Conventions must be established in a manner which protects them from the erosion with which ordinary usage continuously threatens them.

Ritual does so, it seems to me, and it further seems to me that in this respect ritual may be without functional equivalents. Rules promulgated by decree may also be insulated from usage, but they do not, in their promulgation, entail acceptance, and the philosopher John Searle (1969, p. 189, *passim*) has argued that without acceptance there is no obligation. Moreover, the conditions which make it possible for some men to promulgate decrees by which other men must abide are probably relatively recent in human history, not antedating by much, if at all, the advent of plant and animal domestication. One can only speculate, but ritual may have been the primordial mechanism or one of the primordial mechanisms by which conventions were established among humans.

My argument so far, then, is that the very form which is ritual establishes convention. To establish a convention it must (1) be specified, and (2) be accepted. This is to say that in its very form ritual does not merely symbolize but *embodies* social contract, and as such is the fundamental social act—that upon which society is founded.

Ritual not only specifies and accepts conventions but also invests them with morality, for obligation is entailed by acceptance, and breach of obligation, it may be argued, is the fundamental immoral or unethical act. Homicide, for instance, is not. It is killing someone whom there is an obligation not to kill that is immoral. Speech act theory is also instructive with regard to ritual's intrinsic morality. Rituals are full of what J. L. Austin called "performatives", a class of utterances which includes such sentences as "I name this ship the *Queen Elizabeth*", "I pronounce you man and wife", "I promise to do so and so". These utterances are often indistinguishable grammatically from statements, but they are very different from them. They do not report or describe states of affairs: rather, they bring states of affairs into being. Because this is the case their relationship to the states of affairs with which they are associated is inverse to that of statements. This is of importance here because of the matter of assessment. If, for instance, I said "Peace prevails", and you then looked out the window to see tanks followed by infantry coming up the street firing, you would think my statement flawed. It is wrong, you would say, or mistaken, inaccurate, or even a downright lie. Be this as it may, relevant states of affairs are the criteria against which statements are assessed.

Let us contrast this with the performative. Let us say that we have been at war. We come together at the joint border of our territories, as do the Maring, address our ancestors in formal manner, kill pigs and exchange their livers upon which we then dine, plant certain plants and say "Peace prevails". A month later I attack you. We do not say that there was something the matter with the utterance. We say that the state of affairs is faulty. The performative is the criterion against which we assess relevant states of affairs. Liturgies thus establish criteria according to which behaviour is judged and as such whatever they encode is intrinsically moral. It is of interest that the word used in Vedic and Zoroastrian thought to label acts and states of affairs in violation of proper order was also used for lie (Brown, 1972, pp. 252ff.; Guillemin-Duchesne, 1966, pp. 25ff.). A Vedic lie is the inverse of an ordinary life.

I earlier noted that liturgical orders include both word and act. Few, if any, do not include both. Tambiah (1968) and others have discussed differences in the communicative virtues of words on the one hand and acts, substances and objects on the other and I shall not elaborate this matter here. There is another problem, however, that my discussion has raised and which must be taken up. Earlier I suggested that in ritual the transmitter, receiver and message become fused in the participant, but nothing was said about the nature of the participant. Given the possibility of discontinuity, or even conflict between the public act and the private processes of the performer this is not trivial. Indeed, it is highly problematic.

I would suggest that the use of the body defines the self of the performer for himself and for others. In kneeling, for instance, he is not merely sending a message to the effect that he submits in ephemeral words that flutter away from his mouth to dissolve into silence. The subordinated self is neither a creature of insubstantial words from which he can separate himself without loss of blood nor some insubstantial essence or soul that cannot be located in time or space. It is his visible present living substance that he "puts on the line", or that "stands up" (or kneels down) to be counted. In other instances by drawing himself into a formal posture to which ceremonial words give symbolic value the performer incarnates the symbol. That is, he gives substance to the symbol as the symbol gives him form. The canonical and self-referential come together in the *substance* of the *formal* posture. Speech act theory emphasizes that saying is often a way of doing. So it is that doing may be an especially powerful—or rather, substantial—way of saying.

I speak of word and substance, and it may be that in including within its order both word and substance, ritual contains within itself a paradigm of creation.

Myths of creation, as Bateson (1972, pp. xxiii ff) has noted, are seldom, if ever, concerned simply, or even at all, with the creation of matter *ex nihilo*. They are more concerned with the manner in which a primordial matter became ordered. As such creation is conceived as the informing of substance, but not only as the informing of substance. As substance without form is inchoate, so do many myths seem to recognize that form without substance does not exist in this world of chemistry and physics. Creation is, then, understood as both the informing of substance and the substantiation of form. We note this, of course, in Genesis, and in the New Testament the Second Adam is the Word become Flesh. Among the Walbiri of Central Australia, the creative heroes of the dreamtime, the primordial but still continuing time of creation, emerge from a primordial goo which they then form by giving names to its previously featureless regions (Meggitt, 1966, pp. 5ff.). Examples could be multiplied.

The primordial union constituting creation, in some myths at least, is, then, that of what are taken to be two primitive categories: form and substance. In ritual there is, I believe, a reunion of this primordial union. What better way to provide form than the invariant words of canon, or substance than with the living body drawn into the posture which the canon designates? Something similar to this was said about ritual by William of Auxerre in the thirteenth century in a discussion of why it is that all sacraments include acts or substances as well as words. Essential form, he said, can be established only by Word, but pure form cannot exist in this world independently. It must be substantiated (Lacey, 1918, p. 907).

This argument does not purport to explain why men take the

distinction between form and substance to be a problem, or why it should be that in myth form is so often provided by Word. The distinction surely does not arise out of simple perception, and Nature is as full of form as it is of substance. Bateson (1972, p. XXV), in a great throw-away line, has suggested, without elaboration, that it may be implicit in the subject–predicate relationship in language generally. I would suggest, in elaboration, that almost all subjects can be predicated in a number of ways, and almost all predicates can be given to a number of subjects. With predication and lexicon at their disposal language users can conceive of orders alternative to those in accordance with which they live. The conception of alternative not only facilitates change. It also facilitates disorder, for the conception of alternative orders must question, at least tacitly, those that do prevail. Although no man may ever have experienced absolute formlessness all men have experienced what they take to be disorder from time to time, and may be continually aware of its possibility. This possibility is made inevitable by language, for the use of language makes inevitable the confrontation of prevailing social forms, themselves specified in language, by others inevitably emerging out of thought guided by grammar and set in words. It is conventional and not natural form that is problematic and, if the distinction between form and substance is made at all, the association of form with words may be obvious or natural, for conventions must be stipulated in words, and the distinction of form from substance is a product of words.

When I say that the association of form with word is natural I mean to imply more than that it may flow naturally from the operations of language. In those myths which represent creation as the ordering of formless matter by First Word the natural world is *apparently* subordinated to the order of that which is quintessentially conventional or cultural. It may be suggested, however, that the effect is the reverse. The Word that creates seas and light and dry land is the self-same Word that creates kinship and kingship and incest taboos. Nature and conventions are created in the same way by the same classes of agencies, and while it may seem that the notion of Creative Word absorbs the natural world into the cultural, the effect is to transform the conventional, which is *ipso facto* arbitrary, into the apparently natural and, as such, necessary or inevitable. Conventions are made natural by the supernatural. We may note in passing that a likely effect of naturalizing one's own conventions is to make the conventions of others appear to be unnatural, or even abominable.

Myths of creation speak of creative or ordering Words. Such Words are not simply any words. They are very special Words distinguished from and set against ordinary discourse. We come here to another feature of ritual of great importance, namely its invariance. It is from its invariance that sanctity is, I think, derived. It was Anthony F. C. Wallace (1966, p. 234) who noted that if ritual is a mode of communication it is a peculiar one because to the extent that it is invariant it is, in information theoretical terms, devoid of information. In information theory, information is that which reduces uncertainty among alternatives, but to the extent that a sequence of acts and utterances is fixed, it cannot reduce uncertainty among alternatives because there are no alternatives. Information, however, is not synonymous with meaning, he observed, and the meaning of ritual's information-lessness is certainty.

Elsewhere I have proposed that sanctity be taken to be a characteristic of discourse rather than of the objects of discourse. In this usage it is the *credal assertion* that Christ is God and not Christ himself that is sacred. Christ may be divine or at least accorded divinity, but that is another matter. In a corpus of religious discourse sanctity inheres in and flows from certain sentences, which may be called "Ultimate Sacred Propositions". An example might be "The Lord Our God the Lord is One". Such sentences are rather peculiar. Having no material referents they are, in their nature, neither verifiable nor falsifiable, yet they are taken to be unquestionable. I would define the sacred as the quality of unquestionableness imputed by a congregation to sentences in their nature neither verifiable nor falsifiable.

The unquestionableness of such sentences is of the essence. The certainty of that which is encoded arises out of the invariance of the form in which it is encoded. Certainty is one of the grounds upon which unquestionableness stands, the other is the acceptance intrinsic to the performance of that which is certain. Thus it is that the notion of the sacred is engendered by ritual's invariance, and as Maurice Bloch (1974) has suggested, so may the notion of the divine. The words spoken by ritual's performers are not their own words. Their origin is often immemorial. Words imply speakers and immemorial invariant words imply extraordinary first speakers who existed in time immemorial, or even, perhaps, at the beginning of time.

While it may be that the concept of the sacred or the notion of the divine would be literally unthinkable without language it may also be argued that language and social orders founded upon language could not have emerged without the support of sanctity. Earlier we noted one of the problems inherent in language—its extraordinary talent for deceit, and later another, the innate ability of language users to comprehend the arbitrary nature of the conventions to which they are subordinated and their ability, also intrinsic to language, to conceive of alternatives. Lie and alternative, inherent in language, it is interesting to note, are taken by Buber (1952) to be the ground of all evil. At the very least they pose problems to any society whose structure is founded upon language, which is to say to all human societies. If there are to be words at all it is necessary to establish *The Word*. The Word is established by the invariance of liturgy, and it may at least be suggested that it emerged phylogenetically as some expressions drawn from the burgeoning language of earlier hominids were absorbed into, and subordinated to, the invariance of already existing non-verbal rituals which seem to be common in the animal world. Let me put this argument in terms of adaptation. The very versatility that has conferred upon the species the ability to expand into all of the niches and habitats that the world presents, a versatility that rests upon the specification of patterns of behaviour through language rather than through genetic processes and limited non-symbolic learning, has intrinsic to it the problem of disorder. The ability to modify or replace conventions is central to human adaptiveness, but if alternatives to the conventions in accordance with which they live can be imagined (indeed may be inevitably imagined) by the members of any society, how can they be led to abide by those prevailing, particularly if some of the alternatives seem more attractive? It may be suggested that sanctity is a functional replacement for genetic determination of patterns of behaviour, a determination which becomes decreasingly specific as language emerges. The capacity for variation or alternative that is given to the species by language is ordered by sanctity, which is itself a product of language. Flexibility is not a simple product of versatility, but of versatility and orderliness. The innumerable possibilities inherent in words and their combinations are constrained, reduced and ordered by unquestionable Word enunciated in ritual's apparently invariant canon.

Sanctity, then, orders a versatility that otherwise might spawn chaos. While sanctity has its apparent source in ultimate sacred propositions, which are typically without material referents, it flows to other sentences which do have material referents and are concerned with the regulation of society: "Henry is by Grace of God King", "It is more blessed to give than to receive", "I swear in the name of God to tell the truth". Returning to a question raised but not answered earlier: to the extent that the hosts at a Maring festival rely upon their visitors to honour their pledges to help in warfare, they do so, at least in part, because of the sanctification of those pledges entailed by their place in rituals.

In sum, in its flow from ultimate sacred propositions, the unquestionableness of sanctity is transformed into the related notions of authority, correctness, propriety, truth and naturalness, thus certifying the conventional aspects of society, those aspects which Turner calls "structure" (1969).

While sanctity may reduce alternatives, I have been arguing that it may establish and preserve flexibility. Certain characteristics of Ultimate Sacred Propositions are important in this respect. Typically devoid of material terms, they themselves do not specify the usages of social life. Their association with particular social arrangements is therefore a matter of interpretation. Any product of interpretation is open to reinterpretation, of course, but reinterpretation does not challenge Ultimate Sacred Propositions. It merely disputes previous interpretations of them, and thus God can remain unchanged while his man changes—while, that is, the conventions which he blesses are transformed or even replaced. Constant reinterpretation is, by the way, encouraged by the typically cryptic nature of Ultimate Sacred Propositions. What, after all, does it mean to say that God is One or God is Three? If propositions are to be taken to be unquestionable it is important that they be incomprehensible.

We note here, by the way, that those very features of Ultimate

Sacred Propositions that lead positivists and atheists to declare them to be without sense or even nonsense—that they are unverifiable, unfalsifiable, cryptic or incomprehensible—are those which suit them for association with players of the existential game, particularly social systems at the most inclusive level. Specifying nothing, they can sanctify not only conventions but changes in convention. Encompassing everything they provide continuity through transformation. It is precisely when specific material qualities are introduced into them or, as is more usual, when highly specific social institutions or material goals become too highly sanctified, that is, too closely connected to the ultimate, that trouble sets in. For instance, if as Coolidge said, "the Business of America is business", and the United States is One Nation under God, then business is highly sanctified, and the conditions under which the society can persist are limited to those favourable to business. Paul Tillich referred to this "absolutizing of the relative and relativizing of the absolute" as "idolatry" and took it to be evil (1957, p. 11). I take it to be maladaptive. In both his terms and mine the Absolute must remain vague.

Yet, as important as liturgical invariance may be, surely language and the human way of life must be founded upon more than a trick in information theory. So far I have spoken only of the sacred, which is in language and which faces language and the public orders built upon language. But the sacred is only one component or aspect of a more inclusive phenomenon which I call the Holy. The other aspect of the Holy, which, following Rudolph Otto (1926), may be called the numinous, is its non-discursive, ineffable, or emotional aspect—what is called "religious experience" in the broadest sense. We know that this, as well as the sacred, is invoked in at least some rituals. "Communitas" (Turner, 1969) or "Effervescence" (Durkheim, 1961 [1915]) is one of its manifestations. Scholars differ with respect to the nature of religious experience. Some would apply the term to any emotional state taken by the individual to be a response to what is construed to be a divine object. Others, like Rudolph Otto (1926) would take it to be a general undifferentiated "ur-emotion" encompassing love, fear, dependence, fascination, unworthiness, majesty, connection. Witnesses agree that it is powerful, indescribable, and utterly convincing.

I do not mean to make too much of this, but Erikson (1966) suggests that the numinous emotion has its ontogenetic basis in the relationship of the pre-verbal infant to its mother. The child's experience of its mother has characteristics similar to those which Otto attributes to the worshipper's experience of his God: she is mysterious, tremendous, overpowering, loving and frightening. It is learning to trust her upon whom he depends utterly that makes subsequent language learning and, for that matter, continuing socialization possible. This trust is learned in what Erikson calls "daily rituals of nurturance and greeting", stereotyped interactions between mother and child taking place dependably at regular intervals, or at times specified by the child's needs. Through the course of ontogeny the numinous emotions initially associated with mother are displaced to other objects. Of importance here is the bipolar reference of ritual symbols noted by Turner (1973) and Campbell (1959, pp. 461ff.). At one and the same time they point to cosmic and social conceptions on the one hand and psychic and physiological experience on the other. Through the mediation of such representations the conceptual is given the power of the experiential, and the experiential the guidance of the conceptual. Again, we note a relationship here between conceptual form and experiential substance.

Erikson's ontogenetic suggestion has phylogenetic implications. If ontogeny has a phylogeny and if the mother–child relationship among humans is but a variant of the primate or even mammalian pattern, it may be that the basis of the numinous is archaic, antedating humanity, and that religion came into being when the emerging, discursive, conventional sacred was lashed to the primordial, non-discursive, natural emotional processes that in their later form we call "numinous".

Earlier I spoke of the acceptance of convention entailed by participation in liturgy, proposing that it is sufficient to establish the obligations upon which human societies stand. It may be, however, that acceptance in the absence of something more profound is fragile. I would now suggest that the numinous, when it is experienced, supports acceptance with conviction or belief, or perhaps it is proper to say transforms acceptance into belief.

Those who have reached those profound numinous states called mystical report a loss of distinction, an experience of unification with what they take to be the divine object and perhaps the cosmos. The experience, they say, is in some way ultimately meaningful, but being devoid of distinction, is devoid of information and even of reference. It points to nothing but itself. Ultimate meaning is not referential; it is, rather, a state sometimes described as a state of pure being. To say that this state is convincing is, really inappropriate, for, being directly experienced, it simply *is*, and as such is undeniable.

The union in ritual of the numinous, a product of emotion, with the sacred, a product of language, suggests possible grounds for the notion of the divine going somewhat beyond Bloch's ingenious but perhaps too simple suggestion. Because the notion of the divine is a human universal we must search for its ground in a universal experience or condition.

I would suggest that the notion of the divine has at least four features. First, while it may be incarnated, the divine itself is not material in any ordinary sense. Second, it exists, or rather, it has being. It is not deemed to be, simply, a law, like the laws of thermodynamics, or an abstraction, like truth, but a being, like Zeus. Third, it is powerful, or efficacious. It has the ability to cause effects. Finally, it is something like alive. It possesses something like vitality. To use Rudolph Otto's term, it is "urgent".

I would hesitantly suggest that the first three of these qualities are supplied by fundamental linguistic processes as they are expressed in ritual's utterances, the last by the emotions generated in ritual.

First, the existence of the non-material is made conceptually possible by the symbolic relationship between sign and signified. Whereas concept is intrinsic to the symbolic relationship, material reference is not intrinsic to concept. If the sign is not bound to the signified there is nothing to hold the signified to materiality at all, and it can easily escape into the abstract, imaginary or otherwise purely conceptual.

The existence of the conceptual may be made conceivable by the fundamental linguistic process of predication. To say that "X is an aspect of Y" is to endow Y with the attribute X. The copula "is" in this sentence has, simply, a logical function, which is to invest Y with X, but this logical function has an existential implication. Moreover, this implication may be unavoidable. To say that "X is an aspect of Y" might be to say, or to *seem* to say, that both X and Y in some sense exist. Yet the existence entailed by predication may be no more than conceptual existence, like the way in which honour or the axioms of geometry exist. But Gods are Beings. The problem is, then, to transform the conceptual—that which exists merely as concept—into that which seems to have being.

The conception of the non-material as efficacious, i.e., as capable of causing effects, may contribute to such a transformation, for humans generally realize that effects are not directly caused by concepts alone (any more than, let us say, houses are built by plans alone. Houses are built according to plans by builders). The efficacy of the non-material, this is to say, implies the being of the non-material. The notion of the efficacy of divine beings, in turn, might well be founded upon the performativeness and meta-performativeness of language as expressed in ritual. The very invariance of ritual proposes, as Bloch has suggested, an agent to whom the efficacy of performativeness intrinsic to language can be attributed.

Divine beings by the account so far offered remain nothing more than inductions from mystified performativeness. This, however, seems neither satisfactory nor correct, for we know that people are often convinced of the existence of divine beings in the absence of material from which they could induce, however correctly or incorrectly, such beliefs.

We must consider not only the capacities of the propositions and performatives that language may present to the worshipper but also the worshipper's experience of those utterances and acts, and the relationship between their qualities and his experience. A mediating or connecting term may be noted. At least in languages in which it is an independent lexical element, and perhaps in all languages, the verb "to be" may give rise to the notion of being independent of instances of being. It is of interest in this respect that the most sacred name of God in Hebrew, the tetragrammaton, is said to be a form of the verb "to be" (Brandon, 1970, p. 655). Tillich (1957, etc.) refers to God as "The

Ground-of-All-Being" and "Being–Itself". It is of further interest here that the profoundly altered states of consciousness characteristic of religious experience are sometimes described as states of "pure being", the word for trance in Java is "being" (Geertz, 1965, p. 32) and Bushmen refer to the states they achieve in trance dancing as "really being" (Katz, 1974).

The predication of that which is represented in an ultimate sacred proposition may become conflated in ritual with the numinous state of "pure being" of the performer. Numinous experiences, even those which are much less intense than may be suggested by references to Javanese and Bushman trance, are widely described as ones in which the presence of the divine being is "experienced". Sometimes, indeed, with loss of distinction, the worshipper senses that he is participating in, or becoming one with, the divine being. I would suggest that divine objects, which are represented by ultimate sacred propositions, are predicated as living, or even supplied the predicate of being, by the numinous experiences of worshippers. The vitality which the worshipper feels in the divine object is his own, projected upon what he takes to be other or "encompassing". Ritual, then, is possibly the furnace within which the image of God is forged out of the powers of language and of emotion.

Whether or not the notion of the divine is adaptive I would argue that mystical consciousness is. Ordinary consciousness is incomplete and so are its unaided understandings. The common sense of conscious reason which has its loci in individual organisms, proposes a sense of separation. Consciousness separates men from each other, each man in solitude behind his own eyes, each one imprisoned by his own skin, each enclosed alone between the dates of his birth and of his death. The common sense of separation endorses the common sense of self-sufficiency and autonomy, notions that are sanctified virtually to the point of apotheosis in Western capitalist society. But of course they are illusions. Although men are metabolically separate from one another, and although consciousness is individual, men are not self-sufficient and their autonomy is relative and slight. Men are parts of larger systems upon which their continued existence is contingent. But the wholeness, if not indeed the very existence of those systems may be beyond the grasp of their ordinary consciousness. Conscious reason may of course provide us with knowledge about the structure and function of such ecological and social systems and present to us reasonable arguments for complying with their imperatives. But such knowledge and reasons are likely to be overcome by what economists call rationality. To ask conscious reason to lead unaided the separate individuals in which it resides to favour the long-term interests of ecosystems and societies over their own immediate interests may be to ask too much of it. Sustained compliance with the imperatives of larger systems not only may require more than ordinary reason, but may have to be maintained in defiance of a consciousness that *in its nature* informs men of their separateness. It may, indeed, require that the common sense of separation be transcended and replaced from time to time by an extraordinary sense of participation, of being joined together with entities from which one is separated by the evidence of the senses and by competitive rationality, into wholes—societies and ecosystems—that are natural, but not in their nature directly perceptible.

The mode of understanding encouraged by liturgy may make up for some of the deficiencies inherent in consciousness. To perform a liturgical order is to participate in it, act as part of it, and where the ritual is public it is to join with others in this participation. It is obviously important that singing, dancing and speaking in unison are common features of public rituals. To sing or dance in concert or unison with others, to move as they move and speak as they speak is, literally, to act as part of a larger entity, to participate in it, and as the radical separation of the everyday self from other everyday selves dissolves in the communitas (Turner, 1969) of participation—as it sometimes does—the larger entity becomes palpable. Such extraordinary or even mystical experiences seem to be profoundly satisfying but, more important here, they also may provide deeper and more compelling understandings of perfectly natural and extremely important aspects of the physical and social world than can be provided by reason alone. In sum, numinous experience does not always hide the world from conscious reason behind a veil of supernatural illusions. Rather it may pierce the veil of illusions behind which unaided reason hides the world from comprehensive human understanding.

Whether or not this account is correct it is well to emphasize that the numinous and the sacred are the inverse of each other. The sacred is discursive, but its references are not material and therefore its propositions are unfalsifiable. The numinous is non-discursive, but it is immediately material—it is felt—and therefore not only is it unfalsifiable but self-validating. In ritual's union ultimate sacred propositions come to partake of the immediately known and undeniable quality of the numinous. That this is logically unsound is beside the point. It may make problems for logicians, but it does not trouble the faithful. In the union of the sacred and the numinous the most abstract and distant of conceptions are bound to the most immediate and substantial of experiences. We are confronted at the end with a remarkable spectacle. The unfalsifiable supported by the undeniable yields the unquestionable which transforms the dubious, the arbitrary and conventional into the correct, the necessary and the natural. This structure is, I would suggest, the foundation upon which the human way of life stands, and it is realized in ritual.

The phrase "the human way of life" leads us back to the structure of adaptive systems, and we may turn here to the cybernetics of the Holy, more specifically to an ultimate adaptive mechanism residing in the relationship, in particular social systems, between the numinous and the sacred. I have written about this matter elsewhere (1969, 1971a, b) and can therefore be brief here.

Because religious experience is part of the emotional life of humans and because the emotional life of humans must surely be affected by their material condition, it is plausible to believe that the intensity, frequency and object of religious experiences are affected by material conditions. (The time-lag is probably considerable, and should be considerable, in this relationship.) The material conditions to which the members of a society are subject are in some degree a function of the regulatory hierarchies attempting to govern them. These regulatory hierarchies are sanctified by Ultimate Sacred Propositions which, in turn, are supported by the ritual acceptance and numinous experiences of the society.

We may note here a cybernetic loop. It may be suggested that the willingness of congregations to accept in ritual or even their ability to give numinous support to Ultimate Sacred Propositions or, more likely, to the connection of authorities to those Ultimate Sacred Propositions, may be adversely affected by protracted periods of unsatisfactory conditions. Thus, if authorities wish to maintain their sanctity they must keep the operation of their regulatory hierarchies in reasonable order. If they do not they may find themselves deprived of sanctity, either passively as people withdraw their ritual support, or actively as prophets arise declaring new Ultimate Sacred Propositions, or reinterpreting old ones in ways which change authorities or even transform systemic structure. Ultimate responses, involving prophetic or revitalistic movements and the like are, of course, much more radical in their effects than specific systemic adjustments, and are slower to be mobilized.

It is important to make clear that the cybernetics of the holy may be disrupted in technologically advanced societies. This was implicit in the discussion of idolatry earlier and I have discussed it at length elsewhere (particularly 1969, 1976a, b). Here I shall only note that in technologically simple societies authorities are unlikely to possess means of coercion sufficient to found their prerogatives, and therefore must stand upon their sanctity. Technological advance, however, supplies authorities with means of coercion which are at once increasingly powerful and decreasingly available to their subjects. They are therefore able to stand increasingly upon their power, and to rely decreasingly upon their sanctity. Powerful authorities do not dispense with sanctity, but the relationship between sanctity and authority is inverted. Whereas in the technologically simple society, sanctity is the ground of authority, in the technologically advanced society sanctity, or that for which sanctity is claimed, may become authority's instrument, becoming thereby the delusion that Marx claimed it to be. It should not be thought, however, that the ability of the sacred and the numinous to contribute positively to human affairs is terminated by technological advance, for propositions the unquestionableness of which is uncoerced and which are supported by numinous emotions continue to emerge, providing revitalization movements with the guidance and the energy to correct the social ills vexing those participating in them. (For a fuller discussion see Rappaport, 1969, 1971a, b.)

I have spoken of the cybernetics of the Holy, using the term "Holy" to subsume both the discursive sacred and the non-discursive numinous. I do not wish to make too much of it but it seems to me to be appropriate to use "Holy" inclusively, for it shares derivation from the Old English *hale* with "whole" and "health". The sacred and the numinous, the discursive and the non-discursive, the rational and the affective, structure and communitas make up wholes. One term of each of the pairs in the absence of the other is incomplete. Human adaptation resides ultimately in wholes through the mobilization of which the ambitions of separate men may be subordinated to common interest while at the same time the operations of society may be reviewed and tempered by the psychic and physical needs of the humans who compose it. It is through such wholes that the conflicts between individual men and their societies are mediated. Wholeness, holiness and adaptiveness are one and the same.

References

AUSTIN, J. L. (1962) *How to do Things with Words.* Oxford University Press, Oxford.

BATESON, G. (1972) *Steps to an Ecology of Mind.* Ballentine, New York.

BLOCH, Maurice (1974) Symbols, Song, and Dance, and Features of Articulation. *European Journal of Sociology,* **15,** 55–81.

BRANDON, S. G. F., ed. (1970) *Dictionary of Comparative Religion.* Charles Scribner's Sons, New York.

BROWN, W. Norman (1972) Duty as Truth in Ancient India. *Proceedings of the American Philosophical Society,* **116,** 252–68.

BUBER, Martin (1952) *Good and Evil. Two Interpretations.* Scribner's Sons, New York.

CAMPBELL, Joseph (1959) *The Masks of God. Vol. I, Primitive Mythology.* Viking, New York.

CULLEN, J. M. S. (1966) Reduction of ambiguity through ritualization. In *A Discussion of the Ritualizations of Behaviour in Animals and Man.* Julian Huxley, convenor. *Philosophical Proceedings of the Royal Society of London,* Series B, Biological Sciences, **772,** Vol. 25.

DURKHEIM, Emile (1961) *The Elementary Forms of the Religious Life.* Joseph Ward Swan, trans. Collier, New York. (First edition, English translation, 1915).

ERIKSON, E. (1966) The ritualization of ontogeny. In *A Discussion of the Ritualization of Behaviour in Animals and Man.* Julian Huxley, convenor. *Philosophical Transactions of the Royal Society of London.* Series B, Biological Sciences, **772,** Vol. 25.

GEERTZ, Clifford (1965) Religion as a cultural system. In *Anthropological Approaches to Religion* (ed. Michael Banton) ASA Monograph No. 13. Tavistock, London.

102   HUMAN BEHAVIOUR AND ADAPTATION

GUILLEMIN-DUCHESNE, J. (1966) *Symbols and Values in Zoroastrianism*. Harper and Row, New York.
KATZ, Richard (1974) Education for transcendence: Lessons from the !Kung Zhu/Twasi. *Journal of Transcultural Psychology*, **2**, 136–55.
LACEY, Thomas (1918) Sacraments, Christian, Western. In *Encyclopedia of Religion and Ethics* (ed. James Hastings) Vol. 10, pp. 903–908.
MEGGITT, M. J. (1966) Gadjari Among the Walbiri Aborigines of Central Australia. *Oceania Monographs* No. 14. University of Sydney, Sydney, Australia.
NEEDHAM, Rodney (1972) *Belief, Language and Experience*. Blackwell, Oxford.
O'DOHERTY, F. (1973) *Nature, Grace and Faith*. Manuscript.
OTTO, Rudolph (1926) *The Idea of the Holy* (trans. J. W. Harvey) Oxford University Press, London.
PEIRCE, Charles S. (1960) *Collected Papers of Charles Sanders Peirce*, Vol. II. (ed. Charles Martshorne and Paul Weiss) Harvard University Press, Cambridge, Mass.
PIAGET, J. (1972) *Structuralism* (trans. and ed. Chaninak Masckler) Routledge and Kegan Paul, London.
RAPPAPORT, R. A. (1968) *Pigs for the Ancestors*. Yale University Press, New Haven.
RAPPAPORT, R. A. (1969) *Sanctity and Adaptation*. Paper prepared for Burg Wartenstein Conference, No. 44, The Moral and Aesthetic Structure of Human Adaptation, Wenner-Gren Foundation. Reprinted in *Io* 7 (1970), 46–71. Also in *Coevolution Quarterly*, **2** (1974).
RAPPAPORT, R. A. (1971a) Ritual, sanctity and cybernetics. *American Anthropologist*, **73**, 59–76.
RAPPAPORT, R. A. (1971b) The sacred in human evolution. *Annual Review of Ecology and Systematics*, **2**, 23–44.
RAPPAPORT, R. A. (1976a) Adaptation and maladaptation in social systems. In *The Ethical Basis of Economic Freedom* (ed. Ivan Hill), pp. 39–82. American Viewpoint, Chapel Hill.
RAPPAPORT, R. A.(1978) Adaptation in social systems. In *Evolution in Social Sociology of Knowledge and Religion*, **10**, 75–104.
RAPPAPORT, R. A. (1977) Adaptation in social systems. In *Evolution in Social Systems* (ed. J. Friedman and M. Rowlands) Duckworth, London.
ROMER, Alfred S. (1954) *Man and The Vertebrates*. Penguin. First published 1933.
SEARLE, J. (1969) *Speech Acts*. Cambridge University Press, Cambridge.
SIMON, Herbert (1969) *The Sciences of the Artificial*. M.I.T. Press, Cambridge, Mass.
SLOBODKIN, L. (1968) *Toward a Predictive Theory of Evolution in Population Biology and Evolution*. Syracuse University Press, Syracuse.
SLOBODKIN, L., and RAPOPORT, A. (1974) An optimal strategy of evolution. *Quarterly Review of Biology*, **49**, 181–200.
TAMBIAH, S. J. (1968) The magical power of words. *Man*, **3**, 175–208.
TILLICH, Paul (1957) *The Dynamics of Faith*. Harper, New York.
TURNER, V. (1969) *The Ritual Process*. Aldine, Chicago.
TURNER, V. (1973) Symbols in African ritual. *Science*, **179**, 1100–1105.
WALLACE, A. F. C. (1966) *Religion: An Anthropological View*. Random House, New York.

THE RELATIVE IMPORTANCE OF GROUP SELECTION IN THE EVOLUTION OF PRIMATE SOCIETIES

C. PACKER

School of Biology, University of Sussex

Introduction

THE process of group selection is the establishment, in evolutionary terms, of characteristics which favour the survival of a group but do not favour the survival of individual members of that group. It requires an individual to reduce his own fitness in order to prevent his group from going extinct. Group selection is counter to individual selection, where an individual maximizes his own fitness, and if group selection is to have a strong influence on evolution, it must override the effects of selection on the individual. Selfish behaviour will spread because a selfish individual will always have greater fitness than any of the altruists in an altruistic group.

There appears to be a certain amount of confusion over the way natural selection operates on social vertebrates, whether at the level of the social group or at the level of the individual. In this paper I will be discussing the conditions under which group selection is likely to operate and whether or not it is likely to be an important factor in the evolution of primate societies.

Models of Group Selection

Group selection will influence evolution when there is a gene which decreases an individual's fitness while making it less likely that a group will go extinct (Maynard Smith, 1976). For group selection to have strong consequences, the group, population, or species must, by definition, be the unit of selection. For groups to

be the units of selection, they must have the properties of variation, multiplication, and heredity for natural selection to operate
on them in the same way that it operates on individuals. In particular, the rate of group extinction must be high enough to coun-
teract effects of individual death. Genes which benefit groups will
only be likely to spread in small groups founded by a few individuals and be maintained when there are very limited rates of
migration between groups. Group size must be small in order to
allow a trait benefiting the group to be established by genetic drift
and migration must be low in order to reduce the probability of
subsequent "infection" by a selfish immigrant.

Several recent models have been claimed to show that group
selection may have a greater influence than was previously supposed. However, Maynard Smith showed that they do not have
greater generality than the conditions outlined above. Further, he
demonstrated that even when an allele incurs individual advantage but *inevitable* group extinction it will only be removed by
group selection when there is not even one successful migrant out
of that group between the time when the allele first occurs within
the group, either by mutation or immigration, and the time when
the group becomes extinct.

Group Dynamics in Primates

Most species of primates live in well defined social groups and
it is perhaps for this reason that so many evolutionary interpretations of primate social behaviour have either intentionally or
carelessly considered the social group to be the unit of selection.
Primate groups were first considered to be closed social units—in
which case group selection might be considered to be a potentially strong evolutionary force. However, in recent years long-
term demographic records have become available on a variety of
primate species and migration of individuals between groups has
been found to be a regular feature in most. In fact, in four species
(*Macaca mulatta*, Drickamer and Vessey, 1973; *Macaca fuscata*,
Itani, 1975; *Macaca sinica*, Dittus, 1975; *Papio anubis*, Packer,
1975) all males have been found to transfer into a new troop at
some time in their lives. Consequently, all the breeding males in a
particular troop have entered that troop from elsewhere. Most or

all females transfer between groups in chimpanzees (Nishida, 1977, Pusey, 1977) and gorillas (Harcourt *et al.*, 1976).

Thus in most primate species, the level of migration between groups is adequate to prevent group selection from having strong enough consequences to counter individual selection.

Dawkins (1976) has pointed out that selection is not really in terms of groups or individuals, but in terms of *genes*. However, in discussing selection it is convenient to think in terms of individuals since they are the units in which genes are carried. Individuals can benefit their own genes by helping related individuals who share some proportion of their genes by common descent—a process known as kin selection (Hamilton, 1964). When considering the evolutionary consequences of primate social behaviour it is necessary to examine the effects of that behaviour on the fitness of the individual and his relatives—his inclusive fitness. If the behaviour is purported to have a beneficial effect on the group rather than on the individual's inclusive fitness, then this should be justified.

Group Selectionist Arguments

Although many primatologists may consider group selection to be an insignificant force in the evolution of primate societies, there are numerous examples of group selectionist arguments which have been used to explain aspects of primate behaviour. Group selection is often cited by people who are not aware that they are doing so, either by specifically considering group benefit or by considering the group to be the unit of selection.

A clear example of benefit to the group is provided by Wynne-Edwards (1962) in discussing the concept of dominance. He suggests that dominance behaviour ensures that only as many individuals as can be sustained by the remaining food sources are allowed to feed and this ensures that the maximum number will survive. He concludes that the function of the dominance hierarchy is to identify the surplus individuals whenever the population density needs to be reduced and that it thus has an extremely high survival value for the society as a whole.

However, under these conditions the advantages of dominance are clearly on the side of the dominant individuals. By excluding competitors the dominant animal is ensuring his own survival; any advantages dominance may have to the species are secondary to the advantages to the individual and there is no need to consider the behaviour as the product of group selection.

Another example concerns the harassment of copulating pairs of macaques (Gouzoules, 1974). In the species studied, the mounting male sometimes bites, without seriously wounding, the female. Gouzoules suggests that harassment of the pair by a heckler serves to distract the mounting male. Thus the aggression that might be directed to the female is instead directed at the heckler.

As it is stated this implies that an individual is reducing his own fitness in order to benefit other members of the group. If "heckling" does have adaptive significance, then it would be more useful to examine the behaviour in terms of its effect on the reproductive success of each individual involved and how this affects the inclusive fitness of the harassing animal.

Often group selectionist reasoning is less obvious. Researchers who may appreciate that behaviour is unlikely to evolve for the good of the group sometimes consider the group as the unit of selection. I have chosen two common examples. These concern discussions of dominance hierarchies and social roles. Sometimes these are stated explicitly in terms of group benefit, but often the benefits to the group are implicit.

A dominance *hierarchy* is often considered to be a behavioural trait which is selected for in a group (as pointed out by Clutton-Brock and Harvey, 1976). For example, the hierarchy reduces "the power of disruptive forces" (Bernstein, 1976) or it restricts access of expendable individuals to resources (Kummer, 1971). However, as G. C. Williams (1966) has stated, a dominance hierarchy is no more than "the statistical consequence of a compromise made by each individual in its competition for food, water, and other resources. Each compromise is adaptive but not the statistical summation". It is the characteristics which result in greater competitive ability in each individual that are favoured by selection, not the outcome of the variation in ability between individuals, which is often expressed as a hierarchy.

Similarly, social roles in primate societies are often treated as traits selected for in a group. For example, it was recently stated that in a troop of Japanese macaques "each monkey has a specific function or role to perform within the troop . . . together they constitute the essence of a society as opposed to a simple aggregation of individuals. The role of the alpha male appears to be one of directing the movement of the troop and defending it. The primary role of the peripheral males is apparently to give warning of predators and to help the alpha male defend the troop. The role of the adult females is to raise their offspring and protect them" (Eaton, 1976).

Such a view suggests that roles are "designed with reference to the optimum organization of the society" (Wilson, 1975). Instead, from the viewpoint of individual selection, division of labour may arise when each individual acts to increase his own inclusive fitness, but different individuals in the same group may gain from differing sorts of actions. Thus, a female does not have offspring in order to contribute to the efficiency of the group, but to increase her own reproductive success. Differing self-interests are discussed in more detail below.

Selfish Behaviour in Primates

Selfish behaviour is a common feature in primate societies. This occurs to some extent whenever there is competition for food or mates. The most striking example of an individual increasing his own inclusive fitness at the expense of the group as a whole is that of infanticide. Deliberate infanticide is now well documented in several primate species (see Hrdy, 1976 for references; Struhsaker, 1977). In the one-male troops of Hanuman langurs, infanticide is a regular feature of the takeover of a troop by a new male (Hrdy, 1974). By killing all the unweaned infants in the troop, the new male decreases the time he would have to wait before the nursing females resumed sexual receptivity. Hrdy suggests that the new male also reduces the reproductive success of his competitors, in this case the previous male in that troop, by killing their offspring.

Although this behaviour may be advantageous to the male who kills the infants, it is clearly disadvantageous to the mothers of the murdered infants. However, they eventually accept the new male and breed with him.

Altruistic behaviour directed towards close relatives can also be selfish in that it may increase the "altruist's" inclusive fitness.

Primate Groups as the Product of Individual Interests

My own research has been on the olive baboons of Gombe National Park in Tanzania and concerned the transfer of males between troops (Packer, 1977). This particular topic highlights the conflict of individual interests between members of the same group.

All male baboons voluntarily leave their natal troop after reaching sexual maturity and move into new troops in order to mate with unfamiliar females. A male may transfer for a second or third time later in life, in which case he moves into a new troop containing more oestrus females than the previous troop. In both cases, a transferring male is promoting his own reproductive success: in leaving his natal troop he reduces the probability that he will engage in close inbreeding which might result in offspring of reduced viability, and by moving a second time into a troop with more oestrus females, he will have an opportunity to father more offspring than if he had remained in the earlier troop.

The immigration of a new male affects the fitness of different residents in the troop in different ways. To a breeding male, a new male represents an increase in competition for access to resources; to a female, a new male may represent certain benefits. An increase in the number of males in her troop might result in greater competition over access to herself when she is in oestrus and thus the father of her offspring may be the fittest of a larger number of males (Clutton-Brock and Harvey, 1976). Also, the more males who are potential fathers of her offspring, the greater the amount of paternal care it might receive.

It is of interest therefore to contrast the response of males and females when a potential newcomer attempts to join their troop. A resident male generally chases the females of his own troop well away from the newcomer. Such chasing was found to be effective in reducing the contact of females with outsiders. Sometimes a resident male chases the newcomer several hundred metres away from his troop. This often results in the newcomer transferring into a troop other than that of the chasing male.

Because of the behaviour of the males in her troop, a female is often unable to make contact with outsiders. However, in certain circumstances, oestrus females are active in recruiting new males into their troop. During intertroop interactions, when females are usually chased away from the outside troop, an oestrus female is sometimes able to remain if she is being consorted and she and her consort are being followed closely by a rival male. Under these conditions, the consorting male is sometimes inhibited against chasing the female since it might result in her being taken over by the rival male. In these cases the female moves into the midst of the other troop and into much closer vicinity to outside males. Also when a new male enters a troop, oestrus females often go long distances in order to present to him. By presenting, a female encourages a male to copulate with her.

Not only do the responses to newcomers vary between males and females, but they also vary within each sex. For example, resident males show greater efforts to expel new males of approximately their own age. Amongst males, dominance rank and competitive strategies for access to oestrus females vary with age, and a new male is more competition to a resident male of his own age. Females with unweaned infants tend to avoid new males. These are the females who may incur costs from a potentially infanticidal male. An oestrus female, who encourages the entry of such an infanticidal male, loses only to the extent that she may have a lactating relative, the loss of whose offspring would decrease her own inclusive fitness. Previous resident males are protective to their potential offspring, thus the opportunity for infanticide is less in these baboons than in species where a new male evicts the previous males. Therefore, an oestrus female is taking less of a risk to her own inclusive fitness than it might seem at first.

I have discussed this topic in depth in order to stress that a primate group is a complex social environment which affects an individual's reproduction and survival in a variety of ways without being functionally organized for the collective survival of its members. To paraphrase G. C. Williams, a primate group is the statistical summation of a number of conflicts and compromises between a set of individuals with differing self-interests. The resolution of each difference may be adaptive, but the summation of these resolutions is not. There is no need to assume that a troop is the result of selection at the level of the group.

Thus, for example, a multi-male primate troop has not resulted from selection for a multi-male troop structure over that of a single-male troop, but the conditions under which multi-male troops developed may have been such that either it was no longer advantageous for a single male to evict competitors or he was unable to do so successfully.

Conclusions

It is important to distinguish clearly between individual selection and group selection because the level at which evolution is thought to act will determine the kind of research questions which are asked. Functional explanations generated by group selectionist reasoning often sound similar to those of individual selection but there is a basic difference between the two, and sometimes predictions generated by group selection can be opposite to those based on individual selection. On the basis of group selection it was asserted that small clutch size in birds is a form of individual reproductive restraint, since fewer eggs are laid than is physiologically possible. However, detailed study of several species over several years showed that smaller initial clutch size often leads to a larger number of offspring fledged and instead of restricting their reproductive output, individuals are maximizing it (Lack, 1966).

I think the case is very strong that except under special circumstances, not usually applicable to primate species, the predictions from individual selection are much more likely to be correct. Viewing evolution from the perspective of the inclusive fitness of individuals has proved to have great explanatory and predictive power. By strengthening our understanding of the selective pressures acting on individuals we shall increase our understanding of the evolution of primate societies.

Acknowledgments

I am grateful to T. H. Clutton-Brock, P. H. Harvey, J. Maynard Smith, and A. E. Pusey for their valuable discussion on the topics presented in this paper. Field work was supported by the Ford and W. T. Grant Foundations.

References

BERNSTEIN, I. S. (1976) Dominance, aggression and reproduction in primate societies. *Journal of Theoretical Biology*, **60**, 459–72.

CLUTTON-BROCK, T. H. and HARVEY, P. H. (1976) Evolutionary rules and primate societies. In *Growing Points in Ethology* (ed. P. P. G. Bateson & R. A. Hinde) 195–237. Cambridge University Press, Cambridge.

DAWKINS, R. (1976) *The Selfish Gene*. Oxford University Press, Oxford.

DITTUS, W. P. J. (1975) Population dynamics of the toque monkey, *Macaca sinica*. In *Socioecology and Psychology of Primates* (ed. R. H. Tuttle) 125–51. Aldine, Chicago.

DRICKAMER, L. C. and VESSEY, S. H. (1973) Group changing in free-ranging male rhesus monkeys. *Primates*, **14**, 359–68.

EATON, G. G. (1976) The social order of Japanese macaques. *Scientific American*, **235**, (4), 96–106.

GOUZOULES, H. (1974) Harassment of sexual behaviour in the stumptail macaque, *Macaca arctoides*. *Folia primatologica*, **22**, 208–17.

HAMILTON, W. D. (1964) The genetical evolution of social behaviour. I & II. *Journal of Theoretical Biology*, **7**, 1–52.

HARCOURT, A. H., STEWART, K. J. and FOSSEY, D. (1976) Male emigration and female transfer in wild mountain gorilla. *Nature*, **263**, 226–27.

HRDY, S. B. (1974) Male-male competition and infanticide among the langurs (*Presbytis entellus*) of Abu' Rajasthan. *Folia primatologica*, **22**, 19–58.

HRDY, S. B. (1976) Care and exploitation of nonhuman primate infants by conspecifics other than the mother. *Advances in the Study of Behavior*, **6**, 101–58.

ITANI, J. (1975) Twenty years with Mount Takasaki monkeys. In *Primate Utilization and Conservation*, (ed. G. Dermont and D. G. Lindburg) 101–25. John Wiley and Sons, New York.

KUMMER, H. (1971) *Primate Societies: Group Techniques of Ecological Adaptation*. Aldine-Atherton, Chicago.

LACK, D. (1966) *Population Studies of Birds*. Clarendon Press, Oxford.

MAYNARD SMITH, J. (1976) Group selection. *The Quarterly Review of Biology*, **51**, 277–83.

NISHIDA, T. (1977) The social structure of chimpanzees of the Mahali Mountains. In *Perspectives on Human Evolution (Great Apes)*, Vol. 5 (ed. D. A. Hamburg). Staples Press/W. A. Benjamin, New York.

PACKER, C. (1975). Male transfer in olive baboons. *Nature*, **225**, 219–20.

PACKER, C. (1977) Inter-troop transfer and inbreeding avoidance in *Papio anubis* in Tanzania. D.Phil. dissertation, University of Sussex.

PUSEY, A. E. (1977) Intercommunity transfer of chimpanzees in Gombe National Park. In *Perspectives on Human Evolution (Great Apes)*, Vol. 5 (ed. D. A. Hamburg). Staples Press/W. A. Benjamin, New York.

STRUHSAKER, T. T. (1977) Infanticide in the redtail monkey (*Cercopithecus ascanius schmidti*) of Uganda. In *Proceedings of the Sixth Congress of the International Primatological Society*, Volume 1: *Primate Behaviour*, (ed. D. J. Chivers and C. Harcourt). Academic Press, London.

WILLIAMS, G. C. (1966) *Adaptation and Natural Selection*. Princeton University Press, Princeton.

WILSON, E. O. (1975) *Sociobiology: The New Synthesis*. Harvard University Press, Cambridge, Mass.

WYNNE-EDWARDS, V. C. (1962) *Animal Dispersion in Relation to Social Behaviour*. Oliver & Boyd, Edinburgh.

ADAPTATION TO A TROPICAL RAIN-FOREST ENVIRONMENT: ABORIGINAL SUBSISTENCE IN NORTHEASTERN QUEENSLAND

DAVID R. HARRIS

Department of Geography, University College London

IN discussions of cultural adaptation confusion frequently arises from a failure to specify the locus and scale at which adaptive behaviour is said to occur. Biological studies of adaptation tend to focus on the individual or the breeding population, whereas the concern of most anthropological enquiry is with social groups. These groups are not exclusively kin-based breeding populations and they range in scale from hunter–gatherer bands of fewer than fifty individuals to large, complex societies. They are distinguished from animal communities by the extent to which learned behaviour is transmitted between individuals, and from generation to generation, through language and other symbolic means of communicating information. In the analysis of adaptive behaviour it is useful to follow Weiner† in distinguishing four levels of biological adaptation: the physiological and ontogenetic, which relate respectively to the daily and life-span adaptation of individuals; the evolutionary, which relates to long-term changes occurring through generations; and the demographic, which relates to the adaptive behaviour of populations. Cultural and social anthropologists are concerned with the latter two categories in which they examine adaptation at the level of groups rather than of individuals.

Confusion also arises from uncertainty over the environmental factors, cultural as well as natural, to which individuals or groups adapt. In physiological and ontogenetic research, such as the

† Personal communication.

investigation of responses to extreme temperatures or to nutritional privation, it is relatively easy to determine the environmental factors to which individuals adapt, but when group adaptation, whether evolutionary or demographic, is under discussion the relevant environmental variables are seldom precisely defined. This is especially true of highly generalized studies which posit adaptive relationships between a broadly defined type of society and the type(s) of habitat that it occupies. This paper is an example of such a study, with the definitional and operational problems aggravated by the fact that it deals with a society that no longer exists as a living entity. It is all the more necessary, therefore, to specify the scale and levels at which the processes of adaptation are presumed to have operated.

The scene of the enquiry is the tropical rain-forest region of northeastern Queensland, and the temporal setting is the period just prior to European settlement in the late nineteenth century.† Most of the rain forest that formerly flourished on the east-coast mountains, plateaux, and lowlands between Cardwell and Cairns has now been cleared, but when Europeans began to penetrate the area after 1860 it was the dominant type of vegetation (Figure 1). This southern rain-forest region of some 11 660 km² was then occupied, according to Tindale (1974, pp. 164–90), by twelve Aboriginal tribal groups (Figure 2) whose territories were, with the exception of the Keramai whose territory included extensive tracts of open woodland, largely restricted to coastal and inland rain-forest habitats.

Although uncertainty attaches to the precise extent of the rain-forest "culture area" and especially to the location and strength of the tribal boundaries within it (Dixon, 1976, Peterson, 1976), there is no doubt that the Aboriginal populations of this region were in many ways physically and culturally distinct from the occupants of the open-woodland habitats inland. Their material culture clearly reflects the special character of the rain forest as a

† This study is part of a comparative investigation of pre-European subsistence across Torres Strait from southern Papua to the southern Cape York Peninsula on which I have been engaged since 1974 (Harris 1976, 1977, In press). I thank the Australian Institute of Aboriginal Studies, the Leverhulme Foundation, and the Central Research Fund of the University of London for their financial support of the field work.

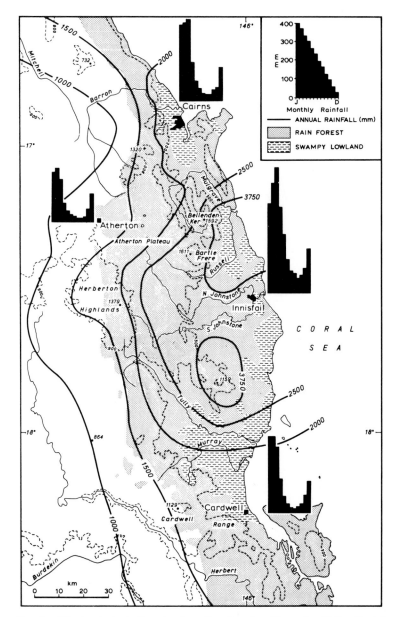

FIG. 1.   The tropical rain-forest region of northeastern Queensland (climatic data from Gibbs, 1971, approximate pre-European distribution of rain forest from Birtles, 1967).

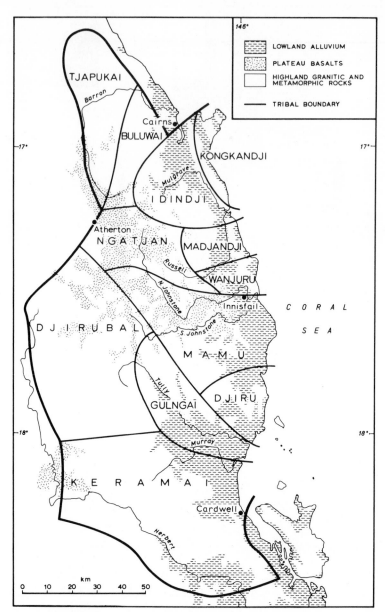

FIG. 2. Tribal territories (from Tindale, 1974) and dominant rock types (modified from 1 : 250 000 Geological Series maps, Bureau of Mineral Resources, Geology and Geophysics, Commonwealth of Australia).

human habitat and it is a basic assumption of this paper that the subsistence economy and general life style of the twelve tribal groups was adapted to the rain-forest ecosystem. But analysis of the pattern of adaptation cannot satisfactorily be carried out at the macro-level of ecosystem and cultural system. These general categories are appropriate containers for the necessary background information, which is summarized in the first half of the paper, but when we ask how habitat, economy, and society articulated in a pattern of adaptation it is necessary to bring the analysis down to more specific levels. Lack of detailed ecological and ethnographic data prevents analysis of a specific tribal group in its own territory, but it is possible to infer some ecologically based variations of tribal population density within the region, to elucidate some of the factors that appear to have regulated the size of band and tribal populations, to model the subsistence cycle of an idealized rain-forest band, and to draw some general conclusions about both demographic and evolutionary adaptation.

The Rain-forest Ecosystem

The pre-European distribution of rain forests in northeastern Queensland correlates broadly with the east-coast zone of high rainfall, although even in the areas of highest rainfall the winter months are relatively dry (Figure 1). Between Cairns and Cardwell the surviving forests vary in structure with differences in altitude, exposure, and soil type. They have been classified by Webb (1968) into six structural types, the most structurally complex and floristically diverse of which is the complex mesophyll vine forest. This type was, before its extensive clearance by European settlers, the dominant vegetation of the alluvial lowlands and of the fertile basaltic soils of the Atherton Plateau and elsewhere (Figure 2). It contains a high proportion of deciduous or rain-green species which dominate the closed canopy. Shrubs and herbs are sparse, but woody lianes, or vines, are abundant. They interlace the trees, reach into the canopy, and effectively bind the forest together, providing aerial pathways for many arboreal animals.

Floristic diversity and endemism are both high. The most

up-to-date list of rain-forest trees common in North Queensland names 260 genera and 514 species (Hyland, 1971), which gives a ratio of only 1·98 species per genus. Indeed, 22 per cent of genera are represented by one species only, and many of those species are endemic. Conversely, six genera contain over ten species each, and two of them—*Cryptocaria* and *Endiandra*—are members of the family Lauraceae which contains the greatest number of species (43), includes many of the largest trees, and contributed many of the edible nuts that were staple Aboriginal foods. In general, the great diversity of the rain-forest flora results in there being relatively few individual plants of any species in a given area. In other words, the diversity index—or ratio between number of species and of individuals—is high and the flora can be said to be generalized. Single species seldom dominate even small areas, so that it is usually necessary to walk considerable distances in order to find more than one or two individuals of a particular species: a characteristic of the "fine-grained" rain-forest ecosystem that has implications for Aboriginal food procurement.

The floristic diversity of primary producers, principally trees, is paralleled by that of the primary and secondary consumers, the herbivorous and carnivorous animals. Diversity is high among the invertebrate fauna, but relatively low among the vertebrates, which represent the main source of animal food for human populations. Birds form the largest group of vertebrates, some 80 species being native to the rain forests. Thirty-five species of snake, and 26 species of mammal, excluding bats, are also recorded (Harrison, 1962, p. 77; Ride, 1970), but comprehensive data on other reptiles and on fish are not available. Despite the diversity of bird life, only three species, all terrestrial—the cassowary (*Casuarius casuarius*) and the two mound-building megapods, the scrub fowl (*Megapodius freycinet*) and the scrub turkey (*Alectura lathami*)—appear to have been important Aboriginal foods, and they were valued more for their eggs than for their flesh. Lizards and snakes, particularly goannas (*Varanus* spp.) and pythons, were eaten, as were a variety of fish caught in the numerous rivers and lakes of the region. The native mammalian fauna contributed to Aboriginal food supplies, but not on a large scale. It consists of 4 species of rat, and 22 species of marsupial comprising 10 possums, 5 macropods (kangaroos and wallabies), 2 bandicoots, 4 antechinuses or marsupial mice, and 1 small tiger cat. It is dominated by nocturnal, tree-living, and tree-climbing animals, most of which are small and elusive. Collectively they did not offer the Aboriginal inhabitants of the rain forests an abundant or easily procured supply of food.

Although the tropical rain forests of northeastern Queensland constitute the most biotically diverse terrestrial ecosystem in Australia they are much less complex biotically than the rain forests of mainland Southeast Asia and Indonesia. They experience a more pronounced dry season, which lasts from about May to December, and which is sufficiently marked to induce some water stress in the forest vegetation. This is expressed both in the high proportion of deciduous or rain-green species and in the periodic rather than perennial flowering of many trees. In Queensland, as in the Malayan rain forest (Whitmore, 1975, pp. 52–9), a majority of rain-forest tree species fruit towards the end of the dry season and early in the wet season (November–December). They include most of the species that provided the edible nuts on which the Aborigines to a large extent depended. Seasonal fruiting peaks also correlate with peaks in the breeding activity of rats, such as the giant white-tailed tree rat (*Uromys caudimaculatus*) which grows as large as a rabbit, and of other fruit-eating species such as the cassowary. According to Tindale (1974, p. 109), cassowary chicks were tethered and tamed by some rain-forest Aborigines until large enough to provide food for a feast, but whether this was done in pre-European times is not certain. Insectivorous birds also show distinct breeding responses to seasonal peaks in insect populations which themselves correlate with dry-season peaks in leaf and flower production. Conversely, breeding among birds is at a minimum during the wet season and their bodies then have least fat. In general it can be said that in the tropical rain forests of Queensland the main wet season, from January to March, is a lean period for animals—and for human foragers—whereas the late dry/early wet season is the time when plant and animal foods are most abundant.

Inter-annual variations in food availability also occur. They relate to unusually dry or wet seasons: for example Webb reports

(1958, p. 225) the popular belief that dry years favour flowering in the rain forests; and exceptionally strong winds and heavy rains accompany the tropical cyclones that sweep in from the Coral Sea on average once every two years (Gibbs, 1971, p. 62). Such cyclones can devastate large tracts of lowland rain forest, and, as Webb remarks (1958, p. 227), they "are a potent ecological factor which regularly upsets forest equilibrium, with far-reaching consequences for the regeneration, suppression, and reproduction of species".

Thus it can be argued that the two most crucial constraints to which a subsistence system based on wild-food procurement must adapt if it is to endure are, first, the spatial pattern of high biotic diversity per unit area, and, second, the seasonal and inter-annual variations in the abundance of many forest foods. Underlying both these constraints is the further fact that animal foods are less abundant than starch-rich plant foods, which implies that a central concern of rain-forest subsistence is likely to be the procurement of adequate supplies of protein and fat.

The Cultural System

Information on the pre-European human populations of the rain-forest region derives unequally from their few living descendants, from historical accounts, and from ethnographic and archaeological collections. Because the rain forests were the last major area of Queensland to be penetrated by Europeans—a process which took place mainly in the 1870s and 1880s in response to gold and other mineral strikes in the interior—several journals and reports written by early prospectors, explorers, and government officials have survived. Collectively these contain sufficient ethnographic information to allow a broad reconstruction of pre-European culture, and they can be supplemented by the more limited data available from surviving Aborigines and from museum and private collections. The main historical sources used in my interpretation, all of which date from the 1880s, are the writings of Christie Palmerston (1883, 1886, 1887), a pioneer prospector; of Carl Lumholtz (1889), a Norwegian zoologist whose main aim was to discover whether the putative tree-climbing kangaroo really existed (it did and is named after him) but who also wrote a detailed account of Aboriginal life in the region; of Archibald Meston (1889, 1904) who led two scientific expeditions to the Bellenden Ker Range south of Cairns; and of Walter Roth (1901–10), the pioneer ethnographer who became the Queensland Government's first Northern Protector of Aborigines in 1897.

These early observers were struck by the relatively small stature and slender limbs of the rain-forest Aborigines, but it was not until Tindale and Birdsell worked with a remnant population on the Atherton Plateau in 1938 that the concept of a distinctively pygmoid racial type was clearly enunciated. This led to a controversy about its racial affinity and role in the peopling of Australia which need not concern us, but Tindale and Birdsell (1941) did identify the central bloc of twelve small-statured tribes to which this paper relates (Figure 2). Study of the languages of the area by Dixon (1972, 1976) lends some support to the observation that these rain-forest tribes differed culturally from neighbouring groups, but it also shows that at least five distinct languages were spoken in the area and that there were linguistic links with peripheral tribes.

In the realm of material culture greater distinctiveness attaches to the rain-forest tribes. Some cultural elements are unique to them and clearly reflect features of the rain-forest habitat. These include dome-shaped, rain-proof, thatched huts used principally in the wet season but lasting from year to year; bark cloth hammered from the inner bark of fig trees (*Ficus pleurocarpa*) which was used to make blankets as well as containers both for carrying water and honey and for leaching bitter yams; baskets made from lawyer cane (*Calamus australis*) and rush (*Xerotes longifolia*) which were used as sieve bags for leaching toxic nuts; huge wooden swords and shields, the latter made from the flange buttresses of fig trees and painted with intricate designs when a boy was initiated into manhood (McConnel, 1935); and, most distinctive of all, two types of specialized nut-processing stone used respectively to crack open the hard nuts of the Queensland almond (*Elaeocarpus bancroftii*) and to macerate nut kernels, especially those of the yellow and black walnuts (*Beilschmiedia bancroftii* and *Endiandra palmerstonii*).

The specialized character of these elements of material culture, many of which are unique to this part of Aboriginal Australia, supports the inference drawn from racial and linguistic data that the rain-forest tribes differed from neighbouring occupants of more open habitats. How far their social behaviour also differed is difficult to determine because of lack of evidence, but several societal aspects of rain-forest culture appear distinctive. They include cannibalism, mummification prior to cremation, and the holding of fighting corroborees to settle disputes. At these corroborees the huge swords and shields were wielded in duels, but combatants were seldom killed. Indeed, as Lumholtz remarks (1889, p. 127), "Mortal wounds are extremely rare" and the combatant knows "that his opponent, through fear of his relatives, will not carry the conflict to the extreme . . . if necessary, they will interfere and prevent his getting wounded".

Any attempt to analyse the pattern of pre-European Aboriginal adaptation in the rain-forest region demands knowledge of the size, structure, and inter-relationships of the social groups that made up the twelve tribes. Information on this aspect of rain-forest culture is extremely meagre, but some evidence can be gleaned from the historical sources and this can be reinforced by reference to more general knowledge of Australian Aboriginal society. Lumholtz distinguishes (1889, pp. 176–7) the "family tribe" of 20–25 individuals from the "tribe" of 200–250, and he comments that "Individuals belonging to the same tribe are usually on the best of terms, but the different tribes are each other's mortal enemies", although "the small subdivisions of the tribes that live nearest the border are on amicable terms with their neighbours". The distinction that he draws between tribes, and sub-tribes or family tribes, corresponds to the well known distinction in Australian Aboriginal society between larger tribes sharing a common language or dialect, and smaller kin-based bands or hordes. His estimate of band and tribal sizes, which implies an average of ten bands per tribe, is reasonable for the early post-contact situation that he witnessed, but it obscures significant ecologically based variations in population density.

Tribal Population Densities

A map giving approximate Aboriginal populations, which was published in 1897 by Parry-Okeden, Queensland Commissioner

TABLE 1. Estimated populations in 1897 and in c. 1800 of twelve rain-forest tribes in northeastern Queensland.

Tribe	Area (km²)	Band or horde	1897 population	1897 Density (km²/person)	c. 1800 population (1897 × 2½)	c. 1800 Density (km²/person)	Principal habitats†
(Data from Tindale, 1974)		(Data from Parry-Okeden, 1897)					
Kongkandji	400	Koongangie	320	1·25	800	0·50	C/RF
Ngatjan	500	Eaton, Hucheon	300	1·67	750	0·67	URF(B)
Djiru	260	Gerra, Gillah	130	2·00	325	0·80	LRF/C
Gulngai	500	Marapunda, Walinganba	120	4·17	300	1·67	LRF/C
Mamu	1300	Woggil, Gijow, Kitba, Ohalo, Warra Warra, Deba	285	4·56	712	1·83	LRF/C
Madjandji-Wanjuru	900	Mooka, ?Maimbie	175	5·14	438	2·05	LRF/C
Idindji	1000	Yellingie	152	6·58	380	2·63	LRF/URF(G)
Keramai	2600	Kirrama	300	8·67	750	3·47	LRF/URF(G) OW
Djirubal	2900	Chirpa, Barbarum (sic), ?Wannagoola, ?Mancobunba, ?Murma, ?Okemo, ?Bool Boora, ?Warry Boora	300	9·67	750	3·87	URF(G)
Tjapukai-Buluwai	1300	?Tuffelgey	100	13·00	250	5·20	URF(G)
Rain-forest total	11660		2182		5455		
Rain-forest average				5·34		2·14	

† C = coastal; OW = open woodland; LRF = lowland rain forest; URF = upland rain forest; (B) = basaltic tableland; (G) = granitic and metamorphic highland.

of Police, provides some information on these variations (Table 1). The correlation of Parry-Okeden's band names with Tindale's tribes presents difficulties, and we cannot be confident that the population estimates for 1897 are themselves accurate, but despite these uncertainties a remarkably consistent relationship of population density to habitat type is revealed by Table 1, which arranges the tribes in order of decreasing population density.

A major distinction can be drawn between tribes occupying mainly lowland rain forests with access to considerable stretches of coast (Djiru, Gulngai, Kongkandji, Mamu, Madjandji-Wanjuru) and tribes of the upland rain forests inland (Ngatjan, Djirubal, Tjapukai-Buluwai). The lowland tribes, whose economies focused on coastal as well as on forest resources, show higher population densities (an average of almost 3·3 km² per person) than—with the notable exception of the Ngatjan—the upland tribes (an average, excluding the Ngatjan, of 10·5 km² per person). If the territories of the three upland groups are examined it is seen that most of the Ngatjan tribal territory was underlain by the fertile basaltic soils of the Atherton Plateau, whereas the territories of the Djirubal and Tjapukai–Buluwai extended over the more sterile granitic and metamorphic highlands to the north and south (Figure 2). The rich soils of the Atherton Plateau, as well as the alluvial soils of the coastal lowlands, supported complex mesophyll vine forest, whereas less luxuriant mixed mesophyll and evergreen vine forests grew on the thinner and less fertile soils of the highlands. The nut-yielding trees on which rain-forest subsistence focused are most abundant in the complex mesophyll vine forest, and this fact, together with the presence on the Plateau of many freshwater streams and lakes, helps to account for the relatively high population density that characterized the Ngatjan. And it is strong testimony to the enduring significance of ecological variables that European colonists have in this century built up a denser network of settlements and achieved a higher level of agricultural production on the fertile soils of the Atherton Plateau than anywhere else in northern Queensland. Two tribes, the Idindji and the Keramai, occupy an intermediate position in Table 1 between the lowland and upland groups, and, as might be predicted, their territories included extensive tracts of granitic upland as well as areas of alluvial lowland (Figure 2).

The 1897 estimates do not of course represent pre-European levels of population because they do not allow for the decimation of Aboriginal groups that followed the arrival of Europeans in the region. No evidence is available on which to base detailed estimates of the post-contact decline of tribal populations, but the consistency of the density-habitat relationship revealed in the Table suggests that the impact of Europeans did not vary greatly overall and that the demographic pattern shown is broadly representative of the pre-contact situation. On the basis of general estimates of the post-European decline in the Aboriginal population of the region, reinforced by extrapolation from comparable resource-rich areas elsewhere in Aboriginal Australia, it appears realistic to estimate the pre-European population as not less than two and a half times the 1897 population. The resultant figures are shown in Table 1. They suggest that the total population in, say, 1800 was between 5000 and 5500 and the average density just over 2·0 km² per person. Although this density is high by comparison with most other parts of Aboriginal Australia, it does not imply that populations attained maximum levels in relation both to available food and to their technological ability to procure it. On the contrary, the evidence suggests that band and tribal populations were regulated by varied means at densities below any upper limits set by available food supplies and technology.

Population Regulation

The historical sources occasionally refer to the limitation of population that resulted from such practices as late marriage, postpartum abstention, prolonged weaning, infanticide, intergroup killing, and cannibalism. Thus Lumholtz states (1889, pp. 184, 163, 134) that: "the majority of young men wait a long time before they get wives", that "it is, as a rule, difficult for young men to marry before they are 30 years old", that "the women bear their first child at the age of eighteen to twenty years, sometimes later, and seldom have more than three or four", that, after the birth of a child, the mother "must keep away from her husband . . . for a long time", and that "the children are weaned late, and it even happens that the child is nursed at its mother's breast with the next older brother or sister''. Commenting on infanticide, Lumholtz points out (1889, pp. 134–5) that

> The advent of a baby is not always regarded with favour, and infanticide is therefore common . . ., especially where there is a scarcity of food, as under such circumstances they may even eat the child. In their nomadic life children are a burden to them, and the men particularly do not like to see the women, who work hard and procure much food, troubled with many children.

It is significant that this comment makes explicit connection between the demands of mobility and food procurement and the wish to limit the number of children. That mobility favoured wide spacing of children and small families can also be inferred from Lumholtz's description (1889, p. 192) of how the mother ''constantly carries [her child] with her at first in a basket, but later on, when it is big enough, on her shoulders, where either she supports it with her hand or else the child holds itself fast by its mother's head. Thus she carries it till it is several years old''.

The demographic significance of inter-group killing and cannibalism is difficult to gauge, but the evidence suggests that neither occurred frequently. The pattern seems to have been one of enmity between widely separated tribes, resulting in occasional killing and consumption, in contrast to prevailing intra-tribal and proximate-tribal friendliness. Movements of individuals from band to band, and of bands within their own and neighbouring tribal territories, were part of the normal pattern of economic and social interaction that sustained the largely autonomous, exogamous bands. Polygyny evidently prevailed (Lumholtz, 1889, p. 162), and because women were valued more as food procurers than as child bearers it is likely to have contributed to the limitation rather than the increase of population growth. Furthermore, the fighting corroborees, a major purpose of which was to settle disputes over wives, probably helped to maintain polygyny by periodically checking tendencies towards a more equal distribution of women among the adult men.

In the pattern of intra- and extra-group behaviour involving polygyny, late marriage, prolonged weaning, infanticide, inter-tribal killing, and cannibalism, we can discern a series of culturally mediated variables that regulated populations in the rain-forest region at levels below the maximum densities attainable with the food resources and technology available. Without more adequate data we cannot specify with any precision the relative importance of the different variables, but it seems clear that those operating mainly within bands and between bands of the same tribe—polygyny, late marriage, prolonged weaning, and infan-ticide—rather than those operating mainly between tribes—kil-ling in raids and cannibalism—were the more effective in limiting population.

There may have been other variables also checking population growth, such as generalized low fertility in women due to their being less well nourished than men. For example, Lumholtz states (1889, p. 161) that the hunter "very often keeps the animal food for himself, while the woman has to depend principally upon vegetables for herself and her child." If, as has been suggested (Frisch and McArthur, 1974, Howell, 1976), lack of body fat delays the onset of menstruation and suppresses ovulation during lactation, then the dietary inequality between the sexes may have helped to limit population. Disease, too, may have regulated population in pre-European times, but the historical sources scarcely mention disease whereas they do comment on the physical prowess and agility of the Aborigines.

The demographic variables, particularly polygyny, late mar-riage, prolonged weaning, and infanticide, can thus be envisaged as having negative feedback effects within and between bands which checked any tendency for populations to increase above an average size of, say, 40–50 per band or 400–500 per tribe. Precisely how the limitation of family and group size was perceived as advantageous by the individuals concerned cannot be ascer-tained, although Lumholtz's comment on the conflict between mobility and child-bearing is suggestive; but it can be assumed that the population was not consciously maintained at a level below some abstractly conceived "carrying capacity" of the rain-forest environment. Instead we can envisage that the demog-raphic sub-system, with its negative feedback effects operating at family and band level, articulated with the rain-forest ecosystem through an annual cycle of subsistence and ceremonial activities. This cycle involved spatial and seasonal variations in the movements of individuals, family or hearth groups, and bands which keyed in to annual changes in the rain-forest ecosystem.

The Subsistence Cycle

If the historical sources are scrutinized for evidence of seasonal variations in social and economic activity, and if that evidence is related to seasonal changes in the ecosystem, it is possible broadly to reconstruct the subsistence cycle of an idealized rain-forest band. The chief natural variable that pulsed the cycle was the seasonality of flowering and fruiting among the rain-forest plants that provided staple foods. As we have seen, the major contrast was between the main fruiting peak in the late dry/early wet season and the relatively lean period of the main wet season, a flux in the supply of many plant foods that was paralleled by corresponding variations in animal populations and to which Aboriginal subsistence was geared. The band was the basic socio-economic unit, containing on average 45 people divided into 7 or 8 family or hearth groups each consisting of 6 or 7 individuals. Although the band exercised customary rights over the use of resources in its own "country" or territory, it did not always act as a single unit for purposes of food procurement. Part of the time individuals and family groups foraged on their own, and at other times bands came together in tribal congregations. And permeating all subsistence activities, at family, band, and tribal level, was an emphatic and unequal division of labour between the sexes. This placed a disproportionate domestic burden on the women as baggage carriers, hut builders, procurers and processors of food, and bearers of children (Lumholtz, 1889, pp. 160–1), and by enhancing the conflict between domestic service and motherhood it reinforced the negative feedback effects that regulated populations at low densities.

If we follow the sequence of a band's subsistence activities through the year we find that in the relatively cool and dry winter season people were more mobile than in the summer wet season. In the dry season the men made hunting trips to the more open habitats within and marginal to the rain forests; they fished in lakes and rivers, using techniques of fish stupefaction in the quieter reaches and water-holes formed at this season of reduced stream flow; they searched for goannas and for cassowaries' eggs on the forest floor; and they climbed to the forest canopy by means of looped lengths of lawyer cane in pursuit of arboreal mammals, birds, and the large pythons that were relished especially for their fat and which often lay dormant at this season curled within the great frond epiphytes that cling to tree trunks and branches (Lumholtz, 1889, pp. 293–8). The women spent a good deal of time locating and digging yams and other tuberous plants as well as searching for insects and other small animals. Some inland groups visited the coast (Mulligan, 1877, p. 399; cited in Birtles, 1967, p. 34), whereas others restricted their movements to the interior plateaus and mountains (Meston, 1889, p. 19). In general the dry season was a time of partial dispersal and relative social isolation.

Towards the end of the dry season and into the early wet season (October–December) production of wild foods in the rain forests reached its seasonal peak. This was the time of most prolific fruiting among rain-forest trees, particularly those nut-bearing species that provided staple foods. At this time bands came together at ceremonial *bora* grounds where fighting corroborees and dance festivals were held. Animal foods, especially the eggs of scrub fowl and scrub turkey, added to the seasonal largesse which supported larger population aggregates and more settled life than characterized the dry season.

At the beginning of the wet season the more elaborate and permanent camps of thatched huts were re-, or more fully, occupied at locations that bore strategic relationships to spatially predictable and seasonally abundant resources. For example, Meston reports (1889, p. 18) of the Aborigines of the Bellenden Ker Range that their "main camps are always built on some healthy dry situation, beside or very near a running stream. These are the "wet weather camps", where they remain during the wet season, and store large supplies of nuts". Easy access to running water was a primary requirement for the wet-season camps. Most of the tree nuts that provided staple starchy food required leaching in fresh, preferably running, water, and access to rivers and streams also favoured the exploitation of fish, including eels and crayfish, which yielded dependable supplies of protein. Rock outcrops along river banks were pitted with water-worn holes convenient for crushing and leaching plant products; pebbles and boulders provided suitable raw material for making axes and nut-processing stones; and large exposures of bedrock offered sites for grinding axes and other stone tools, for fishing, and for general social interaction. Although most wet-season camps were probably located near rivers, the harvesting of particular foods, such as the sweet nuts of the Queensland almond, led to the temporary establishment of more casual camps close to such spatially and seasonally predictable resources (Woolston and Colliver, 1973, p. 106).

The late dry/early wet season was a time of plenty when social life intensified, especially during the fighting corroborees which brought bands together for two to three days at a time on perhaps three or four occasions each wet season (Lumholtz, 1889, p. 127). Dance festivals lasted longer than fighting corroborees but only occurred every few years. According to Lumholtz (1889, p. 236–41), they took place in mid wet season and lasted several weeks as dancers moved from one *bora* ground to another at intervals determined by the need to gather fresh supplies of food, principally walnuts, every few days.

As the wet season advanced the seasonal peak of food availability passed and there was a corresponding decline in social activity. The latter half of the wet season (February–March) was the leanest period of the year, although there is no evidence that bands experienced sustained hunger at this (or any other) time. Tree nuts, collected and stored in the main camps, remained a staple food and perennially available resources such as fish and palm stems continued to be exploited. Bands remained at the home-base camps, occupying their relatively large and rain-proof wet-season huts, although the women continued to forage, as Meston says (1904, p. 6), "every second or third day, regardless of the state of the weather". As the rains gradually diminished in intensity and duration through April and May, bands, family groups, and individuals once again became more mobile. And, with the arrival of the dry season, another annual cycle of subsistence and social life began.

Conclusion

Ethnoecological analysis makes possible a broad reconstruction of pre-European economy and society in the tropical rain forests of northeastern Queensland and suggests some general conclusions about the nature of demographic adaptation in that environment. In a region of some 11 660 km² twelve tribes, numbering perhaps between 5000 and 5500 people in all, lived at an average density of not less than 2·0 km² per person. The pattern of adaptive behaviour that linked the cultural system with the rain-forest ecosystem found expression mainly in the actions of family groups and bands. They selectively exploited the generalized ecosystem, with its "fine-grained" distribution of component species, by following an annual cycle of subsistence and ceremonial activities which involved group aggregation and disaggregation and which meshed with the seasonal reproductive cycles of the principal rain-forest biota that were used for food. Mobility, maximized in the dry season and minimized in the wet season, was an integral part of this pattern of adaptation. But partial sedentism existed, in the sense of the wet-season occupation of home-base huts by the whole band, with a tendency for some of the less mobile individuals to remain at or near the home base all the year round.

Partial sedentism was based on the abundance of wild foods, especially nutritious and storable tree nuts, but it also allowed, and was itself favoured by, the elaboration of material culture that was a distinctive feature of rain-forest society. The relationships between partial sedentism and material culture can be thought of as a sub-system within which positive feedback or deviation amplifying effects promoted a degree of specialization in the use of resources which allowed a relatively dense population to be sustained. But the tendency towards specialization was held in check by the demographic sub-system which linked mobility with the sexual division of labour and with marriage practices in a network of negative feedback effects that regulated populations at densities below the maximum attainable with the food resources and technology available. It is evident that trends towards specialization in the use of resources, and towards sedentism and the build-up of relatively large populations, existed among the rain-forest tribes; but it is also clear that these trends led neither to domestication, in the sense of the incorporation of particular plants and animals into the subsistence economy by selective control over their breeding, nor to full sedentism. If cassowary chicks were tamed and reared by the coastal Kong-kandji and other rain-forest dwellers in pre-European times, as Tindale's report suggests, it could be said that a threshold of domestication was approached. But, if so, the negative factors checking such specialization evidently remained sufficiently strong to maintain the subsistence system as a whole at a level that can be characterized as intensive, selective foraging within a broad-spectrum pattern of resource use.

If it were possible to show how this system arose and developed through time we might be able to formulate some generalizations about evolutionary adaptation in the rain-forest region, but in the absence of adequate archaeological and palaeoenvironmental evidence this must remain a matter for speculation. There is recent proof of human occupation more than 13 000 years ago at Laura some 80 km northwest of the region (Rosenfeld, 1975), and it is now established that man was present farther south in Australia (at Lake Mungo in New South Wales) at least by 32 000 BP (Barbetti and Allen, 1972, Bowler *et al*. 1972). Palynological investigation has demonstrated that complex mesophyll vine forest has been established on the Atherton Plateau for the last 5000–6000 years and that it was preceded by notophyll rain forest in the period 6000–9500 BP and by sclerophyllous woodland between 9500 and about 30 000 BP (Kershaw, 1974, 1976). It is quite probable that human populations were present on the Atherton Plateau before the establishment there of tropical rain-forests and that they then exploited the rain-forests for several millennia before the arrival of the Europeans. If future archaeological work confirms this supposition the pre-European cultural system could be regarded as evolutionarily as well as demographically well adapted to the rain-forest ecosystem.

The evidence summarized and discussed in this paper suggests that the Aboriginal inhabitants of the rain-forest region developed a sufficiently flexible behavioural repertoire to maintain their way of life over the long term in the biotically diverse rain-forest ecosystem. They learned to cope with seasonal and secular changes in the physical environment, but their total population was too small and their cultural system insufficiently resilient to withstand the devastating impact of European settlement. By 1900, barely three decades after European penetration of the rain forests had begun, their economy and society, unique in Aboriginal Australia, had disintegrated.

References

BARBETTI, M. and ALLEN, H. (1972) Prehistoric man at Lake Mungo, Australia, by 32,000 years BP, *Nature*, **240**, 46–48.

BIRTLES, T. G. (1967) *A Survey of Land Use, Settlement and Society in the Atherton-Evelyn District, North Queensland*. Unpublished M.A. thesis, University of Sydney.

BOWLER, J. M., THORNE, A. G. and POLACH, H. A. (1972) Pleistocene man in Australia: age and significance of the Mungo skeleton, *Nature*, **240**, 48–50.

DIXON, R. M. W. (1972) *The Dyirbal Language of North Queensland*. Cambridge University Press, Cambridge.

DIXON, R. M. W. (1976) Tribes, languages and other boundaries in northeast Queensland. In *Tribes and Boundaries of Australia* (ed. N. Peterson). Australian Institute of Aboriginal Studies, Canberra.

FRISCH, R. E. and MCARTHUR, J. W. (1974) Menstrual cycles: fatness as a determinant of minimum weight for height necessary for their maintenance or onset, *Science*, **185**, 949–51.

GIBBS, W. J. (1971) *Climatic Survey Northern Region 16–Queensland*. Bureau of Meteorology, Commonwealth of Australia, Canberra.

HARRIS, D. R. (1976) Aboriginal use of plant foods in the Cape York Peninsula and Torres Strait Islands, *Australian Institute of Aboriginal Studies Newsletter, New Series*, **6**, 21–22.

HARRIS, D. R. (1977) Subsistence strategies across Torres Strait. In *Sunda and Sahul: Prehistoric Studies in Southeast Asia, Melanesia and Australia* (eds. J. Allen, J. Golson and R. Jones). Academic Press, London.

HARRIS, D. R. (In press) *Across Torres Strait*. Cambridge University Press, Cambridge.

HARRISON, J. L. (1962) Mammals of Innisfail, *Australian Journal of Zoology*, **10**, 45–83.

HOWELL, N. (1976) The population of the Dobe area !Kung. In *Kalahari Hunter–Gatherers: Studies of the !Kung San and their Neighbours* (eds. R. B. Lee and I. DeVore). Harvard University Press, Cambridge, Mass.

HYLAND, B. P. M. (1971) *A Key to the Common Rain Forest Trees between Townsville and Cooktown based on Leaf and Bark Features*. Queensland Department of Forestry, Brisbane.

KERSHAW, A. P. (1974) A long continuous pollen sequence from north-eastern Australia. *Nature*, **251**, 222–23.

KERSHAW, A. P. (1976) A Late Pleistocene and Holocene pollen diagram from Lynch's crater, north-eastern Queensland, Australia, *New Phytologist*, **77**, 469–98.

LUMHOLTZ, C. (1889) *Among Cannibals*. John Murray, London.

MCCONNEL, U. H. (1935) Inspiration and design in Aboriginal art, *Art in Australia*, 15 May, pp. 49–57.

MESTON, A. (1889) *Report on the Government Scientific Expedition to the Bellenden-Ker Range (Wooroonooran), North Queensland*. C.A. 95, Queensland Government, Brisbane.

MESTON, A. (1904) *Report on Expedition to the Bellenden-Ker Range*. C.A. 36, Queensland Government, Brisbane.

MULLIGAN, J. V. (1877) Expedition in search of gold and other minerals in the Palmer Districts, by Mulligan and party, *Votes and Proceedings of the Legislative Assembly*, III, Queensland Government, Brisbane.

PALMERSTON, C. (1883) From Mourilyan Harbour to Herberton, *The Queenslander*, 22 September: 477–78, 29 September: 518–19, 6 October: 557–58.

PALMERSTON, C. (1886) From Herberton to the Barron Falls, North Queensland, *Trans. and Proc. of the Royal Geographical Society of Australia, New South Wales Branch*, **4**, 231–44.

PALMERSTON, C. (1887) The diary of a northern pioneer, *The Queensland Figaro*, 12 February: 265–66; 19 February: 291, 295; 26 February: 346, 351; 5 March: 385; 12 March: 433; 19 March: 467; 26 March: 491; 2 April: 545–46; 9 April: 596; 23 April: 651.

PARRY-OKEDEN, W. E. (1897) *Report on the North Queensland Aborigines and the Native Police*. C.A. 10, Queensland Government, Brisbane.

PETERSON, N. (1976) The natural and cultural areas of Aboriginal Australia. In *Tribes and Boundaries of Australia* (ed. N. Peterson). Australian Institute of Aboriginal Studies, Canberra.

RIDE, W. D. L. (1970) *A Guide to the Native Mammals of Australia*. Oxford University Press, Melbourne.

ROSENFELD, A. (1975) Air to ground, *Hemisphere*, **19**, 21–25.

ROTH, W. E. (1901–1910) North Queensland ethnography, Bulletins **1–8**, *Department of Home Secretary, Brisbane* (1901–1905), Bulletins **9–18**, *Records of the Australian Museum*, **6–8** (1907–1910).

TINDALE, N. B. (1974) *Aboriginal Tribes of Australia*. University of California Press, Berkeley and Los Angeles.

TINDALE, N. B. and BIRDSELL, J. B. (1941) Results of the Harvard–Adelaide Universities anthropological expedition, 1938–1939 Tasmanoid tribes in North Queensland, *Records of the South Australia Museum*, **7**, 1–9.

WEBB, L. J. (1958) Cyclones as an ecological factor in tropical lowland rain forest, North Queensland, *Australian Journal of Botany*, **6**, 220–28.

WEBB, L. J. (1968) Environmental relationships of the structural types of Australian rain forest vegetation, *Ecology*, **49**, 296–311.

WHITMORE, T. C. (1975) *Tropical Rain Forests of the Far East*. Clarendon Press, Oxford.

WOOLSTON, F. P. and COLLIVER, F. S. (1973) Some stone artifacts from North Queensland rain forests, *Occasional Papers in Anthropology*, **1**, 104–25, Anthropology Museum, University of Queensland.

TESTING ADAPTIVENESS OF CULTURALLY DETERMINED BEHAVIOUR: DO BUSHMAN WOMEN MAXIMIZE THEIR REPRODUCTIVE SUCCESS BY SPACING BIRTHS WIDELY AND FORAGING SELDOM?

N. BLURTON JONES

Institute of Child Health, University of London

and R. M. SIBLY

Department of Zoology, University of Oxford

MANY recent writings in ecological anthropology or cultural ecology use the term adaptation and are based on the assumption that one can show that cultures are in various senses adaptive and that one way of behaving is "better" (in some economic or ecological sense) than another. Contrary to early anecdotal studies the ecological anthropologists find that when one observes and measures the interaction between people and the material world even quite bizarre practices turn out to appear economically advantageous. But the nature of "advantage" and adaptation is unclear and often refers to energy budgets or to group survival, both of which would no longer be acceptable criteria to evolutionary biologists. We admire this school of anthropology and hope that by discussing the criterion of "adaptation" and "advantage" that comes first to the mind of the biologist we can provoke further research and thinking on the nature of human cultural adaptation.

Important and relevant criticisms of the application of the concept of adaptiveness to human culture (equally applicable to the concept of adaptation in biology) have been set out by Burnham (1973) and Alland (1975). Recent developments have gone far towards solving these problems in biology (Hamilton, 1964; Trivers, 1975; Tinbergen, 1965; Sibly and McFarland, 1976). The ecological approaches to culture seem too valuable to lose merely from isolation from the answers to these problems. Consequently

135

in this paper we aim to contribute to the development of ecological approaches to culture by provoking discussion of biologists' answers to (1) what is the criterion of adaptiveness? What is improved or increased by adaptive behaviour? and (2) how do we test whether behaviour is adaptive or not?

Our approach to the second question illustrates the development from Tinbergen's (1965) comparisons of the outcomes of different behaviour (also called for by Alland, 1975) via his idea of compromise in adaptation to current attempts to use optimization techniques to calculate the behaviour sequence that would maximize reproductive success, the result then being compared with the observed behaviour (Sibly and McFarland, 1976). This is a difficult but potentially extremely powerful approach.

Burnham (1973) raised a third criticism: what is the mechanism by which an adaptive change takes place? The mechanism is clearly not the same as in biological evolution. Many possibilities are conceivable and have been discussed in the literature. One might be able to derive and propose the most efficient but we regard this question as independent from the first two. If cultural change is demonstrably adaptive this is not disproved by our inability to describe the mechanism by which the change occurs. Furthermore, since cultural change is more rapid than biological change, the short-term mechanisms may be of much less practical importance than the pressures towards adaptation, whose effect will be more powerful and remarkably rapid.

Lee (1972) has described various quantitative aspects of birth-spacing and foraging in Kalahari hunter–gatherers. He has shown how the "cost" of having babies in terms of weight carried by mothers increases cumulatively with shortened birth-spacing, the increase in cost from giving birth every three years rather than every four is much greater than the increased cost of giving birth every four years rather than every five. This, and his demonstration and explanation of the changes as Bushmen become more settled, is an elegant example of what contemporary ecological anthropology can achieve. But as biologists we believe that the analysis is incomplete, a further important step is missing—the demonstration that the increased costs of closer birth-spacing are not worth paying. Our proposition is that people, at least in the ancient hunter–gatherer niche, might, like many non-human species (Lack, 1954), tend to have as many babies as they can successfully raise.

Thus in this paper we try to show how one might test whether people in a foraging culture behave in ways which maximize their reproductive success (and perhaps ultimately their inclusive fitness, Hamilton, 1964). Our example is very limited and our approach may or may not be applicable to other hunter–gatherer cultures or post hunter–gatherer societies. In our preliminary analysis of the spacing between births of the !kung Bushmen we are using the ecological data and suggestions published by Lee (1968, 1969, 1972) (see Lee and DeVore, 1976 for reports of the recent series of studies on the Kalahari !kung Bushmen), and physiological data from many people (Durnin and Passmore, 1967, Weiner, 1977), including Bushmen (Wyndham, 1956, 1958, 1964). Bushman mothers average nearly four years between births. Both the mothers themselves and Lee (1972) agree that this is desirable because of the difficulty of carrying two children on their gathering excursions. But what does "desirable" mean? We rephrase this question as: are they, by spacing births so widely, likely to be rearing to maturity more children than they would if they gave birth more often?

By testing the applicability of natural selection theory to human behaviour in this context we are not making any implications of "innateness" in the behavioural mechanisms involved: (1) questions about adaptation are questions about consequences of behaviour (which act as *long-term* causes) and carry only framework-setting implications about the short-term mechanisms of individual development or motivation (Tinbergen, 1951; Harris, 1968; Gross, 1975); (2) we know that all the variables discussed here, even the physiological ones, are strongly modified by physical and cultural environments. Indeed the interest of this exercise is in applying it to culturally transmitted behaviour and individually variable performance. If culture is adaptive, does adaptive mean maximizing inclusive fitness, or maximizing something else (individual wealth, group survival—which biologists regard as unlikely), or not actually maximizing anything—in which case the propositions of cultural ecology become less easy to test. It would seem reasonable to expect hunter–gatherer cultures (particularly when as with the Bushmen, the archaeological record (Yellen, 1976) reveals the great antiquity of their material culture and habitat) to show behaviour that maximizes inclusive fitness. But it would seem very unreasonable to expect this to apply very effectively to rapidly changing industrial cultures, unless culture is even more adaptive than we think. Detailed empirical studies of a variety of cultures have been undertaken in recent years and hopefully our ideas could be tested on several non hunter–gatherer cultures as well as by further analyses of Bushman data.

Thus in this paper we attempt to bring together ecological approaches to human behaviour with data from physical anthropology and environmental physiology and current developments in evolutionary biology, particularly studies in which the techniques of optimisation are applied to the question of compromise in adaptation. Tinbergen showed how any feature of an animal's behaviour is a result of a compromise between conflicting pressures. This line of thought has been elaborated by Sibly and McFarland (1976) and others. In an ideal optimization study, one would know the costs and benefits involved in performing or not performing each activity in an individual's repertoire, so that its optimal strategy could be calculated exactly. This is the strategy one would expect as the ultimate outcome of natural selection.

In practice consideration has to be given to five points: (1) what options are open to the animal and what courses of action is it able to perform? This is partly a matter of discovering what it cannot do, of finding or assuming constraints on its behaviour like some of the "givens" enumerated below; (2) what risks, to personal survivorship or to the survival of kin, and what benefits in terms of the potential production of offspring, are entailed by each course of action? (3) is it feasible to measure these risks and benefits? (4) can a mathematical model of the individual's situation be constructed, and if so, what optimal strategy does it suggest? (5) how does this optimal strategy compare with the animal's actual behaviour?

This approach can embody the normal scientific procedure of hypothesis, prediction and test. A more rigorous account of the method, together with examples, is given in Sibly and McFarland (1976) and McFarland (1976).

Lee has shown that many features of Zhun/twa Bushman society and individual behaviour are readily explicable as successful adaptations to surviving with a hunter–gatherer technology in the sparse habitat of Ngamiland. Most of these are clearly adaptive in almost any sense—personal survival or comfort, survival of children or group. But the observations that we argue need further "explanation" are two which are in some ways "counter-intuitive" and may provoke more precise consideration of the way in which they are adaptive: (1) the interval between births in non-settled traditionally foraging Bushmen is approximately 4 years (this declines markedly when people settle); (2) women (who provide 67% of the calorie "income") only go gathering once every 2 or 3 days. Most of the time they spend talking and singing and visiting or being visited by friends and relatives.

There are several observed aspects of Bushman behaviour, some *very* important, whose adaptive value we have not questioned at this stage of the investigation: (1) mothers carry children of under 2 years old when they go gathering, and frequently carry children under 4 years old. We use Lee's figures on this and *for the time being* assume that a woman makes the maximum possible use of available babysitters; (2) men do not gather, but hunt, acquiring at unpredictable intervals an average 33% of the calorie "income" (but of course acquiring a wider range of proteins); (3) that the women walk quite fast on their journeys to and from the nut groves. We assume a figure of 3 m.p.h. The consequences of higher and, more important, lower speeds for our model can be tested; (4) that the dry season villages are 6 miles from the nut groves and one mile from water and that Lee is correct in calling this optimal for the energy or thermoregulatory budgets; (5) that mongongo nuts (*Ricinodendron rautanenii*) are the most useful plant food source and the main one to consider (other plant foods provide 8·9% of calorie income—Lee, 1968), although (6) they take a very long time to crack (Lee, 1969) which excludes daily gathering excursions; (7) start and end ages for having babies (19·5–45 years) (Howell, 1976); (8) that Lee is correct in arguing that although plant food is superabundant and the supply of mongongo nuts is not exhaustible by foraging, exhaustion of supplies *near* dry season camps is, as Konner (personal communication) and Lee (1969) suggest, a reason for the long "six mile" journeys late in the dry season.

Some further "givens" will arise and be discussed later in this paper. Every given can also be seen as a gateway to a new area of quantitative study linking ever wider facets of Bushman life into one sharply specified system. Regardless of the eventual answer about what is optimised, this procedure of constructing a system that specifies the consequences of one variable upon each other variable is to our minds an attractive potential outcome of the approach that we are proposing.

Birth-spacing, Food Requirements and Back-loads

If a Bushman mother has a baby more often than every 4 years (given that as she does, she carries children up to 4 years old on her foraging trips) she will spend some time carrying two small children when she goes gathering and more time carrying at least one of them. This will reduce the amount of food that she can bring back, if there is some limit to the total weight that she can carry. At the same time it will increase the amount of food her family needs; there are more children to feed then and subsequently. As her payload goes down so the food requirements go up. Obviously at some point shortening the birth interval will lead to a situation where the mother would have to carry extremely high loads to feed her family. But of course there is strong selective advantage in having more children, so long as you can feed them enough for them to grow up and reproduce. If reproductive success is the criterion it would be worth great costs to the extent of risking physical integrity to have just one more baby (provided this meant more babies growing up and reproducing). Since too great a level of risk cannot be worth taking there must be some optimal birth interval which maximizes reproductive success.

The first step in analysing this situation is to work out what maximum back-loads are required to support various sized families. If we treat the number of years for which the woman reproduces as a constant, then family size and birth interval are closely correlated. Much of the relevant data is available. Lee (1972) published weights of children of various ages, and of adults. He also calculated dietary requirements of adults (1968). We have recalculated these and those of children. We have used data from the biological data handbooks for calorie cost of lactation and requirements for babies under one year. Lee (1968, 1969) published data on the food values of a given weight of both prepared and unshelled mongongo nuts. From this we have calculated the weight of nuts a mother would have to carry home to feed her family (given she provides 58·8% of the calories from nuts) for a range of birth intervals (2 to 6 years in steps of 0·1 year), for gathering one day in three and for gathering one day in two, for family sizes that do or do not assume the infant mortality reported by Howell (1976).

Our first objective was to calculate the load of food and children that on average a mother will carry if she spaces births at a particular interval. This load is derived from the probabilities that a child will survive to each age and estimates of weight and food requirements of Bushman children of different ages as given in Table 1. In the computer simulation estimates were made every tenth of a year by linear interpolation between the values shown.

The weight of nuts that a mother will have to carry for each child is calculated as (expected nut requirement/child of given age, kg) = (probability that a child survives to that age) × (energy requirements of a child of that age, calories/day) × (% of Western recommended daily dietary allowance that Bushman children eat) × (% diet that is nuts) × (weight of nut needed to supply 1 calorie, kg/cal) × (number of days nuts must last). We suppose that Bushmen children require 76% of the Western standards for children of that age (based on comparison of Lee's figures for adults with figures in Spector, 1956); that 58·8% of the calories in their diet are from nuts (Lee, 1969), and that 0·00119 kg nuts provide 1 calorie (Lee, 1969; Wehmeyer *et al.*, 1969). Our conclusions are fairly insensitive to small errors in these figures.

Older children are carried progressively less, and we have followed Lee (1972) in supposing that the most important parameter is the average weight carried per journey. Lee's (1972) Table 14.2 is the source of our figure for this: weight of child is multiplied by proportion of mileage for which child is carried. Whether it is correct to consider only *average* weight carried depends on the relative dangers of the different catastrophes that may ensue. If the greatest risk is heat stress, or dehydration, or some consequence of fatigue, then our assumption will be at least approxi-

TABLE 1. Calculation of load of food and child that a mother must expect to carry for a child at each age

Age[1] of child (years)	0	1	2	3	4	5	6	7	8	9	10	11	12	13	14
Survivorship to that age[2] (%)	100	80	74	70	68	67	66	65	64·2	63·4	62·6	61·9	61·2	60·6	60
Bodyweight carried[3] (kg)	0	4·8	8·1	8·7	6·8	1·2	0	0	0	0	0	0	0	0	0
Expected bodyweight to be carried[4] (kg)	0	3·84	5·99	6·09	4·62	0·80	0	0	0	0	0	0	0	0	0
Energy requirement (cal/day)[5]	0	550	850	1200	1330	1470	1600	1730	1870	2000	2170	2330	2400	2550	2700
Expected nut requirement[6,7,8] (kg)	0	1·27	1·82	2·43	2·61	2·11	1·68	1·79	1·91	2·02	2·16	2·30	2·34	2·46	2·58

Notes
1. Age is given in years since conception
2. By interpolation from Howell (1976)
3. By interpolation from Lee (1969). Older children are carried for less of the journey and following Lee we used the average weight carried (see text)
4. Calculated as bodyweight carried times survivorship
5. By interpolation from figures for normal vigorous daily activity
6. We suppose that 45% of the energy content of nut is wasted in providing the energy requirements of children up to 4 years p.c. age, i.e. 3¼ years old, assuming much of their food to be milk at a high calorie cost to the mother
7. Derivation of nut from energy requirements is given in text
8. Assuming nuts have to last 3 days

mately true, especially if reciprocal sharing of loads between mothers functions to even out the load of individual mothers around the average they expect to have to carry. On the other hand, if the major risk is of back injury when positioning the load before carrying it, then our assumption would be invalid. Although there is a surprising lack of evidence on this second risk, we believe, as we shall argue later, that the former is the greater risk, and so we have chosen to use the first assumption rather than the second. Our conclusions are very sensitive to which assumption is made (and so is the applicability of our model to other cultures).

In addition to these variable loads a mother has to carry a constant load, being her contribution to the 3 (or 2) day food requirements for herself at 1750 calories/day (this does not allow for milk supply or growth of foetus which figure as child requirements, a procedure which, along with calculating age from conception, greatly simplifies the calculations), for her husband at 2250 calories/day, and possibly a contribution for a dependent relative (average requirements of, say, 400 calories/day) (Lee, 1969, 1972). Working as above we calculate 3-daily nut requirement for adults as $4400 \times 0.588 \times 0.00119 \times 3 = 9.24$ kg.

The figures in Table 1 are point estimates of, for example, energy requirement at exactly 7 years since conception, whereas the data on which they are based are usually for intervals, giving for example energy requirements of children aged 4–6 years since birth. We have arrived at our figures by interpolation making *ad hoc* assumptions where necessary. We do not give our working in full firstly because the original data is itself sometimes only a "guesstimate" and secondly because our conclusions are insensitive to small errors in our calculations (with the exception of calculation of weight of child carried).

The weight carried by a mother for each child (Figure 1) was combined with the constant load of food for adults in order to calculate the total load carried by a mother in different years. This load is shown for five different birth-spacings that she might adopt in Figure 2. It is clear that for some birth-spacings she has to carry more in some years than in others, the maximum amounts ever carried are shown in Figures 3 and 4.

These calculations produced two unexpected results: (1) a

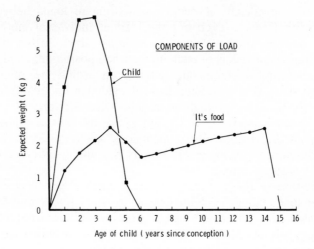

FIG. 1.   The weight carried by a mother for each child as used in the computer simulation. (Data from Table 1.)

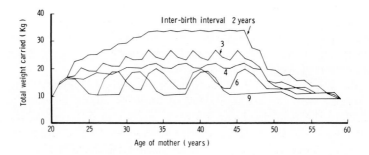

FIG. 2.   Computer simulation of the total weight of children and food for her family, carried by a mother if she collects food every third day.

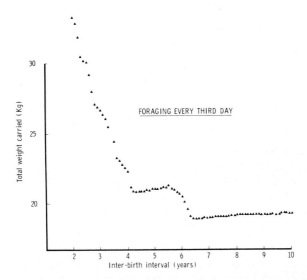

FIG. 3.   The maximum weight ever carried by a mother who goes to collect food every third day in relation to different birth-spacings she might adopt.

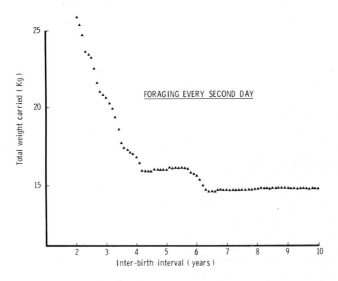

FIG. 4.   As Fig. 3 except that food is collected on alternate days.

sharp upturn in the back-load of food plus babies when birth interval comes below 4 years (Figures 3 and 4); (2) a remarkably even level of back-load through a woman's reproductive career with birth intervals around four years (Figure 2). We had speculated that 4 years might allow a cycle of two easy years in which a woman could give away excess food to her friends or close relatives, followed by two years in which they reciprocated. We do not know any data on the amount of sharing of plant food between specified individuals but this contrasts with the frequent remarks in the literature on exchange of meat and the x'aro system of exchange of objects and so might suggest that the exchange of plant food between women of child-bearing age is minor and unimportant, as our model would predict.

However, the overall levels of back-load that one must expect is less clear. With no infant or child mortality, gathering one day in three, and a four year interval, some extremely high loads are predicted. Including mortality, and with gathering on alternate days, the back-loads decline to near the observations reported by Lee (1968, 1969) and DeVore and Konner (1974). It is important to note that Lee's original measurements of work and food income, although taken at a very hard time of year were, as far as we can judge from his published data, collected from a group of people with only two small children in the entire group. People with more children may indeed carry more or go gathering more often, or have husbands who contribute more calories than average. Thus we currently believe that either women with many children work harder than the literature suggests, that mortality in the first five years must be higher than reported, or birth-spacing wider, or that the population must be increasing. Future publications and analyses of their data by the Harvard team will undoubtedly clarify the situation.

Limits to Back-load and Foraging Frequency

It now becomes clear that if we are to set any limit to family size and birth interval we must know about the limits to how much a woman can carry and how often she can go out foraging.

Bushmen are very small and we may wonder why big women do not manage to support more babies and thus why Bushmen (women, anyway) are not bigger. We have considered several restrictions on back-load: the effect of exhaustion on your ability, even having shed the nut part of the load, to run away from a predator in the unlikely event of having to do so; load of water to be carried to replace sweat loss; and more probable: accidents to backs or ankles from lifting or carrying too much, which would make the mother unable to forage for a dangerously long time; and therefore badly in debt to her friends and relatives. The ergonomics literature (e.g. Davies, 1972) implies that safe limits for women are quite low, lower for smaller women, and that the observed 15–20 kg carried by Bushmen is likely to be about the safe limit. However, this evidence implies that it would be advantageous to Bushwomen to be larger and there is as yet no clear quantitative relation of risk of back injury to load (P. R. Davis, personal communication).

Finally and most promising, we have been considering the effect on the mother's heat balance of the energy liberated by carrying a load. Particularly in September and early October, the hardest months, the hot end of the dry season, there will be days when work of any kind is impossible. We can thus exclude daily gathering as a possibility on these grounds, in addition to the need to spend time processing the nuts that have been gathered, and in other domestic tasks. If we knew the number of days on which work of any kind was possible we would be able to say more about the maximum frequency of gathering excursions to which a woman can commit herself. There will be many days on which high loads cannot be carried without a good chance of collapse from heat imbalance. It is clear that there comes a point past which the more food the mother attempts to bring back the greater the risks she is taking.

A woman should not produce a family which requires her to carry heavier loads on a greater number of days than is safe. But within this limit there must always be an advantage in adjusting the back-load to the weather on any day, either by changing foraging strategies as the day warms up, or by predicting midday temperatures successfully from early morning conditions.

Environmental physiologists use a number of criteria for tolerable thermal conditions, the limit to conditions in which acclimatized people can expect to work without collapse. It is important for the present discussion that once collapse has occurred the risks are severe. It would be very hard for people who collapsed from heat problems in the Kalahari in September–October to get home. If they could not get to shade their problems might worsen, and even if they did get to shade death occurs in a substantial proportion of untreated cases of heat stroke and other forms of heat collapse (Leithhead and Lind, 1964). Several ways of relating these criteria to work levels are available but one of the most appropriate and convenient, and one of the best regarded criteria of tolerable conditions is the Predicted Four Hour Sweat Rate (P4SR) (McArdle et al, 1947). This gives an equation into which one can insert energy liberated by work. Carrying loads requires more energy than walking and thus liberates more heat. Empirically established equations relating energy liberated to body size, speed of walking and load carried, give the heat produced by 41 kg ladies walking at 3 or 4 m.p.h. carrying various loads (e.g. Durnin and Passmore, 1967, and others). Carried loads are, up to a point, similar to increased body weight. Thus although increased size might allow higher maximum loads it would also unhelpfully increase heat production (Robinson, 1942 and others show that large people are at a disadvantage when *working* in heat). The heat produced when carrying various loads can be fed into the P4SR equations and from these the environmental conditions under which it would be possible to carry each load could be ascertained. The P4SR depends on wet-bulb, dry-bulb and globe temperatures, air-speed, level of clothing worn, area of body surface and metabolic rate. In calculating metabolic rate we use the regression formula suggested by Datta, S. R., Chatterjee, B. B. and Roy, B. N. (1973), viz. (metabolic rate, kcal min^{-1}) = 0·0943 × (body weight + load carried, kg) −2·183. This was based on subjects of average surface area 1·62 m^2, and for our purposes we prefer to express it as: (metabolic rate/unit surface area, kcal m^{-2} h^{-1}) = 3·493 × (body weight + load carried, kg) −81. For Bushman mothers weighing 41 kg (metabolic rate/unit surface area, kcal m^{-2} h^{-1}) = 62 + 3·493 (load carried, kg).

Then P4SR is roughly: (P4SR, l/unit surface area) ≈ 0·014 × (metabolic rate, kcal m^{-2} h^{-1}) −0·8 + B4SR where B4SR (Basic Four-hour Sweat Rate index) depends on wet-bulb, dry-bulb and globe temperatures and air-speed. Therefore P4SR $\approx 0 \cdot 1 + 0 \cdot 05 \times$ (load carried, kg) + B4SR.

The average daily maximum dry-bulb temperature in September and October at the nearest meteorological stations is around 90°F, but the relative humidity at midday is low (Met. Office, London). Globe temperature is probably about 30°F higher than dry-bulb temperature (Wyndham, 1956, 1958, 1964). At these temperatures B4SR is around 2·5 so that on an average day in these locations P4SR with a load approaching 30 kg would be around 4 in the critical region (Weiner, personal communication). Lee's published information on temperatures suggests that they are rather higher in the exact region with which we are concerned. He reports dry-bulb readings in September as 35–43°C (1972) and above 33°C on every day in September and October (Yellen and Lee, 1976). Thus it seems possible that in the Dobe area heat stress is a major hazard to anyone carrying heavy loads.

Daily readings of globe thermometer (which assess gain in heat from radiation) or wet-bulb thermometer (both required for P4SR) do not seem to have been taken in any part of !kung Bushman land so we cannot make precise predictions. However, Wyndham (1956, 1958, 1964) mentions that GT readings "of 140°F in the sun . . . were recorded. . . ." (1964) "as high as 50°C" at the cold time of year, and "up to 60°C in the Kalahari accompanying dry-bulb readings of 40°C" and "globe thermometer temperature exceeds air temperature by some 20°C at 2 pm". Lee (1972) gives September shade temperatures at Dobe (where he did his foraging measurements) as showing "highs ranging from 35–43°C". We can thus safely assume that there are many days with globe thermometer readings of 50°C and more. (Shade is negligible on journeys to the nut groves and we propose to leave it out of our calculations. In the habitats of other cultures it could be very important). The actual temperatures are rather critical but even a guess at the distribution of GT readings in September and the assumption of a very low wet-bulb reading (actually humidity rises steadily during September), suggests that there will be few days when 20 kg could be carried, rather more when 15 kg could be carried, very few when 30 kg could be carried. As load increases, number of safe days for foraging decreases. The exact relationship will determine the maximum amount of food that can be brought home and thus the limits to IBI. But we can say that the fragmentary climatic information available suggests that carrying 15–20 kg on gathering excursions around one in two to three days is the best that can be done in the adverse climatic conditions of September and October. This is of the same order as Lee and others report that Bushman women in fact do. The increase in humidity might be expected to interact with family size in determining the date at which people change their strategy, and as Lee describes, cease gathering excursions and move from the dry season camp to the nut groves for periods of a few days, using water from roots.

Discussion

Our basic argument is thus extremely simple. Our method consists merely of questioning each observation of behaviour (what else could they do, is this the right time to do it?) and of seeking measured consequences of each feature of behaviour or physiology. The consequences have all (if we use a criterion of reproductive success) to be reduced ultimately to a cost or benefit measured by number of offspring growing to maturity. Thus even the death of the mother must be costed as the reduction in the number of offspring she leaves due to her dying while needed to support those already born. The different options open to the mother can then be assessed in terms of the mother's reproductive success. It is interesting to note that there must exist some optimum strategy (or maybe a set of strategies) that maximizes reproductive success. Such a strategy can sometimes be found by analytic optimisation, but even if this is not possible it can be found by iteration using a computer. It will predict what the mother should do in order to leave the largest number of surviving offspring, and this can be compared with the observed behaviour of women.

In this study we have considered the different birth spacings and food gathering strategies that a mother might adopt. Under certain assumptions we have calculated the back-load she must carry for each inter-birth interval if her family is to be adequately nourished. As a first approximation it appeared that there would be each day a critical limit below which load-carrying would be safe but above which death would be the probable result. Thus the problem was reduced to that of finding limits to back-load. Within these limits the optimal strategy is clear: to have the largest family that can be adequately fed during the dry season. What the mother should do on a particular day, however, depends critically on temperatures during the day, and without detailed climatic information we have only been able to make a limited assessment of the observed behaviour of the women.

It was our original intention at least to guess at the dependence of mortality on the variables we have calculated. Thus we wished to know how the daily risk (of death or serious accident) to the mother depended on the load that she carried. We recognize that she might suffer any of a number of calamities—heat stress, back injury etc., so that it is necessary not only to evaluate the more serious hazards but to estimate their cumulative consequences in terms of the one common currency, the risk of death. Similarly we hoped to assess the risks attendant on malnutrition (of parents and of children). Knowing these relationships a much more comprehensive study would be possible in which we could calculate the extent to which an extra baby slightly increases the hazards undertaken by each other person in the family. Such a study would still evaluate strategies in terms of the mother's reproductive success. We could however, investigate more of the options that in fact are open to her, for example, to decrease her load on especially hot days at the expense of the adequate nutrition of her family.

Obviously we have left many questions unasked. Besides the "givens" listed above we are assuming that physiological adaptation to heat has reached some limit; that dietary requirements cannot be substantially reduced below the level used in our calculations: that very inadequate nutrition for one or two months every year has a detrimental effect on the survival and reproductive career of the children comparable to the benefit to the mother of one extra child aged 0–4 (the reciprocal effects of nutrition and disease discussed by Morley, 1973, and Scrimshaw, Taylor and Gordon, 1968, is one argument for supposing that this is a reasonable supposition); that building up sufficient store of nuts before September to see the family through September (and until the rains begin sometime in October) would have costs which out-weigh the benefits in increased family size. It is obvious that in Bushman society as it is now this would incur intolerable social costs. But we feel we should regard this as an interim answer, for ultimately we must explain the social organisation that levies these costs; a very general ultimate explanation (reciprocal altruism) is possible (but the advantages of this have yet to be quantified, and we suggested they do not apply to plant resources); but our aim is for a detailed and quantitative argument that this social organisation arises from individuals maximizing their inclusive fitness and that a temporary breaking of the system (e.g. a seasonal holiday from reciprocal altruism, a Bushman *mardi gras*) would not increase the inclusive fitness of individuals partaking in it. We also assume that a woman will not be allowed indefinitely to go into "debt" to her friends and relatives.

Our toleration of "givens" might appear to weaken our argument. But at any step in our analysis the results could have dif-fered from those obtained, and they could have differed in the direction of saying that Bushman mothers perform at a much lower level than possible. Quantitatively they tend in the opposite direction.

However, just as we took the mother's carrying capacity as a given in the first stage of our model, so any of these other givens can be the starting-point for a further investigation of the complex compromise which must be any adaptation. No scientific inves-tigation is ever completed and we would feel it quite unjustified to use the incompleteness of any optimisation study as a reason for not pursuing this general approach. A much more important criti-cism would be that we fail to test our model against one in which a measure other than reproductive success or inclusive fitness is examined. We have to confess to some difficulty in thinking of an alternative, anything concerning, e.g. individual wealth precludes having any children at all. Inclusive fitness is the only measure for which it is not necessary to ask: why maximize that? But we feel that discussion and testing of different "target variables" is what is now required. The omission of any discussion of group advantage or even constancy of population may surprise the cul-tural ecologist reader. The omission is imposed on us by our choice of inclusive fitness as an ultimate criterion. But we do have in due course to compare our model with for example one that supposes a restraint on over-exploitation of the habitat both for plant food and for animal food.

Ultimately one should be able to test our particular model against the known reproductive record of individual women. Those who give birth at the right time should raise more children than those who give birth at the wrong time. The analysis would have to be restricted to families that were dependent entirely on foraging and not using outside income (if a man finds some kind of work that reduces the need for his wife to forage by increasing his contribution to the family income, or which gives her greater access to babysitters, she should be able to give birth more often without detriment to her reproductive success, as they indeed do). Due account would also have to be taken of the value of giving birth quickly after the death of a child under 4 (still carried) and the costs of giving birth quickly after the death of a child over 4 whose successor survives and is still carried. It may be better to predict patterns of individual reproductive careers than the crude mean birth-spacing. But aside from these important points our basic prediction would be that women who gave birth substantially more often than once every four years (or whatever our eventual calculated optimum turns out to be), should raise fewer children than those who gave birth at around 4 year intervals (Lee, 1972 observes an average of 3·88 years). If this prediction is not borne out then wide birth-spacing and "part time" foraging are not maximizing reproductive success. They may be minimizing effort (in which case why have any babies!), or maximizing inclusive fitness (those who have more babies may be having a detrimental effect on the reproductive success of their relatives of a size which outweighs their own success, e.g. if they had one extra baby at a cost of two or more to their sisters). Or they actually may be adapted to extreme conditions as Lee suggests, with good evidence from several sources. The data for assessing some of these things may already exist.

While we have shown how we attempt to determine whether some culturally variable aspects of women's reproduction and foraging behaviour are adaptive for RS or inclusive fitness, we cannot claim to be showing anything about the classical core issues of social anthropology. Though we could make some predictions about male and female dress from work and climate, we have not shown whether all-night trance dances are good for inclusive fitness rather than something else, nor that "bird medicine" is good for the reproductive success of the mother who goes to the trouble of practising it (or alternatively for those who persuade her to practise it). But we do hope that we have raised a possibility that others will wish to follow further.

Many criticisms of our approach will be based on what to a biologist (and to cultural ecologists such as Harris, 1968, 1974 and Gross, 1975) would appear to be a confusion between function (long-term consequences, survival value, sometimes referred to as "ultimate causes") and development and causation (motivation or short-term "proximate causes"). We are talking about ultimate causes (i.e. remote causes) and make no statement about development or motivation. We would argue that the latter are the short-term mechanisms that ensure that functional behaviour is performed. It does not matter much for survival value exactly how the short-term mechanisms achieve the goals, so long as they do achieve them. In fact a good deal of work is now under way on the physiological mechanisms underlying the long birth-spacing of Bushman women and its rapid shortening when people settle.

In many animals, where long and short term are clearly separable, there is no problem here. Difficulties may indeed arise when long and short term come closer together, as they do when one proposes that rapidly changing cultural behaviour is adaptive. As biologists we would note that the propensity for culture evolved, that culture is clearly a major part of human adaptation, but that it can only have been adaptive by producing adaptive behaviour, in other words behaviour which maximizes inclusive fitness. Culture can have evolved only if individuals transmitted what it was in their inclusive fitness interests to pass on, and if individuals only acquired what it was in their interests to acquire (and the interests of transmitter and receiver can differ, even if they are parent and child, Trivers, 1974). Thus natural selection could have given rise to constraints on imitation; a little specificity about who an individual imitates, and under what circumstances, could have important consequences for cultural transmission. Beyond this we offer no suggestions as to how cultural transmission might maximize inclusive fitness. But we hope that our proposals will help to unearth the most useful questions in this area, and help to allow cultural ecology to make even more use of its basic research strategy.

Acknowledgments

We are extremely grateful to Professor J. S. Weiner for discussing with us the possibility of heat stress as a limiting factor, for giving us the relevant references and balancing our view of the literature on this subject. Likewise we are very grateful to Professor P. Davis for discussing risks of back injury and load lifting and giving us helpful references on this topic.

Besides remote antecedents in discussions with M. J. Konner and D. J. McFarland, this study owes its inception to Richard Lee for giving N. Blurton Jones a copy of his paper on birth-spacing on the day that an unknown travel agent had booked the authors into the same compartment on the Orient Express bound for the International Ethological Conference. We are very grateful to all these people, as well as admiring of the lively ladies whose toils we have attempted to analyse.

References

ALLAND, A. (1975) Adaptation. In *Annual Review of Anthropology*, **4**, 59–73.

BURNHAM, P. (1973) The explanatory value of the concept of adaptation in studies of culture change. In *The Explanation of Culture Change* (ed. C. Renfrew). Duckworth, London.

DATTA, S. R., CHATTERJEE, B. B. and ROY, B. N. (1973) The relationship between energy expenditure and pulse rates with body weight and the load carried during load carrying on the level. *Ergonomics*, **16**, 507–13.

DAVIES, B. T. (1972) Moving loads manually. *Applied Ergonomics*, **34**, 190–94.

DEVORE, I. and KONNER, M. J. (1974) Infancy in hunter–gatherer life; an ethological perspective. In *Ethology and Psychiatry* (ed. N. F. White). University of Toronto Press, Toronto.

DURNIN, J. V. G. A. and PASSMORE, R. (1967) *Energy, Work and Leisure*. Heinemann, London.

GROSS, D. R. (1975) Protein capture and cultural development in the Amazon Basin. *American Anthropologist*, **77**, 526–49.

HAMILTON, W. D. (1964) The genetical theory of social behaviour. I, II. *Journal of Theoretical Biology*, **7**, 1–52.

HARRIS, M. (1968) *The Rise of Anthropological Theory. A History of Theories of Culture*. Crowell, New York.

HARRIS, M. (1974) *Cows, Pigs, Wars and Witches. The Riddles of Culture*. Hutchinson, London.

HOWELL, N. (1976) Toward a uniformitarian theory of human palaeodemography. *Journal of Human Evolution*, **5**, 25–40.

LACK, D. (1954) *The Natural Regulation of Animal Numbers*. Oxford University Press, London.

LEE, R. B. (1968) What hunters do for a living, or, how to make out on scarce resources. In *Man the Hunter* (eds. R. B. Lee and I. DeVore). Aldine, Chicago.

LEE, R. B. (1969) !Kung Bushman subsistence: an input–output analysis. In *Environment and Cultural Behavior* (ed. A. P. Vayda). Natural History Press, Garden City, New York.

LEE, R. B. (1972) The !Kung Bushmen of Botswana. In *Hunters and Gatherers Today* (ed. M. G. Bicchieri). Holt Rinehart Winston, New York.

LEE, R. B. (1972b) Population growth and beginnings of sedentary life among the !Kung Bushmen. In *Population Growth: Anthropological Implications*. (ed. B. Spooner). M.I.T. Press, Cambridge, Mass.

LEE, R. B. and DEVORE, I. (eds). (1975) *Bushman Hunter–Gatherers*. Harvard University Press, Cambridge, Mass.

LEITHEAD, C. S. and LIND, A. R. (1964) *Heat Stress and Heat Disorders*. Cassell, London.

Meteorological Office (Met. O. 617d) (1967) *Tables of temperature, relative humidity and precipitation for the world. Part IV*. London, Her Majesty's Stationery Office.

MORLEY, D. (1973) *Paediatric Priorities in the Developing World*. Butterworth, London.

MCARDLE, B., DUNHAM, W., HOLLING, H. E., LADELL, W. S. S., SCOTT, J. W., THOMSON, M. L. and WEINER, J. S. (1947) The prediction of the physiological effects of warm and hot environments: the P4SR index. *Medical Research Council (London), R.N.P. Report., 47/391*.

MCFARLAND, D. J. (1976) Form and function in the temporal organisation of behaviour. In *Growing Points in Ethology* (eds. P. P. G. Bateson and R. A. Hinde). Cambridge University Press, London.

ROBINSON, S. (1942) The effect of body size upon energy exchanges in work. *American Journal of Physiology*, **136**, 363–68.

SCRIMSHAW, N. S., GORDON, J. E. and TAYLOR, C. (1968) The interaction of nutrition and infection. *WHO Monograph Series No. 57*. World Health Organisation, Geneva.

SIBLY, R. M. and MCFARLAND, D. J. (1976) On the fitness of behaviour sequences. *American Naturalist, 110*, 601–17.

SPECTOR, W. S. (1956) *Handbook of Biological Data*. Saunders, London and Philadelphia.

TINBERGEN, N. (1951) *The Study of Instinct*. Oxford University Press, London.

TINBERGEN, N. (1965) Behaviour and natural selection. *Ideas in Modern Biology*. (Vol. 6 of Proceedings of the XVIth International Zoological Congress, Washington, 1963) (ed. J. A. Moore). New York.

TRIVERS, R. L. (1974) Parent–offspring conflict. *American Zoologist*, **14**, 249–64.

TRIVERS, R. L. and HARE, H. (1976) Haplodiploidy and the evolution of the social insects. *Science*, **191**, 249–63.

WEHMEYER, A. S., LEE, R. B. and WHITING, Marjorie (1969) The nutrient composition and dietary importance of some vegetable foods eaten by the !Kung Bushmen. *South African Medical Journal*, **43**, 1529–30.

WEINER, J. S. (1977) Human ecology. Part V of *Human Biology* (ed. G. A. Harrison, J. S. Weiner, J. M. Tanner and N. A. Barnicot). Oxford University Press (2nd edition 1977).

WYNDHAM, C. H. and MORRISON, J. F. (1956) Heat regulation of MaSarwa (Bushmen). *Nature*, **178**, 869–70.

WYNDHAM, C. H. and MORRISON, J. F. (1958) Adjustment to cold of Bushmen in the Kalahari Desert. *Journal of Applied Physiology*, **13**, 219–25.

WYNDHAM, C. H., STRYDOM, N. B., WARD, J. S., MORRISON, J. F., WILLIAMS, C. G., BREDELL, G. A. G., VON RAHDEN, M. J. E., HOLDSWORTH, L. D., VAN GRAAN, C. H., VAN RENSBURG, A. J. and MUNRO, A. (1964) Physiological reactions to heat of Bushmen and of unacclimatised and acclimatised Bantu. *Journal of Applied Physiology*, **19**, 885–88.

YELLEN, J. E. (1976) Settlement patterns of the !Kung: an archaeological perspective. In *Kalahari Hunter–Gatherers* (eds. R. Lee and I. DeVore). Harvard University Press, Cambridge, Mass.

YELLEN, J. E. and LEE, R. B. (1976) The Dobe-Du/Du environment: Background to a hunting and gathering way of life. In *Kalahari Hunter–Gatherers* (eds. R. Lee and I. DeVore). Harvard University Press, Cambridge, Mass.

PART II

SHORT-TERM ADAPTATION:

BEHAVIOUR AND PHYSIOLOGY
IN HEALTH, STRESS AND BREAKDOWN

INTRODUCTION

V. Reynolds

Department of Biological Anthropology, University of Oxford

THE concept of adaptation is not an easy one to handle, partly because the word is used in different senses by different people. The point is usefully discussed by Pittendrigh (1958; pp. 390–92). What is the central component of the idea of adaptation? Presumably all adaptation involves some kind of adjustment, past or present. If we say an organism is in a *state* of adaptation, we presumably mean that because of past adjustments, genetic and otherwise, it is now in balance with its environment. Because it is in a state of adaptation, it is not, in this case, undergoing any adjustment at the present time (except within the limits of its own, already established, control systems).

A different sense of the word arises if we say that an organism is in the *course* of adaptation. Here we *do* mean to imply that adjustment is taking place; not just that it has been in the past, but that it is doing so in the present. For instance, we can say that the development by certain birds of the habit of opening milk-bottle tops to get at the cream is a case of adaptation. In this case, adaptation is a dynamic, learning *process*. It is a *process* rather than a *state*. It is in fact the process that leads to the state. Probably we should do better to have different words for the two, for instance, we could go on calling the *process* "adaptation", but refer to the *state* as "adaptedness".

If we focus on the process of adaptation, we find again that the term has many usages and shades of meaning. Professor Weiner in a recent talk (unpublished) distinguished four kinds of adaptive responses: physiological, developmental, disease resistance, and demographic.

(a) *Physiological*: these are primarily homeostatic body mechanisms that become more efficient with use. They are not genetic adjustments but rather the results of experience.
(b) *Developmental*: by developmental adaptations Weiner meant those occurring over a longer time-span than the physiologi-

cal ones. For instance, the development by an individual of age-characteristic endocrine secretion rates during his or her life cycle can be distinguished from that person's immediate endocrine responsiveness to a given situation.

(c) *Disease resistance*: this kind of adaptation is rather specific and relates to the build-up of immune resistance systems to invading pathogens. The form it takes depends entirely on the kinds of pathogens encountered. It is neither homeostatic, like Weiner's type (*a*), nor a long-term, progressive development like type (*b*).

(d) *Demographic*: this is a very different type of adaptation from the three described above, signifying a deployment of the resources of whole populations to their environments. An example used by Weiner of this kind of adaptation was birth rate. Birth rates in some African countries are around 45 per 1000, as opposed to 16 per 1000 in the developed world. These figures can be said to be adaptive to the prevailing rates of mortality in the areas concerned.

Before commenting specifically on Weiner's four types of adaptation, there is one general comment to be made, namely that in singling out certain kinds of adaptive processes and comparing them with one another, one is essentially engaging in the art of *analysis*. This may not seem a very important point, but it needs to be stressed that analysis *per se* does not imply that any one process that is isolated in the course of analysis is physically or functionally separate or separable from any other process. Thus, having separated demographic adaptation from other types, one would quite possibly want to include physiological, developmental and disease adaptations in any discussion of demographic adaptation and the same would apply whatever one's starting-point.

The above-mentioned distinctions (made by Weiner in another context) are not quite the same as those underlying this Symposium. For instance, we are not concerned at all directly with disease adaptations of the immune response type. An underlying distinction fundamental to the present Symposium is the distinction between long-term behavioural adaptations, be they demographic, cultural, ontogenetic or genetic (mainly discussed in Part

I) and short-term physiological, often homeostatic processes by which the organism adapts to prevailing circumstances (mainly discussed in Part II). If we ask: where is the dividing line between long-term and short-term adaptation?, we can answer that any adjustment of the ongoing life process is a part of long-term adaptation in so far as it relates to inbuilt constitutional limits and predispositions, while it is short-term in so far as it consists of a number of immediate adjustments that bring the organism into a viable relation to the immediate prevailing circumstances.

Dichotomies, however, are notoriously misleading, and none more so than this one, unless it is realized that it is only analytic. Thus in the case of cultural adaptations such as patterns of food gathering, these are long-term in the sense of being transmitted down the generations, but short-term in the sense that each individual has to learn them in his or her lifetime. Again, with physiological adaptations such as shivering in the cold or increased respiratory rate as one climbs a mountain, these are long-term in the sense that we are pre-adapted to these changes by virtue of our phylogeny, but short-term in the sense that they do actually occur and function over limited periods in the here and now. The general point being made is that short-term, physiological adaptations of the kind we are concerned with in the second part of the Symposium are only short-term in the analytical sense, and are in fact securely rooted in a limited range of possibilities determined by longer-term processes, some phylogenetic, others cultural. Short-term human adaptations are thus "gene-bound" and "culture-bound". Broadly generalizing, culture provides individuals with socially acceptable methods of adaptation, while genes provide the physical mechanisms that enable the adaptive process to take place and these mechanisms to some extent control the nature of the adaptive process.

This approach sees man as a sort of powered mechanism inhabiting a physical environment and responding to environmental changes by reference to a set of cultural instructions. Here, therefore, culture is being seen as a *means* to an end, namely adaptation to the physical environment. Among social anthropologists, Malinowski (1944) was perhaps the most widely known to employ such a model. But Malinowski and his system of "basic needs and cultural responses" (see Table 1) has now passed into the history of social anthropology, having been labelled a "functionalist".

TABLE 1.   Basic needs and cultural responses (from B. Malinowski, 1944, p. 91).

Basic needs	Cultural responses
1. Metabolism	1. Commissariat
2. Reproduction	2. Kinship
3. Bodily comforts	3. Shelter
4. Safety	4. Protection
5. Movement	5. Activities
6. Growth	6. Training
7. Health	7. Hygiene

What, it may be asked, were the shortcomings of the functionalists that led them to be superseded by the forward-looking social anthropologists? The answer, I think, was the increasing realisation that culture forms such an integral part of human life that we cannot get far simply by seeing it as a means to a more basic, biological adaptation. In short, a man is a bit of a culture, cultures consist of people, and in this sense culture is not a *means* to anything, but rather *it is culture itself to which each individual must adapt.*

Our model is now getting a little more complex: individuals adapt to cultural circumstances which are in some sense adapted to environmental circumstances; the physical means available to individuals to adapt to their cultures and the forms by which cultures are adapted to the physical environment are inherited, through genes and traditions respectively.

Now we come to the question of behaviour or, as I prefer to call it in the case of man, "action" (Reynolds, 1976). What determines our actions? Clearly they are in many cases the result of our own choices, and this raises the issue of free-will, but this Symposium is not about free-will and I shall feel free to dodge that issue for now. What, then, determines the set of choices within which action occurs? Clearly, genes set certain limits to these, while our learning of what is culturally approved sets most of the rest.

Let us now try to move forward a little to the questions of what we might mean by "health", "breakdown", and "stress", all terms that are very difficult to define satisfactorily. The working model suggested here for the study of adaptation in man looks something like this: within the limits of the genetically possible lie the possibilities that are culturally approved; within this range of possibilities most actions take place. Such actions serve to maintain a harmonious interaction between internal body processes and all external conditions. If they succeed we have what can roughly be called *"health"*, i.e. a good adaptation. If they fail we have a *breakdown* of some kind: social, mental or physical. *Stress* has something to do with the conditions intermediate between normal healthy functioning and breakdown.

Just where stress begins and ends is highly dependent on the individual's interpretation of cultural demands and expectations. But leaving aside the question of the precise circumstances that will be perceived as stressful, we can say that when those circumstances are reached certain physiological and psychological processes set in, together with certain kinds of action. At the physiological level there is what Levi (1971) calls "stress (Selye)"—departure from normal levels of functioning followed by homeostatic processes and a return to normal levels. At the psychological level, stress is the element of intrusive confusion that calls for cognitive re-structuring to re-establish mental order. At the level of action, stress brings about the taking of "remedial" measures to return to a more desirable state. All these processes are adaptive in so far as they tend to convert stress as defined above (i.e. a state intermediate between a state of health and a state of breakdown) in the direction of health and away from the state of breakdown.

This kind of adaptation, with which we are mainly concerned in Part II, thus bears mainly on a continuum with health at one end, and disease or breakdown or maladjustment at the other. There now arises the further issue, relating back to Part I, of the relation between such "health adaptation" and the issues of survival and reproductive fitness. Our definition of health (above) was not in terms of survival or reproductive fitness, so we can ask without fear of circularity: is health conducive to survival and reproductive fitness?

This is a curious question. Initially it would seem laughably obvious that the answer was yes. But on reflection it is possible to see that the correct answer is no. If health is defined as a state of "perfect equilibrium" at one end of a continuum, then almost all real-life situations must fall somewhere between this and the other, breakdown, end. The existence of hunger, and consequent food-seeking behaviour, are not in themselves signs of health but of a lack of it. Likewise for all other activities and physiological conditions. In fact, "health" is rather unusual as an existential state. Stress is the usual existential state.

The units with which the animal or human converts stress in the direction of health are units of energy. Any cost function has got to take into consideration energy output balanced against the various benefits that may accrue to the individual concerned. It is the fact that health in the absolute sense is not present that leads to activity at all three levels (physiological, psychological and behavioural). This applies both to situations of more or less immediate gratification such as hunger and thirst, and to situations where longer-term processes are at stake, in particular sex activity and reproduction. It is thus stress, rather than health, that is conducive to survival and reproductive success. Health in itself, though a pleasant state to be in, is no guarantor of either survival or reproductive fitness, both of which demand energy expenditure, often in quite enormous quantities, and can bring animals (and people) to the limits of their endurance. In the animal kingdom we have the examples of bird migration in the food quest, of feeding nestlings in the field of parental behaviour, and of mate-finding, keeping and territorial defence in the field of reproductive behaviour.

In man a curious set of secondary problems arises. As social anthropology and sociology show, man is a product of his culture and finds his motivations and energy outlets in its terms. But its reward system is not always geared to biological health or reproductive fitness, whereas in animal social organizations the reward system *is*, by and large, inclusive fitness, and individuals' motivations revolve around this reward system. In human societies anything can happen. Some societies do have conventional rewards for longevity and fecundity, and in this respect their values accord with biological rewards. Others, our own included, do not; we relegate the old (by definition the "best" survivors) to poverty and inconsequentiality, and we do not hold those who reproduce most efficiently in particular esteem. In each human society we have to establish the relation between cultural and biological activities *de novo*.

How do the contents of Part II relate to what has been said in general terms above? It seems clear that the facts of human physiology do accord with the idea that man adapts to his culture, so that the question is now: in what specific ways does the body adapt (or try) to situations presented by modern society? In answer, Hutt and Hutt show that even in early childhood, heart rate variability decreases with increased 'mental load', in this respect being a better discriminator between mental and physical load than crude HR which increases with both increased mental and physical load. They find a difference between individuals with regard to HRV, and contrast volatile systems, where HRV is very responsive to situation changes, with those where the system is well damped, suggesting that the latter is more useful under affectively demanding conditions but not when proficiency is required. This reminds one of the finding by Johansson, Frankenhaeuser and Magnussen (1973) that adrenally responsive but affectively calm children did best in a mathematics test. The implications of these findings are considerable: they suggest that coping strategies developed quite early in life not only, as is well known, affect performance itself in cultural settings, but also subject the person to physiological stress to a greater or lesser extent, thus perhaps pushing him or her more or less often towards the breakdown end of the health–breakdown continuum.

In their comparison between normal and autistic children, Helevuo and Reynolds continue a comparable line of thought: if, again in young children, arousal (both psychological and physical) too frequently or even chronically exceeds acceptable limits, behavioural adjustments are made to buffer off the environment by perceptual 'cut-off'. This enables body systems to resume working at normal levels (*overall* autistic children did not excrete more catecholamines than normal ones, but were highly responsive if their defences were broken), but at the expense of non-involvement in social activity.

At the Symposium, interest among participants in the work of Montagner and his associates was considerable; it is here presented for the first time in the English language. The major findings of the French team are that there are different kinds of

children, and that the differences are related to home environment. One especial difference is that some children show a
socially positive, appeasing, object-offering behaviour profile,
while others show behaviours that bring about aggression, breaking of social contacts, retreat or escape. The former pattern is
able more easily to adapt to daily life situations than the latter.
These patterns are already shown between six months and two
years of age, and on them are built the more complex patterns
seen at 3–4 years. At the physiological level, the Montagner team
shows that, although there are individual differences, socially
positive 'leaders' consistently show lower adrenal corticosteroid
levels than 'dominant-aggressives', and their diurnal rhythms
tend to be more regular than those with certain other behaviour
profiles.

These studies of children show the body at work adjusting to
life situations, 'adapting' in the short-term, here-and-now sense.
When we look at the adult stage of the process we have an additional interest: here is the 'pay-off' of what has gone before. Here
we have man with a cigarette in his mouth, ulcers in his stomach,
and a calculable risk of myocardial infarction (MI). Theorell
shows how early MI can be a result of a pre-occupation with work
and deadlines, with the now well-known 'behaviour pattern A'.
MI is now to a great extent predictable. The child has grown up;
its behaviour patterns have set; society continues to press for the
competitive spirit; some respond 'well' but the price of long-term
social coping begins to tell. Others develop "low back pain", and
in other ways (type B) opt out of the most competitive (and often
financially rewarding) jobs, and their susceptibility to early MI is
correspondingly reduced.

Carruthers, in similar vein, points to the danger to health of the
hard-driving, aggressive life-style our culture tends to value. He
suggests that one reason we actually enjoy stressful situations
may be that there is a hypothalamic link-up between noradrenaline release and the brain pleasure centres. Whatever the
facts may turn out to be, it is clear that unless such physiological
processes as lipid release and metabolism are dealt with satisfactorily, health can be impaired and early death result.

Johansson and Lundberg show how study of particular life
situations can illustrate these processes. Working men in a saw-

mill were divided into two groups: those with a good degree of control over their work schedule, and those whose work was repetitive and machine-paced. In terms of subjective reports of job satisfaction, the latter were far less happy than the former, and in terms of catecholamine excretion rates, the latter showed higher levels than the former. These effects are chronic, i.e. in a highly controlled job the individual may not be able to sit back and relax when he needs to. In their second study, they show how the subjectively felt stress of overcrowding, and catecholamine levels, were both increased in train commuters when they travelled on crowded trains. During the recent oil crisis, which produced petrol rationing in Sweden, more people travelled by train; feelings of overcrowding increased, and so did catecholamine levels.

We can see in these chapters the beginnings of clear evidence for differential physiological adaptability to modern life. Relating this back to the long-term, evolutionary picture, most workers would agree that present-day adaptability must be assessed in terms of evolved potentials. Theorell and Carruthers explicitly, and others implicitly, see man as a creature responding to new environmental demands in terms of very old mechanisms. To the extent that individuals can adjust to the situations that society imposes on them, they can enjoy long and pleasant lives. The adjustment process starts in early childhood, and runs right through the reproductive period and the period of child-rearing. How the coping strategies employed at work, at home, and at leisure relate to each other and to natural selection however, remains poorly understood.

References

JOHANSSON, G., FRANKENHAEUSER, M., and MAGNUSSON, D. (1973) Catecholamine output in schoolchildren as related to performance and adjustment. *Scandinavian Journal of Psychology,* **14,** 20–28.

LEVI, L. (ed.) (1971) *Society, Stress and Disease.* Oxford University Press.

MALINOWSKI, B. (1944) *A Scientific Theory of Culture and Other Essays.* University of North Carolina Press. Chapel Hill.

PITTENDRIGH, C. S. (1958) Adaptation, natural selection, and behaviour. In *Behaviour and Evolution* (ed. A. Roe and G. G. Simpson). Yale University Press, New Haven.

REYNOLDS, V. (1976) *The Biology of Human Action.* W. H. Freeman, Reading and San Francisco.

HEART RATE VARIABILITY—THE ADAPTIVE CONSEQUENCES OF INDIVIDUAL DIFFERENCES AND STATE CHANGES

CORINNE HUTT and S. J. HUTT

Department of Psychology, University of Keele

Introduction

IN relaxed individuals, heart rate generally fluctuates from beat to beat, a phenomenon referred to as Heart Rate Variability (HRV). In the mid-1960s Kalsbeek, a Dutch ergonomist (Kalsbeek et al., 1963, 1965), found that changes in such variability could be related to changes in mental load. His work demonstrated that increases in information load were associated with a *decrease* in HRV. From that time, this relationship has been used in assigning the task demands of many flight, vigilance, and industrial operations. In fact, many international airports are graded in their difficulty of take-off and landing operations in terms of the suppression of HRV they cause. Nevertheless, despite its potential, HRV was not a phenomenon widely studied or reported until the devotion of an entire issue of *Ergonomics* (Vol. 16, No. 1, 1973) to its applications.

Heart Rate Variability and Respiration

In part, the reluctance of behavioural scientists to incorporate this phenomenon in their studies may be due to the common supposition that cardiovascular changes are simply epiphenomena of respiratory ones. For instance, Sayers (1976) regards respiration as being a principal factor influencing cardiovascular control. However, the nature of this influence is far from simple or unequivocal. Boyce (1974) showed that, when physical and mental load were independently varied in adults, mean heart rate increased under both conditions, whereas HRV *decreased* under conditions of mental load and *increased* under physical load. Furthermore, spectral analysis of cardiac inter-beat intervals and of respiration frequency demonstrate a small but not a dominant effect of respiration on HRV (Luczak and Laurig 1973); the respiratory amplitude spectrum reveals a peak in the frequencies 0·25 to 0·40 Hz, equivalent to 15 to 25 cycles/min., whereas the maximum of the amplitude spectrum of inter-beat intervals lies at a frequency of 0·10 Hz. Finally, by far the most influential signals and pathways controlling HRV are likely to be neural rather than mechanical. Thus, it seems reasonable to use heart rate measures as indices of autonomic arousal, as they have indeed been shown to be, although speculation regarding causal mechanisms of the effects must necessarily be circumspect.

Studies of Behaviour and Heart Rate Variability

Our own attention was drawn to HRV as an aspect of cardiovascular function during studies of autistic children who characteristically showed a high degree of cardiac arrhythmia, particularly in association with the performance of stereotyped activities (Hutt *et al.*, 1975) (Figure 1). In subsequent studies of normal children who were observed at 6 months, 12 months and 24 months of age, we therefore paid special attention to this phenomenon (see Figures 2 and 3). At a behavioural level we were looking at patterns which in early childhood show what Kagan (1971) has called heterotypic continuity, i.e. stability between classes of response which are very different in manifesta-

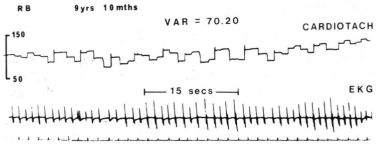

FIG. 1.   Record of a highly variable heart rate from an autistic boy. At the bottom is a time-trace.

tion but are nevertheless theoretically related. Our dependent variable was the response to novelty; such responses can reliably be expected to reveal individual differences together with associated HR changes.

The experimental procedure adopted was essentially the same on each occasion: infants were seen with their mothers and their reactions both to a novel toy and to a stranger were recorded. It has been argued that reactions to novelty are a function of the

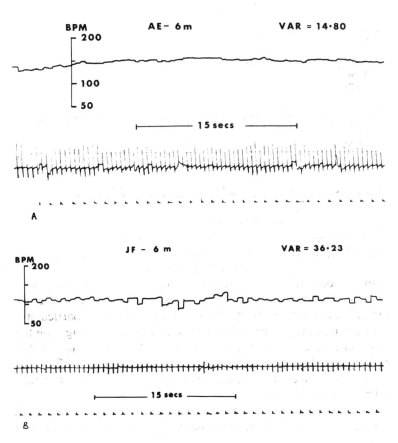

FIG. 2.   Records of two 6-month old infants showing: A, low heart rate variability; B, high variability.

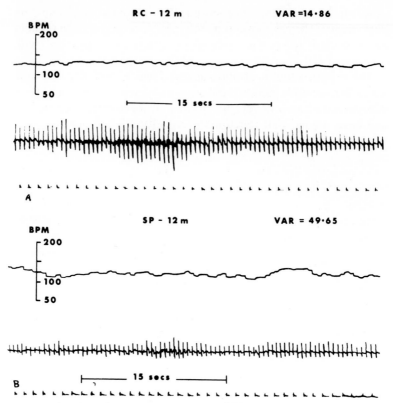

FIG. 3.   Records of two 12-month old infants showing: A, low heart rate variability; B, high variability.

source from which the novelty emanates and that differences between reactions to a novel adult and to novel objects are not simply quantitative (Hutt, 1970). Hence we were particularly interested in the *pattern* of heart rate change to a stranger on the one hand, and a new toy on the other. It seemed too, that if individuals differed in their level of arousal, such differences would be reflected in responses to an alerting, but familiar, stimulus like their name.

During a preliminary acclimatisation period of approximately 3 minutes, the child played with the mother and looked at cartoon pictures. This period was followed by a 3-minute play period with three toys. The toys were then removed for 30 seconds, one of them was changed and the new group of three toys brought back for 1 minute: this we called the *exploration* phase. After a pause of one minute a female stranger walked into the room, stood one metre in front of the child, and twice said 'hello'; 15 seconds later she crouched down so that her face was level with the child's and said 'hello' again. After 15 seconds she left the room and the child played with the toys again for 3 minutes. During this period a male voice from the entry cubicle called out the child's name three times at intervals of 30 seconds. The session was then terminated. The stranger episode was omitted for 6-month old children.

Heart rate was recorded using a telemetry link. Devices disposable stick-on electrodes filled with Neptic electrode jelly were attached to the child's chest and a radio transmitter (Devices SNR 102F) was pinned to the child's clothing. The ECG signal was received by means of a Devices 102R FM receiver, amplified by a specially designed unit (Forrest, 1974) which also eliminated artefacts due to movement. The R-wave in this modified signal was then used to trigger a cardiotachometer (Devices Ratemeter Type 2751). The rate so derived, together with the modified ECG signal, was displayed on a two-channel pen-recorder (Washington 400 MD2).

The child's behaviour was recorded by one video-camera and the paper trace of the ECG and the cardiotachometer write-out by another, the two pictures then being superimposed by means of a Sony video-camera switcher/fader to yield a composite behavioural and accompanying heart rate record. In this manner, behaviour and cardiac changes could be simultaneously monitored and detected.

Individual Differences in Heart Rate Variability

To compute a basal heart rate level for each infant, three artefact free epochs of 15 seconds each were selected from the latter part of the acclimatization period; the variances of these basal-rate epochs were also calculated.

Although mean heart rate ranged from 83 to 172 BPM, and

variances from 5·5 to 52·6, both basal heart rate and HRV remained remarkably stable over time within individuals. Figure 4 shows the ECG of child SP at 2 years of age. Comparison with his record at 12 months (see Figure 3) reveals that his HRV one year later is still high. Despite the reduction of both mean heart rate and variance with age, the rank order correlations for HRV was 0·74 between 6 and 12 months, and 0·71 between 12 and 24 months. Variability is found to be independent of basal heart rate (Porges, 1972; Porges *et al.*, 1973; Hutt *et al.*, 1975). This finding supports Lacey's original supposition (1967) that HRV is a temperamental or constitutional characteristic of the individual.

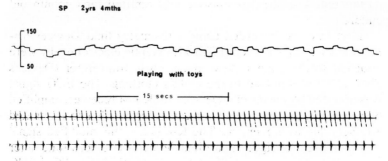

FIG. 4.   Heart rate record of 2-year old with high variability.

Many studies have shown changes in heart rate to be a singularly sensitive measure of attention and arousal, particularly in children (see Graham and Jackson, 1970). Such changes of course, are phasic responses to changes in stimulation. The phenomenon of HRV, on the other hand, received scant attention in psychology until the work of Porges and his colleagues. The evidence hitherto suggests that it reflects the *state* of the organism; changes in HRV therefore reflect changes in states of arousal and attention. Moreover, as we shall see, Porges' work suggests that the phasic HR responses are, in part, a function of the magnitude of the individual's HRV.

Porges (1972, 1976) proposed a 'two-component' hypothesis of attention: the first component is the phasic, directional response determined by attributes of the stimulus and the second is the tonic suppression of HRV which accompanies attention. More importantly Porges (1972) showed that the primary phasic heart rate responses of adults showing high variability differed considerably from those showing low variability.

We therefore divided our group of 26 children at the median to form high-variability and low-variability sub-groups; records typical of these groups were illustrated in Figures 2 and 3. As in Porges' studies, we found that the phasic heart rate response to certain environmental events was distinctively different in the high- and low-variability sub-groups. For instance, the predominant response of both groups to the presentation of a *novel toy* was a decelerative one at all three ages, though at each age the magnitude of deceleration of the high-variability group was greater. There was no relation however between a behavioural measure such as the amount of looking, and magnitude of deceleration.

We next looked at the heart rate responses of the two sub-groups to the advent of the *stranger*; the low-variability group showed a predominantly decelerative response and a relatively slow return to baseline. The high-variability group, on the other hand, showed a multiphasic response—a brief deceleration followed by a sustained accelerative phase and no evidence of a return to baseline within the 15 second period (Figure 5).

The evoked heart rate response elicited by *name-calling* was again a predominantly decelerative one in the low-variability group, though of smaller magnitude than the response to the stranger. The response of the high-variability group was considerably more exaggerated and again essentially multiphasic in nature, though with a swifter return to baseline values (Figure 6).

Correlative studies between behaviour and whatever physiological variable can only be informative in so far as they are able to tell us something about the processes of behaviour change and organisation. For this reason, Lacey's theories, contentious though they be, have an immediate attraction. Lacey (Lacey and Lacey, 1970; Lacey, 1972), has deduced the generalization that heart rate decrease accompanies attention to environmental stimuli and heart rate increase accompanies exclusion of environmental stimuli. In tasks where the subject has to attend to incoming stimuli, heart rate decreases, but when the subject is engaged in mental concentration and therefore inattentive to external stimuli (as when doing mental arithmetic), heart rate increases. Lacey does not see these heart rate changes as

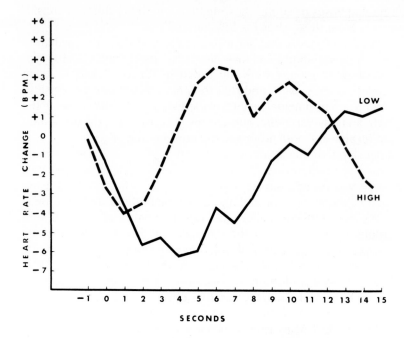

Fig. 5. Averaged heart rate response to entry of a stranger in 2-year olds showing high or low heart rate variability.

resultant events, but accords to the cardiovascular system an active, instrumental role. He argues that it constitutes a negative feedback pathway to the central nervous system: increase in blood pressure and heart rate stimulates the baroceptors in the carotid sinus and aortic arch resulting in increased firing along the glosso-pharyngeal nerve. This sympathetic activity, Lacey argues, has a number of other effects, notably a reduction of muscle tone, sensorimotor activity, and an increase in slow wave activity in the EEG. Conversely, heart rate decrease results in cortical activation, lowering of sensory thresholds and so on. Apart from the fact that such a formulation leaves us considering the rather improbable situation of an individual performing mental calculations and other complex tasks with a relatively inactivated cortex, there are several other difficulties with regard to Lacey's view of cardiovascular function.

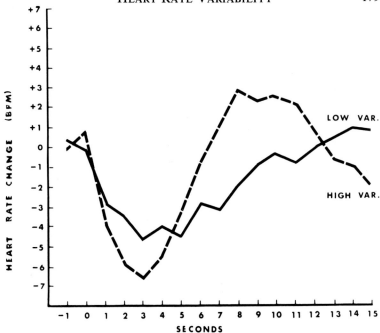

FIG. 6. Averaged evoked heart response to the child's name in 2-year olds showing high or low heart rate variability.

Critics of the Lacey position—among them Duffy (1962), Obrist and Elliot (see Lacey and Lacey, 1975 for these arguments), consider that if the cardiovascular system is to function as such a sensitive gating process, it surely requires instructions from cortical decision centres. Moreover, since Lacey is considering changes which occur over a minute, he is concerned with changes other than those phase relationships with which most workers have been preoccupied. We would suggest a rather simpler model of cardiovascular functioning, a somewhat oversimplified one, based upon the work of Uvnas (1960), Hilton (1965), and Korner (1971); this model takes account of cortical processes in the evaluation of situations and events (Figure 7).

As far as subcortical mechanisms are concerned, cardiac control may be treated as a closed-loop system. Incoming stimuli invariably activate the pressor centre of the medulla and, via the sympathetic effectors, increase heart rate. The increase in heart

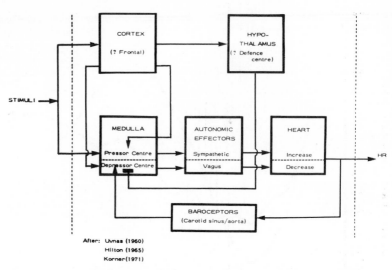

FIG. 7.   A tentative and simplified model of the significant components in cardiovascular control, and the links between them.

rate leads to increased baroceptor stimulation which in due course will result in increased vagal stimulation with a consequent slowing of heart rate. If, however, as is more likely, cortical evaluation governs medullary activation, either the pressor or depressor centres may be activated, depending upon the nature of the stimulus and the response required. When orienting and attending to neutral events, it is the depressor centre which is activated, resulting in heart rate decrease. If, on the other hand, the stimulus or event is also *affectively* evaluated then the hypothalamic centres may amplify the input. Hilton has found, for instance, that stimulation of a 'defence centre' in the hypothalamus inhibits vagal discharge. This would have the effect of producing open-loop in the subcortical control system, with a consequent and marked increase in cardiac activity.

Such a model would also take account of the reactive and sustained components of attention postulated by Porges (1976), the reactive component consisting of a vagally-mediated short-latency parasympathetic peripheral, and cholinergic central state followed by a longer latency sympathetic/catecholaminergic state due to vagal inhibition. The sustained component is again a vagally mediated parasympathetic cholinergic state but of longer latency.

There is independent evidence that a highly variable cardiovascular system is likely to be sympathetically dominated: Levy *et al*. (1966) have shown that the latency of the effect of vagal stimulation upon heart rate is considerably shorter than for the effect induced by sympathetic activation, thereby suggesting that vagal activation and inhibition would result in a speedy correction of the cardiovascular deviations. The converse would be true of sympathetic activation, and the system would thus behave as a poorly damped one.

Other behavioural evidence is also in accord with the notion of the sympathetic domination of the high variability sub-group: we found a significant negative correlation between duration of visual fixation upon the stranger and HRV at both 12 and 24 months of age (Spearman's $r = -0.41$, $P < 0.05$ and -0.39, $P < 0.05$, respectively). In other words, the greater the heart rate variability, the less the infants engaged in eye-contact. Since gaze-avoidance is commonly regarded as a negative affective state of high arousal, it seems reasonable to suppose that it is predominantly associated with sympathetic activation.

Korner (1971) has recently suggested that the processes underlying cardiovascular regulation may profitably be analysed by employing a set of models developed by systems engineers to describe physical control processes (Bayliss, 1966; Milsum, 1966). Chief amongst these, and the most plausible from a biological point of view, are: (1) a first derivative model, describing a process designed to reduce hunting about a particular set point; (2) a derivative plus integral model, describing a process designed to eliminate steady-state errors. Given equivalent environmental inputs, each model is capable of 'damping' the output, but the latter model should lead to a greater and faster reduction of HRV than the former; this, in practice, is what occurs. Thus, it is tempting to postulate that the development of cardiovascular control represents a progression from a derivative to a derivative-plus-integral model.

High variability in adults has been shown by Porges (1972) to be associated with faster reaction times and by Lacey and Lacey (1958) to be positively correlated with the length of time an individual can maintain maximal readiness to respond. If we may assume that a similar relationship appertains during development, we may see high variability as reflecting a labile and sympathetically dominated autonomic nervous system which nevertheless promotes prompt and effective processing of information under affectively neutral conditions. The low-variable or well-damped autonomic nervous system, while functioning better under affectively demanding conditions, is less at an advantage when speed and sustained proficiency are required.

What is particularly significant about these individual differences in relation to cultural adaptation are the strategies of coping that the individuals are constrained to develop. The behavioural consequences of these strategies are in turn dependent to some extent upon the parameters of the particular physiological system we have been considering. Many germane questions have still to be answered before further elucidation is possible: can we specify the conditions under which the subcortical mechanism is likely to go open-loop and what implications may these have for behaviour? Do the time-constants of the constituent processes in the control system change with age, and if so, with what consequences for behaviour? In both high- and low-variability groups, is the first-order derivative model eventually replaced by a derivative-and-integral model? Further psychophysiological research within a developmental context may provide some of the answers.

State Changes and Heart Rate Variability

We have already seen that during attention and conditions of mental effort HRV is suppressed. Playful behaviour, however, is not commonly associated with mental effort. An ostensibly insurmountable difficulty with the concept of play in children lies in the matter of its definition. Colloquially, and somewhat tautologically, much of what a child does is referred to as play. But if play is to be distinguished from other behaviour some working definition must be proposed. Bateson (1956) argued that definitions of a class must also imply what is *not* properly in that class. Acting upon such a directive, Dearden (1967) concluded that play is a non-serious activity which is not obligatory or constrained. While such a negative definition is of limited heuristic value, other workers have attempted to sharpen the distinction between play and non-play: psychologically, play may be distinguished in terms of motivating conditions (Berlyne, 1960), internal states (Berlyne, 1969) and covert processes (Nunnally and Lemond, 1973): empirically, play may be shown to have certain behavioural characteristics (Hutt, 1966), to have specific temporal relationships with other behaviours (Hutt, 1967) and to be systematically related to other psychological functions (Hutt, 1970; Hutt and Bhavnani, 1972; Cazden, 1974).

In the present study therefore, play epochs were distinguished empirically—according to morphological aspects of the child's behaviour. Most of these play epochs occurred during the initial and final phases. To elicit exploratory activity, the "new" toy that was introduced was Galt's "pop-up" toy with the following modifications: the case which contained the four "pop-up men" was mounted on a bright red base which also housed a buzzer connected to the spring of one "man" and a light connected to the spring of another. Pressure on these two activated buzzer and light respectively. The toy was thus visually attractive and complex whilst also providing a variety of contingent effects. In the studies already recounted, we introduced a six-piece formboard problem for the two year olds, so that comparison of HRV during different epochs might reveal the relative degrees of "mental effort" involved in each type of behaviour. HRV was analysed only in those epochs where the prior operational criteria had been met. The data discussed here are only those for the two year olds.

Heart rate variability was greatest during playful episodes (Figure 8) and was considerably suppressed during solution of the formboard (Figure 9). HRV as a variance score for the three behavioural categories are illustrated in Figure 10. Since the variances were proportional to the means, a square root transformation of the data was carried out. Analysis of variance for repeated measures and unequal samples yielded a significant F ratio for type-of-behaviour ($F = 6 \cdot 80$, d.f. 2/36, $P < 0 \cdot 01$) and a marginally significant ratio for sex $F = 4 \cdot 82$, d.f. 1/36, $P < 0 \cdot 05$). Scheffé's test for *post-hoc* pair-wise comparisons showed that for both boys and girls the differences between variability during play and during problem-solving were highly significant ($P < 0 \cdot 01$ for

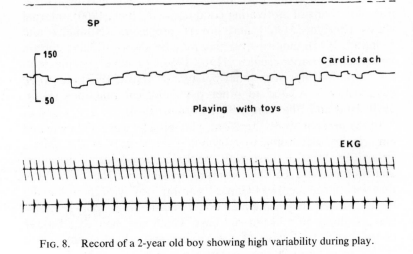

FIG. 8.   Record of a 2-year old boy showing high variability during play.

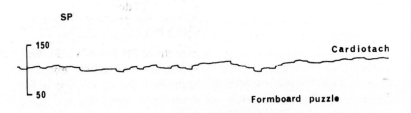

FIG. 9.   Record of the same boy as in Figure 8, showing suppression of variability during performance of a task.

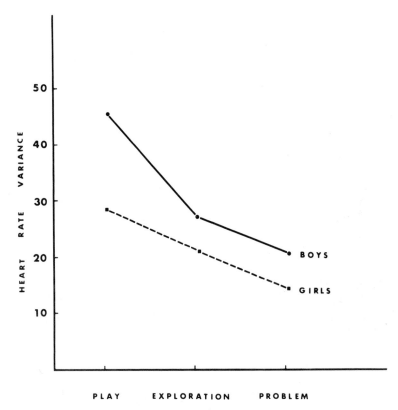

FIG. 10. Heart rate variability expressed as mean variance scores in boys and girls while engaged in different kinds of activity.

both). Furthermore, in boys, exploration differed significantly from play ($P < 0.05$), but not from problem-solving: in girls, exploration did not differ significantly from either.

These results suggest that the mental effort involved in play is minimal, relative to task behaviours. In boys, exploration appeared to involve greater mental effort and attention than did play. In view of the exploratory proclivities of males in most species (Hutt, 1972), the adaptive consequences of vesting such behaviour with greater attentive capacity are self-evident. The failure of exploration to be significantly differentiated from play or task activity in the girls may be due to adventitious social factors: sitting on their mothers' laps, the girls were prone to communicate frequently with their mothers—by look, word or gesture, and continued to do so except when occupied with the task. Although this fact exemplified the greater person-orientation of the girls, it probably also served to reduce the mental effort expended in the exploratory activity.

In interpreting these results it may be informative to consider the nature of other behavioural states which are associated with high HRV. In older children HRV is great during periods of reminiscence, reverie or imagination (Figure 11). Such variability however is almost wholly suppressed upon involvement in a task (Figure 12).

The performance of stereotypies by autistic children and REM sleep in normal adults are also states associated with high HRV. All these states have a common feature—namely a high level of central arousal or, to put it another way, a low level of stimulus input. HRV is associated therefore, with response systems which serve an arousal-modulating function.

The principal function of the nervous system is as an information-processing system. As Delius (1970) has argued, to be effective, much of an organism's information processing

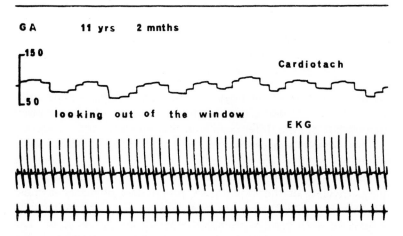

FIG. 11.   Record of an older child, showing high heart-rate variability during reverie.

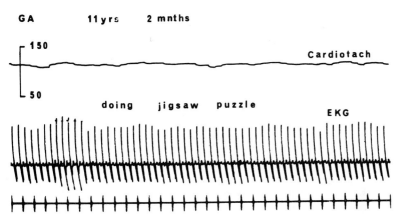

FIG. 12.   Record of the same boy as in Figure 11, showing suppression of variability during performance of task-like activity.

depends on behavioural activities which require a varying distribution of metabolic energy, the autonomic responses being particularly adapted to achieve this. But there is some incompatibility in these two functions: the channel capacity of the nervous system depends on whether it is chiefly engaged in metabolic recovery or in information processing. While operating in the former mode in particular, organisms must resort to mechanisms which prevent further information influx, or, in other circumstances, which overload channel capacity.

Delius has persuasively reinterpreted arousal in terms of information processing rate, and argued that mechanisms for the reduction of processing rate are selected for. Whatever mechanisms are employed however, they have in common the transient uncoupling of cortical regulatory centres from subcortical and autonomic processes. This uncoupling is reflected in a relative increase in HRV.

In play, information processing is reduced, metabolic recovery is facilitated and energy redistribution ensured, but by its activities the organism nevertheless keeps its nervous system primed for coping with potential demands on channel capacity. Similar functions may be ascribed to covert thought processes of an associative kind. During REM sleep there is more direct evidence of metabolic recuperation; and in the extreme case of the autists, the endeavours are principally directed at reducing information input to an already overloaded channel. That such state changes form an integral part of the human adaptation process is only too evident when we consider that play, for instance, is most common in those societies and cultures which are most emancipated from the immediate demands of their biological livelihood.

References

BATESON, G. (1956) The message "This is play". In *Group Processes* (ed. B. Schaffner). Josiah Macey Foundation, New York.

BAYLISS, L. E. (1966) *Living Control Systems*. English Universities Press Ltd., London.

BERLYNE, D. E. (1960) *Conflict, Arousal, and Curiosity*. McGraw-Hill, New York.

BOYCE, P. R. (1974) Sinus arrhythmia as a measure of mental load. *Ergonomics*, **17**, 177–83.

CAZDEN, C. B. (1974) Play with language and metalinguistic awareness: one dimension of language experience, *International Journal of Early Childhood*, **6**, 12–24.

DEARDEN, R. F. (1967) The concept of play. In *The concept of education* (ed. R. S. Peters). Routledge and Kegan Paul.

DELIUS, J. D. (1970). Irrelevant behaviour, information processing and arousal homeostasis. *Psychologische Forschung*, **33**, 165–88.

DUFFY, E. (1962) *Activation and Behaviour*, John Wiley, New York.

FORREST, S. J. (1974) An ECG telemetry coupler for use with a ratemeter. Technical note. Available on request to author.

GRAHAM, F. K. and JACKSON, J. C. (1970) Arousal systems and infant heart rate responses. In *Advances in Child Development and Behaviour*, Vol. 5, (eds. H. W. Reese and L. P. Lipsitt). Academic Press.

HILTON, S. (1965) Hypothalamic control of the cardiovascular responses in fear and rage. *Scientific basis of medicine: Annual Reviews*, 217–38.

HUTT, C. (1966) Exploration and play in children. In *Play Exploration and Territory in Mammals*. Symposium Zoological Society, **18**, 61–68.

HUTT, C. (1976a) Temporal effects on response decrement and stimulus satiation in exploration. *British Journal of Psychology*, **58**, 365–73.

HUTT, C. (1970) Specific and diversive exploration. In *Advances in Child Development and Behaviour*, Vol. 5, (eds. H. W. Reese and L. P. Lipsitt). Academic Press.

HUTT, C. and BHAVNANI, R. (1972) Predictions from Play. *Nature*, **237**, 171–73.

HUTT, C., FORREST, S. J., and RICHER, J. (1975) Cardiac arrhythmia and behaviour in autistic children. *Acta Psychiatrica Scandinavica*, **51**, 361–72.

KAGAN, J. (1971) *Change and continuity in infancy*. John Wiley, New York.

KALSBEEK, J. W. H. (1967) Measurement of mental work load and of acceptable load, possible applications in industry. *International Journal of Production Research*, **7**, 33–45.

KALSBEEK, J. W. H. and ETTEMA, J. H. (1963) Continuous recording of heart rate and the measurement of perceptual load. *Ergonomics*, **6**, 306–07.

KORNER, P. I. (1971) Integrative neural cardiovascular control. *Physiological Review*, **51**, 312–67.

LACEY, B. C. and LACEY, J. I. (1975) Studies of heart rate and other bodily processes in sensorimotor behaviour. In *Cardiovascular Psychophysiology–Current Issues in Response Mechanisms, Biofeedback and Methodology*. (eds. P. A. Obrist, A. Black, J. Brener and L. Di Cara). Aldine-Atherton, Chicago.

LACEY, J. E. (1967) Somatic response patterning and stress: Some revisions of activation theory. In *Psychological Stress: Issues in Research* (eds. M. H. Appley and R. Trumbull). Appleton, New York.

LACEY, J. I. (1972) Some cardiovascular correlates of sensorimotor behaviour: examples of visceral afferent feedback? In *Limbic System Mechanisms and Autonomic Function* (ed. C. H. Hockman). Ch. Thomas, Springfield.

LACEY, J. I. and LACEY B. C. (1958) The relationship of resting autonomic activity to motor impulsivity. *Research Publication in Nervous and Mental Disease*, **36**, 144–209.

LACEY, J. I. and LACEY, B. C. (1970) Some autonomic-central nervous system interrelationships. In *Physiological Correlates of Emotion* (ed. P. Black). Academic Press Inc.

LEVY, M. N., DeGEEST, H. and ZIESKE, H. (1966) Effects of respiratory centre activity on the heart. *Circulation Research*, **18**, 67–78.

MILSUM, J. H. (1966) *Biological Control Systems Analysis*. McGraw-Hill, New York.

NUNNALLY, J. C. and LEMOND, L. C. (1973) Exploratory Behaviour and human development. In *Advances in Child Development and Behaviour*, Vol. 8, (ed. H. W. Reese). Academic Press.

PORGES, S. W. (1972) Heart rate variability and deceleration as indexes of reaction time. *Journal of Experimental Psychology*, **92**, (1) 103–10.

PORGES, S. W., ARNOLD, W. R. and FORBES, E. J. (1973) Heart rate variability: an index of attentional responsivity in human newborns. *Developmental Psychology*, **8**, 85–92.

PORGES, S. W. (1976) Peripheral and neurochemical parallels of psychopathology: a psychopharmacological model relating autonomic imbalance to hyperactivity, psychopathy and autism. In *Advances in Child Development and Behaviour*, Vol. 11 (ed. H. W. Reese), Academic Press.

SAYERS, B. McA. (1975) Physiological consequences of informational load and overload. In *Research in Psychophysiology* (eds. P. H. Venables and M. J. Christie). John Wiley, New York.

UVNAS, B. (1960) Central cardiovascular control. In *Handbook of Physiology*, Section 1, *Neurophysiology*, Vol. 2 (eds. J. Field, H. W. Magoun, and V. E. Hall). American Physiological Society, Washington, D.C.

THE BEHAVIOUR OF NORMAL AND AUTISTIC CHILDREN AND THEIR CATECHOLAMINE EXCRETION RATES IN RELATION TO PREVAILING "STRESS" THEORIES

H. Helevuo and V. Reynolds

Department of Biological Anthropology, University of Oxford

Introduction

We report here on some aspects of the work we have been doing over the last three years in the Department of Biological Anthropology at Oxford University. During that period we have been looking for links between observable aspects of human action, recorded in the form of named behaviour "units", and levels of catecholamine hormones excreted in the urine. Studies conducted elsewhere have for some years now shown that the level of urinary catecholamines, mainly epinephrine and norepinephrine, will increase either as a result of psychological inputs such as watching exciting films, or after strenuous physical activities, such as weight lifting and running. Previous work has not, however, achieved much precision in the recording of the behaviour accompanying catecholamine increase: this we hoped to rectify. Since behaviour is generally considered to be the way life-forms adapt to environmental conditions, it seems necessary to be as objective as possible in recording it, a point stressed by ethologists from whom indeed we have largely borrowed our recording methods.

It would be generally agreed that some kinds of behaviour, such as kicking, punching, fleeing, indicate a higher level of psychophysical arousal than others, such as sitting still, playing alone, or chatting to a friend. On this basis, we could test the hypothesis that low levels of arousal were correlated with low levels of excreted catecholamines. In order to try to separate the

191

purely motor from the psychological aspects of arousal we recorded the extent of locomotor activity on a four-point scale. All other kinds of behaviour were recorded as individual occurrences of particular named activities. We ensured that behavioural observations were made over the time of urine formation.

Some of our subjects were ordinary 5–7-year-old children at school, but in order to have a group against which to test any ideas resulting from the study of normal children, we also studied a group of autistic children. Such children are known to show aberrant behaviour patterns, a point our study amply confirmed. Also it has been suggested (by the Tinbergens (1972), Richer (1976) and others) that they are reacting to what they perceive as a highly stressful environment, such children being, for a wide variety of reasons ranging from the genetic to the psychogenic, unduly intimidated by their social environment. The deep-set and far-reaching developmental failures of autists, described first by Kanner (1943), later refined by Creak (1961) and again by O'Gorman (1970), have thus, in one theory, been related to process of maladaptation, which without help would probably be lethal and even with help usually leads to reproductive failure. We wanted to test the hypothesis that such a maladaptation would show up at the endocrinological level as well as the behavioural level—perhaps, for example, in an unduly high level of excreted catecholamines.

Subjects and Methods: First Year

In the first year we worked with a small sample of 10 normal and 4 autistic children. Our normal subjects were selected for us by the willingness to participate of the head of an Oxford school, the class teacher and the childrens' parents. In the case of the autists we studied a group in Henley attending Smith Hospital day school. One of these children was a weekly boarder; the other three attended from home. Within the hospital, the children were observed, like the normals, in their classroom situation. Each normal child was observed over three consecutive days in the first half of term, and again during the second half of term. Autists were observed on five afternoons at fortnightly intervals, during the term. Observations were recorded on a check-sheet, two children at a time being observed semi-continuously during the urine formation time. The children emptied their bladders before observation. During observation, all urinations were pooled into a sample overlapping the behavioural records. At the end of this, the urine samples were collected and aliquotted for storage and subsequent analysis of primary catecholamines E and NE, and their metabolites MN, NMN and VMA.† In addition, for each child, three baseline night-time samples were obtained from the child's home, with the help of the parents. These three night-time samples were for the nights preceding the observation days during the second half of term.

Table 1 gives details of subjects for year 1. As can be seen, the autistic children were older than the normals, a fact that was unavoidable. O'Gorman (1970) has, however, shown that autists are small for their age. Table 2 shows the behaviour catalogue developed and used in this study.

TABLE 1. Age, sex and weight of children in the first sample.

Child	Normal or autistic	Sex	Age (months)	Wt (kg)
Anna	normal	F	68	19
Christine	normal	F	68	20
Helen	normal	F	68	23
Laura	normal	F	67	22
Linda	normal	F	65	33
Andrew	normal	M	67	20
Alex	normal	M	66	20
Michael	normal	M	62	18
Peter	normal	M	70	23
Tom	normal	M	63	19
Darrell	autistic	M	118	28
Henry	autistic	M	112	28
Ken	autistic	M	88	19
Sam	autistic	M	93	24

Results: First Year

Results are presented in two parts—first, those concerning *all* the children studied (i.e. both normal and autistic), and second, those relating to differences between normal and autistic children.

†These abbreviations are explained under Table 3. VMA is 3-methoxy-4-hydroxymandelic acid (vanilmandelic acid).

TABLE 2. Behaviour catalogue used. Units of behaviour recorded are shown in the body of the table. Column heads denote names of categories into which units were grouped.

Locomotion 0 (Immobile)	Locomotion 1 (Minor)	Locomotion 2 (Medium)	Locomotion 3 (Major)	Solo Behaviour	School-Orientated Behaviour	Initiate Associative Behaviour	Receive Associative Behaviour	Initiate Assertive Behaviour	Receive Assertive Behaviour	Initiate Aggressive Behaviour	Receive Aggressive Behaviour
Sit doing nothing	Sit & write	Climb	Run	Self groom	Be given task	Smile	Be approached	Command	Be commanded	Provoke	Be provoked
Stand doing nothing	Stand & paint	Walk	Jump	Talk to self	Be commanded	Go to	Receive object	Try to take	Be taken from	Hit	Be hit
Crouch doing nothing	Stand & play	Crawl	Hop	Vocalize to self	Do task	Give object	Be helped	Akimbo	Be pointed at	Push	Be pushed
Lie doing nothing	Sit & drink	Shrug	Swing	Self display	Play	Help	Be soothed	Search	Be asserted to	Grab	Be grabbed
	Kneel	Place walk	Hang	Mouthe	Go to teacher	Soothe	Be hugged	Point		Wrestle	Be kicked
		Twist	Dance	Gaze	Talk to teacher	Hug	Be patted	Demand		Kick	Be bitten
		Balance	Play beat	Look at object	Show to teacher	Pat	Be kissed	Take		Bite	Be scratched
		Roll	Move heavy things	Glance	Comply	Kiss	Receive contact	Assert		Scratch	Be shown tongue
		Any Tremor		Stare	Non-comply	Physical contact	Receive attention			Tongue out	Be banged
				Watch	Listen	Hand in hand	Be shown to			Bang obj. with obj.	Be thrown
					Question/ask permission	Seek attention	Be asked company			Tantrum	
					Be scolded	Show to X	Be talked to by peer			Rough and tumble	
					Look at teacher	Ask company	Be looked at			Throw	
					Be talked to by teacher	Talk to peer	Be talked to by me				
					Be praised	Talk to me					
						Look at peer					
						Look at me					

All children

There was a positive correlation between epinephrine and its metabolite metanephrine in all children (Table 3). This was validated by the fact that the two sets of measurements (i.e. for E and NE on the one hand, and for MN and NMN on the other) were made "blind" and in two different laboratories.

TABLE 3. Catecholamine: metabolite correlations, first sample.

Hormones	Type	r_S	$P <$
E : MN	day	0·516	0·05
	night	0·499	0·05
	day/night	0·231	ns
NE : NMN	day	0·073	ns
	night	0·257	ns
	day/night	0·129	ns

r_S: correlation coefficient of excretion levels of epinephrine to metanephrine (E : MN) and norepinephrine to normetanephrine (NE : NMN)
ns: not significant

(Spearman Rank Correlation $N = 14$)

Intra-individual variation was consistently less than inter-individual variation for certain catecholamine levels (E, MN and VMA day and night values). Put differently, individual children can be said to show a considerable consistency of diurnal rhythm in their catecholamine excretion rates. These results are shown in the form of means and standard errors for the whole study period for each child. (Figure 1 shows the results for E).

As with the catecholamines mentioned above, behavioural variation within subjects was slight compared with between-subject variability. (Figure 2 shows the results for solo behaviour).

Regarding correlations between endocrine excretion rates and behaviour, we ranked all 14 children for the catecholamines measured and compared these rank orders with those for the behaviour categories. This analysis gave rise to the correlations shown in Table 4.

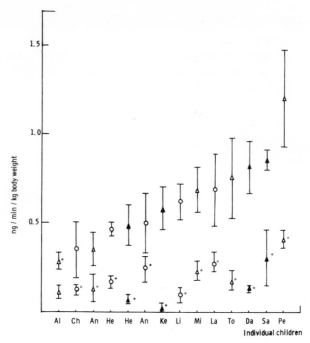

FIG. 1. Individual variation in epinephrine excretion rates, first sample.
○ Normal female, △ normal male, ▲ autistic male.
* Night period, mean ± SE. Other values: Day period, mean ± SE.

Normals v. autistic children: year 1

Confirming earlier studies, clear behavioural differences were found between the two groups, mainly in the overall level of school activity (lower in autistics), level of solo behaviour (higher in autistics), level of associative behaviour (lower in autistics) and level of aggressive behaviour (comparatively high in autistics, especially in view of their low general sociability). (Figures 2 and 3 show the results for solo and initiate associative behaviour respectively).

Regarding catecholamine differences, the only significant difference found was that autistic children showed a greater increase from night resting levels to daytime levels in epinephrine than did normals (see Figure 4).

However, the number of subjects was low, especially in the

autistic group. In view of this, it was decided to repeat the entire study with a larger sample, in an effort to confirm or otherwise the correlations found in the first study.

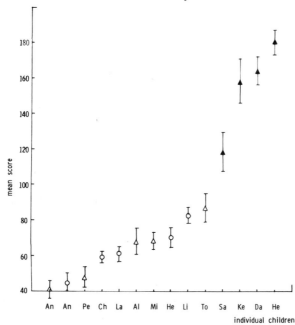

FIG. 2. Individual variation in solo behaviour, first sample. (Means ± SE.)
○ Normal female, △ normal male, ▲ autistic male

TABLE 4.   Correlations between behaviour scores and catecholamine excretion rates; first sample.

Behaviour	Catecholamine	r_S	$P <$
High initiate associative	low E d/n*	0·568	0·05
High initiate aggressive	high MN d	0·542	0·02
High solo	high E d/n	0·749	0·01
High receive associative	low E d/n	0·547	0·05
High initiate assertive	low E d/n	0·640	0·05
High total locomotion	high NE d/n	0·644	0·05
High total locomotion	high MN d/n	0·532	0·05
High total locomotion	high VMA d/n	0·552	0·05

* d, day; d/n, day/night.
r_S: correlation coefficient between behaviour score and catecholamine excretion
    level.
(Spearman Rank Correlation, $N = 14$, 10 normals, 4 autists)

TABLE 5.   Subjects studied in the second sample.

Child	Normal/ autistic†	Sex	Age‡	Wt (kg)
Nora	N	F	81	26
Margaret	N	F	65	20
Patricia	N	F	65	19
Julie	N	F	62	17
Nina	N	F	81	21
Suzanna	N	F	61	19
Rosemary	N	F	63	24
Elizabeth	N	F	62	17
Jayne	N	F	83	23
Carol	N	F	65	22
Richard	N	M	82	24
Bob	N	M	63	20
Shaun	N	M	66	22
Barry	N	M	65	21
John	N	M	63	22
Brian	N	M	83	23
Tim	N	M	62	18
Steve	N	M	82	22
Martin	N	M	81	28
Jeremy	N	M	81	24
Cecily	A	F	125	28
Adam	A	M	120	35
Sam•	A	M	111	27
Ken•	A	M	106	22
Robin	A	M	69	15
Darrell•	A	M	135	35
Henry•	A	M	129	33
Arthur	A	M	136	25
Colin	A	M	125	25
Hubert	A	M	130	29
Terry	AS	M	101	23
Mel	AS	M	137	28
Randolph	AS	M	69	25
William	AS	M	62	23
George	AS	M	155	47
Hamilton	AS	M	118	32
Edward	AS	M	85	26
Ben	AS	M	113	42

† N = normal, A = autistic Smith, AS = autistic Springhallow,
‡ = age in months, • = also studied in sample I.

Subjects and Methods: Second Year

In the second year we worked with a larger sample of 20 normal and 18 autistic children. The normal subjects were from an

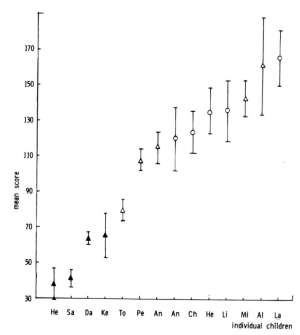

Fig 3.   Initiate associative behaviour scores, first sample.
○ Normal female, △ normal male, ▲ autistic male.

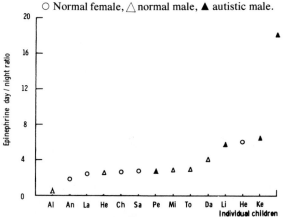

Fig 4.   Ratio of mean daytime epinephrine excretion rates to night-time excretion rates, first sample.
○ Normal female, △ normal male, ▲ autistic male.
Normal mean 2·9, autistic mean 8·3.
t test, 2·55, $P < 0·05$.

Oxford school (not the same one as was used in the first year). The autistic children consisted of the 4 studied in the first year together with a further 6 from the same Smith Hospital school in Henley, and an additional 8 in an autistic school, Springhallow, in Ealing. Recording methods used were as in year 1. Data were collected over four consecutive mornings, for all the children. Table 5 shows the subjects studied in year 2.

TABLE 6.   Catecholamine: metabolite correlations, second sample.

Hormones	Type	r_S	$P <$
E : MN	day	0·470	0·01
	night	0·286	0.05
	day/night	0·340	0·05
NE : NMN	day	0·240	ns
	night	0·377	0·05
	day/night	0·473	0·01

r_S: correlation coefficient of excretion levels of epinephrine to metanephrine (E : MN) and norepinephrine to normetanephrine (NE : NMN).
ns: not significant.

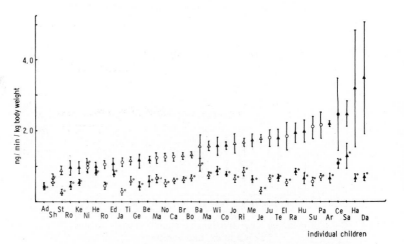

FIG. 5.   Individual variation in norepinephrine excretion rates, second sample.
○ Normal female, △ normal male, ● autistic female, ▲ autistic male.
* Night period, mean ± SE. Other values: Day period ± SE.

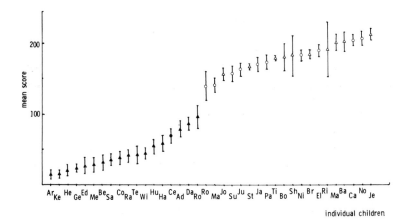

Fig. 6.   Individual variation (means ± SE) in Initiate Associative behaviour,
second sample.
○ Normal female, △ normal male, ● autistic female, ▲ autistic male.

Results: Second Year

All children

As in the first year, there was a positive correlation between levels of free catecholamines and their metabolites in all children and this time the correlation also held for NE: NMN (Table 6). As before the two sets of measurements were made entirely separately.

Again, as in the first year, individual consistency with regard to catecholamine excretion rates was found to be great. We added to the results achieved in year 1 by showing that increasing the sample size not only confirmed the results achieved in year 1, but also led to the addition of NE and NMN. (Figure 5 shows results for NE).

As in year 1, behavioural consistency of individuals was great. (Figure 6 shows results for initiate associative behaviour.)

None of the behaviour: endocrine correlations proposed as a result of the first year's study was confirmed in year 2. Possible reasons for this are discussed below.

Normals v. autistic children: year 2

Regarding behaviour differences, these were largely the same as in year 1, but in addition autists initiated more aggressive behaviour than normals.

There were also some differences between the two autistic groups in year 2: there was more locomotor activity in the Henley Hospital school sample than in the Ealing school sample; there was more solo behaviour in the Henley sample than in the Ealing sample, and the latter initiated more school behaviour than the hospital school children (Figure 7). It is possible that the existence of two sub-groups in the autistic sample has affected some of the results, a point which must have great importance in the study of autistic children generally.

We failed to confirm the finding deriving from the first year, that autistic children showed a significantly greater increase from night resting to daytime levels in epinephrine than normals. The earlier result may have been due to small sample size and increasing the sample eliminated it. Alternatively, it may have been due to the fact that in year 1 autistic children were studied in the early afternoon whereas normals were studied in the morning. In year 2

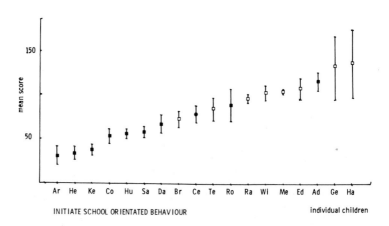

FIG 7.   Differences between the two autistic groups in sample 2: Initiate school orientated behaviour.
Smith versus Springhallow: ● Smith female, ■ Smith male, □ Springhallow male.
Smith mean 62·0, Springhallow mean 103·6, *t*-test 3·59, $P < 0.01$.

all children were studied in the morning. This change, aimed at improving comparability in year 2, may have been responsible for the change in results, since the catecholamine diurnal rhythm is known to lead to higher excretion levels as the morning proceeds, leading to a peak at or around midday (see Fröberg *et al.*, 1972).

Discussion

This study has increased our understanding of catecholamine excretion rates in a number of ways. We have established, by measurement of both primary catecholamines and their metabolites, that these metabolites co-vary in quantity with their primary antecedents. This indicates that in this type of study, at any rate in the present state of our knowledge, there is little to be gained by separate analysis of the metabolites and workers can derive the necessary information about excretion levels from measurement of the primary catecholamines alone.

We have also confirmed the findings of earlier workers (e.g. Pátkai and Frankenhäuser, 1964) that there is great intra-individual consistency of catecholamine excretion rates. This is sufficient to make the search for behavioural or other correlations worth continuing, although it would certainly be useful to have more genetic and physiological data available.

The failure of the second year's data to confirm the general hypotheses regarding behaviour–endocrine correlations that arose out of the first year's work indicates that the smaller initial sample may have been biased in certain respects. It also indicates that narrower hypotheses need to be formulated for testing, working with individuals under intensive study, or small groups under semi-experimental conditions. We have examined the details of some individual cases and found clear indications of individual responses to environmental stresses that did show up in both behaviour patterns and catecholamine excretion rates.

Consider, for example, the two cases illustrated in Figure 8. On the left is shown an autistic boy, Hamilton; on the right a normal boy, Jeremy. In the case of Hamilton, over the 4-day observation period, peak scores for two behaviour categories, Initiate Aggressive and Solo, and for epinephrine excretion rate, were achieved on the same day, day 4. In her additional notes the

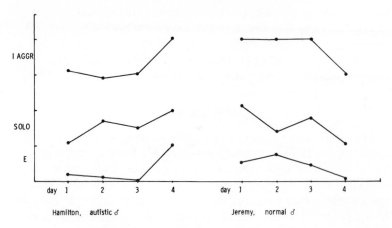

FIG 8. Two individual cases selected to show correspondence between behavioural and catecholamine measures (see text).

observer (H.H.) recorded that he was "very tense and excited", "restless", and that he was scolded by a secretary during the morning concerned when he dropped and broke a milk-bottle.

In the case of Jeremy, we can see the opposite tendency on day 4, i.e. a reduction in levels of initiated aggression, solo activity, and epinephrine excretion rate. This was just a quiet, uneventful day for him. On day 2 his E rate was high, and in her additional notes the observer recorded that he "seemed preoccupied or agitated in some way".

Thus there is evidence of a case-study kind, showing that when inner mental and external environmental factors are considered alongside the behaviour records, a clearer picture sometimes emerges. Individual cases are, however, idiosyncratic and do not lend themselves to statistical analysis or objective enquiry.

If one thing does seem clear, however, it is that we need new and more complex models to pin our ideas on. This study may have helped if it has shown that behaviour is not directly related to urinary excretion of catecholamines. Perhaps this is because of the fact, stressed by Lazarus (1971) and again by Johansson and Lundberg (this volume, p. 285), that at any given time, an individual's interpretation of the environment will render it more or less familiar to him, more or less disturbing, more or less demanding of some kind of action. It is this interpretation rather than the actual stimulus from the environment that will determine the extent of psychophysiological arousal, and how he or she acts.

To give an example, rather than saying that some kinds of environmental change produce an increase in epinephrine and a certain kind of behaviour, we ought to say that when an environmental change is perceived by an individual, it may or may not surmount a level of arousal that he/she accepts as normal. If it does, physiological systems respond in given ways by increased or decreased activity beyond the normal range of variation for that individual. Together with these physiological changes goes a series of behavioural changes which are functional, i.e. they serve to reduce the impact of the perceived environment. In so far as they succeed, physiological systems revert to normal functioning, and the behaviour stops. This general hypothesis clearly gives to behaviour a central adaptive role in the regulation of environmentally produced physiological upsets. It fits well with our own data, and with existing studies showing that environmentally induced psychological arousal *without* behavioural response (e.g. when watching films) leads to marked physiological effects (see, for example, Levi, 1972).

This hypothesis also helps to make sense of our finding that whereas autistic children show aberrant behaviour patterns, they are physiologically indistinguishable from normals. Their behaviour is their way of coping with their perception of the world. If they show "cut-off" behaviour, as most do, then we can join Tinbergen (1974), Richer (1976) and others in suggesting that at the psychological level their problem is one of over-arousal by situations that normals handle with comparative ease. The cause of their over-arousal may involve a failure of coping mechanisms at the physiological level which appears to be linked with brain malfunction, which in turn appears to be connected with both genetically inherited factors and brain damage (Folstein and Rutter, 1977).

References

CREAK, E. M. (1961) The schizophrenic syndrome in childhood. Progress report of a Working Party. *British Medical Journal*, **2**, 889–90.

FOLSTEIN, S. and RUTTER, M. (1977) Genetic influences and infantile autism. *Nature*, **265**, 726–28.

FRÖBERG, J., KARLSSON, C.-G., LEVI, L. and LINDBERG, L. (1972) Circadian variations in performance, psychological ratings, catecholamine excretion and diuresis during prolonged sleep deprivation. *International Journal of Psychobiology*, **2**, 23–36.

FRÖBERG, J. E. (1974) Circadian rhythms in catecholamine excretion, performance and self ratings. *Reports from the Laboratory for Clinical Stress Research*. Dept. of Med. & Psych., Karolinska Institute, No. **36**, April 1974.

KANNER, L. (1943) Autistic disturbances of affective contact. *Nervous Child*, **2**, 217–50.

LAZARUS, R. S. (1971) The concepts of stress and disease. In *Society, Stress and Disease* (ed. L. Levi). Oxford University Press, London.

LEVI, L. (1972) *Stress and Distress in Response to Psychosocial Stimuli*. Pergamon Press, Oxford.

O'GORMAN, G. (1970) *The Nature of Childhood Autism*. Butterworth, London.

PÁTKAI, P. and FRANKENHÄUSER, M. (1964) Constancy of urinary catecholamine excretion. *Perceptual and Motor Skills*, **19**, 789–90.

RICHER, J. (1976) The social avoidance behaviour of autistic children. *Animal Behaviour*, **24**, 896–906.

SIMON, G. B. and GILLIES, S. M. (1964) Some physical characteristics of a group of psychotic children. *British Journal of Psychiatry*, **10**, 104–07.

TINBERGEN, E. A. and TINBERGEN, N. (1972) Early childhood autism—an ethological approach. Advances in Ethology. Suppl. 10, *Journal of Comparative Ethology*.

TINBERGEN, N. (1974) Ethology and stress diseases. *Science*, **185**, 20–27.

BEHAVIOURAL PROFILES AND CORTICOSTEROID EXCRETION RHYTHMS IN YOUNG CHILDREN PART 1: NON-VERBAL COMMUNICATION AND SETTING UP OF BEHAVIOURAL PROFILES IN CHILDREN FROM 1 TO 6 YEARS

H. Montagner†, J.Ch. Henry‡, M. Lombardot†,
A. Restoin†, D. Bolzoni†, M. Durand†, Y. Humbert†
and A. Moyse†

† Laboratory of Psychophysiology, Faculty of Sciences, Besançon, France
‡ Laboratory of Biochemistry, Faculty of Medicine, Besançon, France

Introduction

For the last six years we have been trying to understand how the young child of one to six years organizes his behavioural and physiological responses when confronted with questions that are posed to him by various natural or cultural environments which are imposed on him. Children from 2 to 3 years old, and from 14 to 24 months, were systematically and continuously observed and filmed 1, 2 or 3 hours per day every week, from October to June, in a day care centre, when they were left or placed in free activities with their peer mates. They were also observed and filmed every 2 or 3 days, or every week, in situations that gave rise to competition for a reduced number of objects that were usually attractive and sought after. Children from 3 to 6 years were seen in 2 kindergartens in the same situations.

Our attitude, principles and methods for studying children's behavioural mechanisms have already been set out in some detail (Montagner *et al.*, 1973–76) and discussed in a book published by Stock in Paris in 1978: *L'Enfant et la Communication*. However, we would just mention that like Blurton Jones (1967, 1971, 1972). Eibl-Eibesfeldt (1968, 1972, 1973, 1974), McGrew (1969, 1970, 1972) and Reynolds and Guest (1975) we adopted, from the very outset, an attitude and a methodology used by ethologists to study communication behaviour. But we did not try *a priori* to establish a taxonomy of the child's motor acts (ethogram) or to isolate behavioural releasers. For six years we have been trying to find out how the acts and vocalizations of children follow one another when the child begins, maintains and ends communication with another child. Thus, as is often done in ethology, we attributed a meaning or a function to a motor sequence using as a basis the form of the response that the sequence had brought about. This does not imply that there is necessarily and invariably a correspondence: the response can be absent or take a different form in accordance with the previous exchanges, the type of situation experienced, the physiological state and the background of each child. Before being analytical and determinist our intended approach was firstly functional, multifactorial and probabilistic. In this way we managed to isolate the most probable act sequences of each child in a communication situation. Thus we were able to show behaviour that links and appeases and behaviour that brings about aggression, breaking of contact, retreat or escape. Within these two main groups of behaviour sequences we examined the ontogeny of certain motor sequences which led us to make behavioural profiles that we had previously noted in children between 2 and 3 years (Montagner *et al.*, 1973–76).

I. Non verbal exchange sequences†

A. Linking and appeasement behaviour
(*a*) *Offering*. It is often by an offering behaviour or a simulated offering that a child of 2 to 3 years establishes or re-establishes contact with other children. This behaviour causes the receiving child either to stop crying, to accept the presence of the offerer, or there is a sequence of appeasing acts (see *b*) followed by one child imitating the other, or a return to exchanging appeasement acts or reciprocal imitation after a conflict, or a channelling of the threat.

Offering and offering simulation are already frequently found when children of 14 to 20 months and up to 2 to 3 years play

† For further details see: *L'Enfant et la Communication.*

together and it is especially so when they are in a competitive situation. In 242 out of the 291 cases observed in 1973 and 1974, the presence of these children was then accepted without threat or aggression by the receiving child. In 105 cases, the offering child was then able to actually touch the construction or objects of the receiver without being pushed away, threatened or attacked. Offering children of 14 to 20 months are also those who organize their linking and appeasement acts into complex sequences that are devoid of aggression (see *b*). These are the future leaders or dominated children with leader mechanisms (profile *d:* cf. section II). However, those children who rarely or never offer are also those who do not organize their linking and appeasement acts into sequences or, if there are sequences, these only contain 2 or 3 elements or are mixed with grasping, threats and aggression. In the same situations as the former children, they attract pushing back, threatening and aggressive behaviour in 70% to 80% of the cases (future dominant-aggressive or dominated-aggressive children). Between 3 and 6 years offering and offering simulation continue to play an important role in establishing and reinforcing non-aggressive contact.

(*b*) *Linking and appeasement acts*. The stroke, kiss, certain bodily contacts such as taking another child by the hand, or putting his head on another's shoulder, bending the head sideways on to the shoulder, sideward movements of the body, swinging and waddling, jumping and hopping, turning round oneself, smiling and offering, form sequences and regulate the establishing and maintenance of non-aggressive communication between children from 2 to 3 years. In section II we will see that all children did not express these sequences regularly or in an harmonious order and that some only rarely responded, and in this case the response was most often threat, refusal or aggression (dominant-aggressive and dominated-aggressive).

Thus, putting the head or the head and bust to one side expressed alone or with a smile, an offering, a non-insistent touch, swaying of the top of the body or clapping of the hands brings about a non-aggressive communication in more than 90% of the cases (619 out of 678 observed over a 3 year period: Figures 1, 2 and 3) except when this act is preceded by other acts of grasping, threatening or aggression (see below). Three types of response

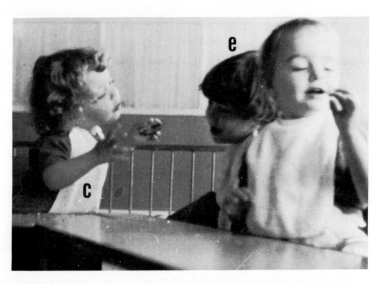

FIG. 1.   The boy C (27 months) puts his head on his shoulder and stretches out his hands turned towards each other and turned in the direction of the boy E (25½ months) who is crying after having suffered aggression. This is one of the most efficient sequences for obtaining a non-aggressive communication and appeasing a child who is crying. The boy C is a leader.

can be seen in the case of the receiver:

(1) Accepting and appeasing responses (Figures 1 and 2). The motor sequence that appeared to us to be the most efficient in appeasing a child who is crying is: kneeling in front of him, putting the head to one side, smiling, swaying of the head and bust (this sequence is more specially expressed by leaders: 80% of the cases). In 40% of the cases observed (66 out of 165), the child stopped crying.

(2) Offering (Figure 3). The offering figure of 55% of the cases is only an approximate figure as it varies according to the composition of the group. It can go up to 70% when there are six or seven leaders and only one or two dominant-aggressive children in the group.

(3) Reducing or stopping threat (see H. Montagner, 1978).

In approximately 80% of the cases, the establishing of contact, offering or stopping threat were followed by reciprocal imitation

FIG. 2.   The boy I (17 months) accepts that the boy Y (22 months) takes his car after this boy has expressed the motor sequence: slowly advancing the hand towards the car—bending sidewards of head and bust. The expression of such a sequence brings about an offering in at least 55% of the cases.

(a)  (b)

(c)

FIG. 3.   After exchanging smiles and gestures similar to those that she expressed in (a), the girl K (24 months) gives in (c) her cake to the boy L (24 months), approximately three seconds after he has put his head on one side in front of the girl (b). Putting the head and bust on one side can bring about offering in 70% of the cases when the two children are leaders (the boy L) or dominated children with leader mechanisms (profile d : the girl K) as is the case here.

or exchanges where linking and appeasing sequences were predominant.

However, a more detailed analysis of the motor sequences showed that the acts that precede and follow the bending sideways of the head can make this movement lose its function of linking, appeasing, soliciting and channelling threat. Thus, when a child who wants an object suddenly advances his hand and grasps the object or stretches out his arm with his hand opening downwards at the same time or after he has put his head and bust on one side, he receives a refusal and is pushed back with threat or aggression in 85% of the cases (Figure 4). This percentage does not vary when the soliciting child smiles and expresses these same behavioural sequences or when he puts out his arm or tries to grasp the object without putting his head or bust on one side. Such behaviour sequences can be expressed by all children, but they are more characteristic of the dominant-aggressive and the dominated-aggressive types (cf. section II).

When a threatening act is included in the sequence (see below) or when there is an ambiguous motor activity (advancing of the hand or head towards the object and the vocalizations usually associated with threat) in linking and appeasement act sequences, the sudden arrival of the soliciting child, especially when there is physical contact between the soliciting and solicited children, the sequence brings about refusal and pushing back, threat and aggression in the solicited child (68% to 83% of the cases observed, depending on the child population). This behaviour characterizes mainly the dominant-aggressive and the dominated children and

Fig. 4. The act sequences like putting the head and bust on one side usually bring about appeasement and offering or stop threat, but they generally lose their function when they are preceded by (a) and or are accompanied by (b) the act of taking (hand positioning) as is the case here, or by threat. The boy m (26 months) is dominant-aggressive (cf. II).

those whose behaviour fluctuates (profile c : cf. section II). In other words, the ambiguous behaviour of the soliciting child hesitating between a non-aggressive soliciting tendency and a second tendency to take without soliciting, and the too short or precipitate expression of soliciting acts are the factors which prevent non-aggressive communication and the effectiveness of the offering itself which was the origin of the non-aggressive contact. An offering by bodily solicitation thus depends on all the behavioural sequences expressed by the soliciting child and not on one single motor act even if this act (putting the head and bust on one side) brings about more often than other acts an appeasing contact followed by non-aggressive communication and an offering.

Linking and appeasing act sequences become free of grasping, threatening and aggression between 14 and 20 months. Firstly, there are short sequences of two or three acts, then more complex sequences appear which resemble those expressed by three-year-olds, i.e. in front of a child who is crying (see above), but this only takes place in certain children. These children have a developed offering behaviour (see (a)) and are those who are more often seen with or near the dominant children of 28 to 36 months. They receive less aggression, are pushed away less or left apart from the children of their age whose linking and appeasing acts are ambiguous or are not organized into homogeneous sequences (for more detailed results, see Montagner, 1978). Between 14 and 20 months the sequential organization of acts which normally regulate non-aggressive exchanges between children of 2 and 3 years appears to be an essential factor in the acceptance of a younger child by the older children and in his integration into the activities of the older group.

Linking and appeasing act sequences continue to play an essential role in the acceptance, attraction, leadership and offering in groups of children from 3 to 6 years (see Montagner, 1978).

B. Behaviour which brings about refusal, breaking of contact or aggression
(a) *Absence of response to offerings and to soliciting sequences.* The child who has received a refusal or who has not received a response to his offering or soliciting has a tendency to isolate

himself, to threaten or to become aggressive towards this soliciting child or another child. Out of 1243 cases of refusal or absence of response to an offering or solicitation the tendency to isolate oneself was observed 328 times; the tendency to take the desired object (Figure 5) or to express aggression was observed 491 times. In 212 cases the aggression was redirected toward a third person who, in 78% of the cases, was a youngster between 14–20 months or a dominated child.

(b) *Threatening behaviour*. The desire for an object, competition and conflict bring about behavioural sequences which have a threat value (Figures 6 and 7) and which bring about: acts of the same kind; the receiver abandoning the desired object; turning the top of the body away; retreating; escaping or fleeing; aggression.

It would appear that the youngster whose toy has been taken most frequently reacts by widely opening his mouth with accom-

FIG. 5.   In (b) the boy P (25 months) is taking the cushion that he wants by opening wide his mouth and letting out a vocalization like "ah" (sequence with a threat value: see figures 6, 7 and 8) after he had vainly solicited (a) the girl O (16 months) who did not see him and who thus was not able to respond.

Opposite, above
FIG. 6.   The boy R (36 months) who is one of the leaders (cf. II) is taking over the central leg of a three-legged table that is turned on another one by opening wide his mouth, letting out a vocalization and throwing out his arm in the direction of the boy Q (21 months), but he does not touch him *(b)*. R is expressing one of the most frequent threat behaviour sequences in children of from 2 to 3 years. There were five seconds between *(a)* and *(b)* and three seconds between *(b)* and *(c)*.

Opposite, below
FIG. 7.   Twelve minutes later, we see the breakdown of the threat sequence expressed by R in Figure 6 : (1) opening of the mouth and emitting a vocalization sounding like "ah" *(b)* when the boy S (33 months), one of the dominant-aggressive children, comes within at least two metres of him; (2) throwing forward of his arm in the direction of S *(c)*. There were 3 seconds between *(a)* and *(b)* and five seconds between *(b)* and *(d)*.

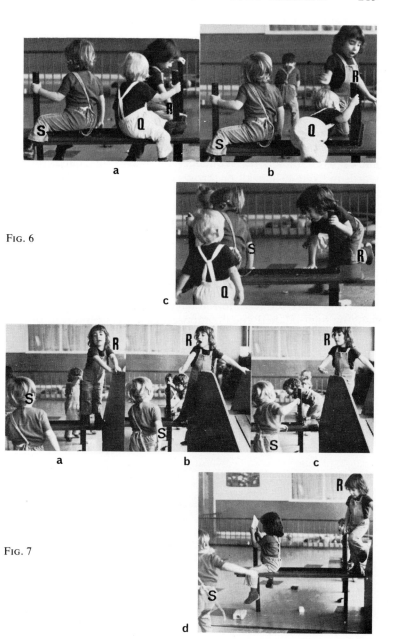

FIG. 6

FIG. 7

the most frequent forms of threat (Figure 8). Contrary to what we wrote earlier (Montagner *et al.*, 1975), this refusal expression already exists in the child of 10 months when someone tries to take his toy away. The sudden opening wide of the mouth and the production of high-pitched vocalizations which are often accompanied by a sudden bending forward of the bust appear in children of 15 months who turn or go towards children who are fighting or taking objects. The 15 to 18-month-old child who has just had something taken from him despite his refusal expression then often shows a characteristic sequence: he waves his hands downwards in front of himself or throws his arm out towards the other child; produces high-pitched vocalizations; cries; falls down.

The sudden opening wide of the mouth and the production of high-pitched vocalizations, the sudden bending forward of the bust and a single or repeated throwing out of an arm in front of himself represent the sequence that is often found in children from the age of 20 months when they defend an object, a situation or another child. From two to three years this sequence becomes more and more reduced and in leader children (see section II) it panying high-pitched vocalizations. These acts represent one of

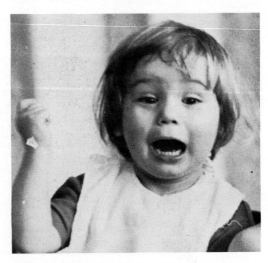

FIG. 8. Expression of threat characteristic of children from 2 to 3 years (this child is 32 months old).

often only includes the lifting of the arm or throwing out the arm towards the other child. This tendency to reduce the threatening sequence continues between 3 and 6 years. Moreover, from the age of 30 months a threat can be expressed by a look and, in this case (78% and 93% of the cases according to the child population), it is to be found nearly always in the leaders or the dominated children with leader mechanisms. If we compare the threatening sequences of a child of 10 months with those of a child of 4 years everything would appear to indicate that the ontogeny of the expression of threat has a progressive passage from the oral area to that of the limbs and then to the look even if at 4 years and over the whole threat sequence of the 15–18 month child is still often expressed.

The responses to the threat sequence vary between 20 and 36 months according to the behavioural profile of the other children who are present. For example, a leader responds to the threat of another leader, either by a threat of the same kind (548 cases out of 1230) or by turning the head away or retreating (461 cases out of 1230). When the receiver replies by throwing out his arm towards the other child, he does not reach him or if he does it is only in a very light way (we observed continued or repeated aggression as an immediate response in only 68 out of 1230 cases). Reciprocal imitation follows (755 out of 1230) during which linking and appeasement acts replace threatening acts and beginnings of aggression (we observed only 87 cases of aggression out of 755 cases). However, when the sequence is produced by a leader toward a dominant-aggressive child, the child responds either by aggression (521 out of 1072 cases) or by behaviour of the same kind (312 out of 1072 cases) which is often followed by continuous and repeated aggression (139 out of 312 cases) or by escape (159 out of 1072 cases). But all the leader has to do is to introduce appeasing or unusual acts into his responses and the other child subdues his aggression or stops, then smiles or tries to express the same acts as the other child (see ''La canalisation de la menace'' in L'Enfant et la Communication, Montagner, 1978).

Children from 14 to 20 months who often link up threatening and aggressive acts in the same sequence (threatening acts can precede, accompany or immediately follow aggression) are also among the children who rarely or never offer and who do not express complex appeasing sequences at 20 months. In all cases between 2 and 3 years they became dominant-aggressive or dominated-aggressive children.

(c) *Aggressive behaviour*. The aggressive behaviour that we took into consideration to make the behavioural profiles in section II are: biting, scratching, grabbing or pinching the cheeks, nose or arms, pulling until the other child falls, sudden pushing, hard kicking or hitting with arm or hand with or without an object in the hand. We did not consider as aggression the restrained blows which most often appear as warning behaviour (they bring about the same responses as threatening behaviour) or even soliciting (they bring about the same responses as soliciting behaviour).

Aggression appears in almost all situations that give rise to competition for a number of scarce objects which are attractive and sought after. It also occurs in competition for a unique and usually attractive position (for example, an upturned table). As we have already seen, aggression also appears when the child has received a refusal or has not received a reply to his soliciting. As well, the child that has been isolated for a few minutes (most often it is a dominated or dominant-aggressive child: cf. section II) can express sudden aggression without an immediate apparent reason towards a child who comes too close to him. Loud crying or crying that lasts longer than a certain time (not yet calculated) brings about aggression or subdued blows according to the "social status" of the child who goes up close. Thus, it is relatively easy to determine the situations which favour or bring about the expression of aggression. Contrary to the ethological studies of animal aggression (see for example: *On Aggression* by Lorenz (1966), and the reports of the numerous seminars that have been held on this subject over the last ten years), we were unable to isolate mechanisms which specifically trigger off aggression in the young child. The expression or non-expression of aggression depends mainly on the situations and successive interactions that the child has experienced since his arrival at the child-care centre or kindergarten and secondly on the type of relationships he has with his family (see Montagner, 1978). We have already seen that competitive situations, conflicts, behavioural ambiguities, absence of response to soliciting and threatening often bring about aggression. The detailed results are given in *L'Enfant et la Communication* (Montagner, 1978). However, in a great many cases children express aggression when they arrive at the child care centre or the kindergarten, when they stop engaging in solitary activity, or often after appeasing exchanges without it being possible to establish a connection between this apparently spontaneous outburst of aggression and particular types of situations and exchanges. It appears as if these aggressions just happen without any apparent reason or cause, as if the children naturally have an internal force which pushes them towards aggressive acts. However, we have shown (Montagner and Henry, 1975; Montagner, 1978) that in particular it is the quality of the exchanges with the home environment and especially with the mother which lead the young child spontaneously to express aggression as a mode of communication (see section III and Table 2).

Finally, it must be mentioned that repeated and very sustained aggression, whether it be given or received, brings about a prolonged isolation in 70% to 80% of the cases. Moreover, aggression is more easily brought about after being isolated than following on an interaction which only contains slightly sustained aggression or no aggression at all. Here it is often very sustained and repeated: the children who have the longest periods of isolation (dominant-aggressive, dominated-aggressive and dominated-frightened) with the exception of those who often keep away from the others (profile *g*: see section II), are also those who express the most violent aggression.

II. Behavioural Profiles

As we have already shown (Montagner *et al.*, 1973–1976) and explained in detail (Montagner, 1978), the analysis of communicative behaviour and the creation of competitive situations enabled us to show several behavioural profiles in children from 2 to 3 years:

(*a*) *dominant-aggressive* children show frequent, repeated and lasting spontaneous aggression and very ambiguous sequences where acts of linking, appeasement, threat and aggression can be seen together (profile *a*);

(b) *leaders* who are also dominant express themselves in non-ambiguous sequences of appeasement acts which become more and more complex from 2 to 3 years; their offerings are frequent and spontaneous aggression is rare (profile *b*);

(c) *fluctuating* children whose behaviour alternates from day to day and week to week between dominant aggressive and leader profile (profile *c*);

(d) *dominated* children who do not participate in competitive activities, but who have leader behavioural sequences when they approach another child or see another child approaching them (profile *d*);

(e) *dominated-frightened* children whose behavioural sequences are often mixed with or followed by acts of fear, withdrawal, retreat and escape (profile *e*);

(f) *dominated-aggressive* who do not succeed or do not try to impose themselves in competitive activities, but who have the same characteristic behaviour as the dominant-aggressive children during their exchanges with others (profile *f*);

(g) very *isolated* children who keep apart from the others (profile *g*).

We have tried to see whether these behavioural profiles could already be distinguished between 14 and 24 months and if they continued in children of 3 to 6 years. At the same time we tried to see if the correlations that we had made between certain behavioural parameters between 2 and 3 years were to be found.

Table 1 shows that there is a good correlation ($r = +0.89$) between the frequency of appeasement sequences and the power of attraction and leadership of children from 17 to 25 months. In other words, the children of this age are very attractive and much imitated when they are very appeasing even if the frequency of their aggression is very high. However, as we have already shown, it is not the same between 2 and 3 years since the most attractive and followed children (leaders) are not only the most appeasing, but also among the least aggressive (there is a positive correlation between the coefficient

$$\frac{\text{Frequency of appeasement sequences}}{\text{Frequency of spontaneous aggressions}}$$

and the power of attraction and leadership in dominant children).

TABLE 1. The correlation between "power" of attraction and leadership (b) of children from 17 to 25 months and the frequency of their offerings and sequences of linking and appeasing acts (a).

	Age of children (2/20/75) (months)	No. of months at the day care centre (2/20/75)	No. of one hour observations	Number of appeasing sequences a	Number of attractive and leadership acts b	Coefficient appeasements aggressions c
Claire	17	15½	7	27	50	27
Damien	19	16½	8	45	47	1·21
Christelle	20	4½	7	11	8	11
Celine P.	22	1	4	10	11	10
Lionel	22	20½	8	61	63	10·16
Laurent	22	5	6	28	41	3·50
Frédéric	23	17½	8	36	53	12
Audrey	24½	5	4	3	6	3
Alexandre	25	17½	8	22	25	4·40
Géraldine	25	17½	7	2	8	2
Catherine	25	24	8	29	17	3·22
Celine B.	25	17½	6	12	10	4

Coefficient of correlation between a and b, r = 0·89; Between b and c, r = 0·40.

When the children of 14 to 36 months were followed up we observed that the most appeasing and the least aggressive between 14 and 20 months became the leaders between 2 and 3 years (see part 2, p. 229) or close to leader profiles at 3 years or between 3 and 5 years. In contrast the most aggressive children and those with the most fluctuating behaviour lost a considerable part of this attractiveness between 2 and 3 years and became the dominant-aggressive children.

The study of the ontogeny of communication mechanisms from the age of 10 to 12 months enabled us to understand better the differentiation of the different behavioural profiles that we had distinguished between 2 and 3 years. Firstly, we found that all the children can express at one time or other all the communication items that have been isolated: bending the head sideways, offering, clapping hands, threatening, etc. However, it is not the same if we examine the sequence of items: the rarely aggressive children who offer and appease and who do not vary much in their appeasement/aggression coefficient between 15 and 20 months are characterized by frequent sequences of unambiguous linking and appeasement acts and by threat sequences which are not followed by aggression. Between 2 and 3 years these children become leaders (profile *b*) or the dominated children who develop towards the leader profile either at 3 years at the child care centre or between 3 and 5 years at the kindergarten (profile *d*). The children of 15–20 months who are very aggressive and fluctuating in their behaviour express ambiguous sequences where offering, appeasement, threat and aggression are most often mixed. The threat acts of these children do not fulfil their warning function in most cases, since they immediately precede or accompany aggression. These children become dominant-aggressive between 2 and 3 years (profile *a*). The fluctuating children who occasionally between 15 and 20 months express behaviour that is comparable to that of children who become leaders develop either towards a leader or a dominant-aggressive profile according to the evolution of the mother's attitude towards them (see Montagner, 1978). The children who appear to be dominated and frightened (profile *e*) between 2 and 3 also have sequences of ambiguous acts between 15 and 20 months: acts of fear, withdrawal, retreat or escape often appear in their appeasing or threat sequences. The children whom we have characterized as dominated-aggressive between 2 and 3 years have at between 15 and 20 months alternating periods of prolonged isolation (sometimes for 15 to 20 minutes) and sustained aggression. During their rare exchanges with others they appear to have the same characteristics as do those who become dominant-aggressive children between 2 and 3 years. They develop a behaviour of fear and escape at 3 to 4 years when they are at the kindergarten. Some of the isolates of profile *g* develop towards profile *d*. In all cases these children occasionally presented between 15 and 20 months, particularly in the absence of the dominant children, communication acts structured like those of the leaders. The other isolated children who only have rare or no exchanges remain isolated at the kindergarten.

Everything would appear to show that between 1 and 2 years there are processes of organization or non-organization of behavioural items which participate in a very fundamental way in the building up of a behavioural profile of the child between 2 and 3 years or for some between 3 and 5 years. There are the children who structure their behaviour in the most unambiguous motor sequences where appeasement and threat and aggression are separated. These are the most attractive children who are followed: they are in harmony with their environment (see part 2, p. 229). There are those who prefer isolation, fear and/or aggression and who develop a hypergestuality without a definite structure; these have difficulty in achieving a non-aggressive communication and in adapting to new structures that they have to experience (coming from the family to the kindergarten, changing schools, changing teachers, changing babysitter, etc.).

III. Factors that can influence the ontogeny of a behavioural profile

At the present time we do not have any method of evaluating with certainty the genetic factors in the ontogeny of communication mechanisms. We have tried to seek out the possible influences of different environmental factors on the setting up and modifications of behavioural profiles. In particular, we have tried

to evaluate parental influence using three methods:
(1) analysing the welcoming behavioural sequences of both parents when they came to collect the child at the child care centre, at the end of the afternoon (H. Montagner, 1978; see the film *Mechanisms of Non-verbal Communication in the Young Child*).

(2) the quantification of the behavioural sequences of the parents when in the morning and late afternoon the parents were together or separately with the child in the dressing room to get him ready to enter the day care centre in the morning and to go home in the afternoon. This way we can calculate for each parent a coefficient

$$\frac{\text{Frequency of appeasement sequences}}{\text{Frequency of threats and aggressions}}$$

(3) the study of the child's behaviour on Mondays at the child care centre and on Mondays and Thursdays at the kindergarten (in France Wednesday is a holiday for school children) according to the modifications that had taken place in the family during the week-end (child care centre and kindergarten) and on Wednesdays (in the kindergarten). Questionnaires were used to obtain information concerning the social and physiological events that took place within the family during the week-end and on Wednesdays.

Table 2 shows that there is a high positive correlation between the appeasement/aggression coefficient of the dominant children and the appeasement/threat and aggression coefficient of the mother. There is no correlation with that of the father.

Each time that we saw an important variation in the mother's coefficient we found a variation in the same direction in the child's coefficient. Table 3 shows that from one month to another, certain children always have a coefficient higher than 2 (the case of Frédéric and Claire : cf. also Table 1). At the age of 2, the children still had a leader or near-leader profile (profile *d*). The mother of these children still appears to be very appeasing and stable in her behaviour (cf. the coefficients in Table 2; for Claire, see part 2). The mothers who have a coefficient which changes from one month to the next (the mother of Damien and

TABLE 2. Comparison between the coefficient $\dfrac{\text{frequency of appeasements}}{\text{frequency of spontaneous aggressions}}$ of the child and the coefficients for the mother and father: $\dfrac{\text{frequency of appeasements}}{\text{frequency of aggressions and threats}}$

The coefficient for each child is calculated from the appeasing sequences and spontaneous aggressions that the child expresses towards others when in free activities (10 observation sessions staggered over 1 month period). The coefficients of the parents are calculated from the relative frequence of appeasing sequences, threats and aggressions that the parents express towards the child when bringing him to the day care centre in the morning and undressing him as well as in the evening when greeting and dressing him (20 observations of approx. 15 min. each. Ten were in the morning and 10 in the evening). The children figuring in this table have been characterized as leaders or dominant-aggressive.

	Age of children (months) at the end of a series of observations over 2 consecutive years	Coefficient of the children: appeasements aggressions C_1		Coefficient of the mothers: appeasements aggressions & threats C_2	Coefficient of the fathers: appeasements aggressions & threats C_3
Leaders					
O. (boy)	32 (71–72)	5·20		15·30	2·03
L. (boy)	31 (72–73)	4·15		8·43	3·49
A. (girl)	34½ (72–73)	3·57		4·82	1·20
S. (boy)	33 (72–73)	3·24		7·38	?
E. (boy)	31 (72–73)	2·90		8·43	3·49
Ed. (girl)	31 (72–73)	2·85		5·10	1·12
Ar. (boy)	36 (71–72)	2·85	Coefficient of the correlation between C_1 and C_2 $r = 0.932$	8·55	1·50
St. (boy)	36 (71–72)	1·54		2·37	5·62
Dominants by Number of Aggressions					
S. (girl)	34½ (71–72)	0·96		1·20	Mother unmarried
Er. (boy)	36 (71–72)	0·82		1·39	8·31
Ch. (boy)	36 (71–72)	0·74		1·10	Mother unmarried
Al. (boy)	36 (71·72)	0·37		0·88	Mother unmarried
P. (boy)	31 (72–73)	0·26		0·75	2·70
Em. (boy)	27 (71–72)	0·26		0·87	1·36
F. (boy)	28 (72–73)	0·22		0·48	4·25

TABLE 3.   Variations of the coefficient
frequency of appeasing sequences
frequency of spontaneous aggressions
from 20 January to 28 April 1975 for children who were together in free
activities.

Age of children (2/20/75) (months)		20 Jan	3 Feb	17 Feb	3 Mar	10 Mar	17 Mar	7 Apr	28 Apr
Claire	17	2	7	3	3	2	8	—	3
Damien	19	0·35	11	6	0·33	1·50	1	0·33	0·60
Christelle	20	1	2	0	0	2	0	7	0
Celine P.	22	—	4	—	4	—	1	1	—
Lionel	22	7	24	9	1	6	3	0	5
Laurent	22	1	—	6	2	1·66	2·66	—	6
Frédéric	23	3	11	3	3	4	2	6	4
Audrey	24½	0	0	—	—	1	—	2	—
Alexandre	25	2	9	2	0·33	0	6	0	2
Géraldine	25	—	0	0	0	0	0	1	0
Catherine	25	2	2	5	1	1	1	1	3
Celine B.	25	1	4	—	2	1	0	—	4

0 corresponds to the absence of offerings and sequences of linking and appeasing acts.

Alexandre : see also Table 1) are more often threatening and aggressive than the mothers of the previous leader children (cf. the coefficients of Table 2; the differences between the frequency of aggression and the appeasement/aggression coefficients of these two populations of mothers are significant at P <0·01). In a general manner (this point is not of real concern in this chapter) the appeasement/aggression coefficient and the differentiation of the behavioural profile of the child are directly linked to the type of relationship that the family, and in particular the mother, develops with the child aged between 1 and 3 years (for more detailed results, see *L'Enfant et la Communication*).

Conclusions

Ethology has provided us with its principles and methods for studying the behaviour of individuals in free activities and has, thus, enabled us to see various behavioural structures (or behavioural profiles) in the child from 2 to 3 years and to begin a systematic study of the precursors of motor sequences that have a communication value. Thus it appeared that offering, smiling, stroking, certain bodily contacts, bending the head sidewards on the shoulder, sidewards movements of the body, swinging and waddling, jumping and hopping, turning round oneself, form motor sequences which express and often bring about appeasement. Attractiveness, mutual tolerance and long-lasting exchanges rest on such sequences which usually originate with leaders, dominated children with leader behavioural sequences (profile d) and some isolated children with profile g. These children are easily accepted by older children and adults in every social context. Everything would indicate that they are most often in harmony with their environment: they adapt better (or show the least marked behavioural modifications) to the changes that take place in their daily life (absence or replacement of teacher, changing schools, etc. . . .). However, those children who prefer isolation, fear and/or aggression and who develop a hypergestuality without a definite structure have difficulty in achieving non-aggressive communication and in adapting to new structures that they have to experience (coming from the family to the kindergarten, changing schools, etc. . . .).

The period from the beginning of the walking stage to 2 years appears to us to be vital in the sequential organisation or non-organisation of behaviour and of the differentiation of the behavioural structure the child usually expresses at 3 or 4 years. The behaviour of the mother appears to play an important role in these processes.

References

BLURTON JONES, N. G. (1967) An ethological study of some aspects of social behaviour of children in nursery school. In *Primate Ethology*, D. Morris (Ed.), 347-68, Weidenfeld and Nicholson, London.

BLURTON JONES, N. G. (1971) Criteria for describing facial expressions in children. *Human Biology*, **43**, 365–413.

BLURTON JONES, N. G. (1972) *Ethological Studies of Child Behaviour*. Cambridge University Press, London.

EIBL-EIBESFELDT, I. (1968) Zur Ethologie des menschlichen Grussverhaltens, I. Beobachtungen an Balinesen, Papuas und Samoanern nebst vergleichenden Bemerkungen. *Zeitschrift für Tierpsychologie*, **25**, 727–44.

EIBL-EIBESFELDT, I. (1972) Similarities and differences between cultures in expressive movements. In R. A. Hinde (Ed.) *Non-Verbal Communication* (ed. R. A. Hinde), 297–314. Royal Society and Cambridge University Press, Cambridge.

EIBL-EIBESFELDT, I. (1973) Taublind geborenes Mädchen-Ausdruckverhalten. *Homo.*, **24**, 39-47.

EIBL-EIBESFELDT, I. (1974) Les universaux du comportement et leur genèse. In *L'unité de l'homme*, 233–45. Editions du Seuil, Paris.

LORENZ, K. (1969) *L'agression – Une histoire naturelle du mal.* Flammarion, Paris, (1966) *On Aggression*, Methuen, London.

MCGREW, W. C. (1969) An ethological study of agonistic behaviour in preschool children. In *Proceedings of the Second International Congress of Primatology, I. Behavior* (ed. C. R. Carpenter), pp. 149–59. Karger, Basel.

MCGREW, W. C. (1970) Glossary of motor patterns of four-year-old nursery school children. In *Direct Observation and Measurement of Behavior* (ed. S. J. Hutt and C. Hutt) pp. 210–18. Thomas, Springfield, Ill.

MCGREW, W. C. (1972) *An ethological study of children's behavior.* Academic Press, New York and London.

MONTAGNER, H., HENRY, E. and CARDOT, N. (1973) Sur quelques variations du rythme circadien des 17-hydroxycorticostéroïdes urinaires chez les jeunes enfants en fonction de leur profil comportemental. *C.R. Acad. Sc.* (Paris), **277**, 101–04.

MONTAGNER, H., (1974) Communication non-verbale et discrimination olfactive chez les jeunes enfants : approche éthologique. In *L'Unité de l'Homme*, 246–70. Editions du Seuil, Paris.

MONTAGNER, H., ARNAUD, M., JEANDROZ, M., RENNER, N., ROSIER, M., HENRY, E.,HENRY, J.Ch., HERBSTMEYER, M., HUMBERT, Y., KARSENTY, Ch. and CHAVANNE, J. (1974) Les activités ludiques du jeune enfant : jeu ou ontogenèse. *Vers l'Education Nouvelle* (Paris), Numéro hors-série, 15–44.

MONTAGNER, H., ARNAUD, M., BONY, M., CARDOT, N., CHAVANNE, J., FROIDEVAUX, J., HENRY, E., HENRY, J.Ch., HERBSTMEYER, M., HUMBERT, Y., JEANDROZ, M., KARSENTY, Ch., RENNER, N. and ROSIER, M. (1974) *Phénomènes de hiérarchie entre les enfants d'une crèche—approche étho-physiologique.* Film 16 mm distributed by le Service du Film de Recherche Scientifique, 96 Bd. Raspail, Paris 6è.

MONTAGNER, H. and HENRY, J.Ch. (1975) Vers une biologie du comportement de l'enfant. *Revue des Questions Scientifiques* (Bruxelles), **146**, 481–529.

MONTAGNER, H., BENEDINI, M., BOLZONI, D., BONY, M., BURNOD, J., HENRY, E., HENRY, J.Ch., HUMBERT, Y., LOMBARDOT, M., MOYSE, A., NICOLAS, R. M., ROSIER, M. (1976) *Mécanismes de la communication non-verbale chez les jeunes enfants.* Film distributed by le Service du Film de Recherche Scientifique, 96 Bd. Raspail, Paris 6è.

MONTAGNER, H. (1978) *L'enfant et la communication.* Stock, Paris.

REYNOLDS, V. and GUEST, A., 1975. An ethological study of 6–7-year-old school children. *Biology and Human Affairs*, **41**, 16–29.

BEHAVIOURAL PROFILES AND CORTICOSTEROID EXCRETION RHYTHMS IN YOUNG CHILDREN PART 2: CIRCADIAN AND WEEKLY RHYTHMS IN CORTICOSTEROID EXCRETION LEVELS OF CHILDREN AS INDICATORS OF ADAPTATION TO SOCIAL CONTEXT

H. Montagner[†], J.Ch. Henry[‡], M. Lombardot[†],
M. Benedini[‡], J. Burnod[‡] and R. M. Nicolas[‡]

†Laboratory of Psychophysiology, Faculty of Medicine, Besançon, France
‡Laboratory of Biochemistry, Faculty of Medicine, Besançon, France

Introduction

It was possibly F. Beach (1948) who, in his book *Hormones and Behaviour*, was the first to make a true synthesis of the relationships that exist between hormonal secretion and behavioural expression. Since the publication of Beach's work, there has been much research done on the effects and the role of hormones in releasing and regulating behaviour and on the modifications that behavioural expression brings about in the functioning of endocrine glands. B. E. Eleftheriou and R. L. Sprott (1975) have recently published two volumes entitled *Hormonal Correlates of Behaviour*. This work brings together twenty articles which deal with behavioural endocrinology in vertebrates including man and in particular presents a series of articles which provide a synthesis on current available data on the role of social factors (specific stimuli or dominance relations) in adrenal cortex physiology in mammals (J. Lloyd, J. J. Christian), on circadian biological rhythms (A. H. Meier) and on the correlation between psychiatric disorders and adrenal-cortex physiology (M. H. Sheard). In the first volume of this work, J. J. Christian summarizes the research that he has been doing since 1950 on psychophysiological regulation in rodents. His studies confirm that increase of the population density and differentiation of a low level of dominance are accompanied by both an increase of adrenal-cortex secretions and a decrease in sexual hormone

229

secretions. Thus, it would appear that the more the population increases, the more the number of subordinated animals increases and the more the average adrenal-cortex activity increases in the whole population. Bronson and Eleftheriou (1964) have shown that in a mouse population the level of corticosterone in subordinate animals increases as the number of daily contacts with the most aggressive animals increases. The amount of corticosterone is maintained at a high level in subordinate mice as long as these mice are left with the aggressive ones. After the first initial contact, further physical contact is not even needed to bring about these effects: interactions that take place at a distance are all that are needed (Bronson and Eleftheriou, 1965; Archer, 1969). Ropartz (1968) has shown that specific olfactory stimuli supplied by secretions of glands annexed to the genital tract are sufficient to induce an increased activity of the adrenal-cortex in male mice. Now, if one looks at the work that has been done on the adrenal-cortex reactivity of various species of monkeys in relation to a specific environment, one finds contradictory results. Thus, Sassenrath (1970) found that in pairs and groups of rhesus macaques the level of ACTH secretion is higher in subordinate animals. When the stress on these animals is reduced by isolating them in individual cages or by withdrawing the dominant elements from the group the ACTH level of the subordinate animals decreases. However, Leshner and Candland (1972) showed that in the case of the squirrel-monkeys (*Saimiri sciureus*) living in groups the level of 17-hydroxycorticosteroids is on the contrary higher in the dominant animals. This confirms Hayama's (1966) observations with *Macaca irus* where the dominant animals have heavier adrenal glands than the subordinate animals.

The common aim of these research projects was to show that the adrenal-cortex activity of mammals develops according to the dominance relationships that are established within this group. The numerous experiments that have followed on the work of Christian on rodents (1963, 1968) have clearly demonstrated that a persistent increase in adrenal-cortex activity is accompanied by a decrease in resistance to infectious diseases and following on this an increase in mortality of the overall population (Christian, 1975).

Levine (1962, 1969) and Levine *et al.* (1967) have shown

that when young rats are handled by the research workers or undergo weak intensity electric shocks for a few minutes per day almost immediately after birth, they have a weaker emotionality than control animals of the same age which have had no early stimulation. Handled rats that have received electric shock treatment when adult show a greater increase of corticosteroids than rats which had not been handled, fifteen minutes following the shock in the same conditions. Then the level of corticosteroids progressively decreases in the handled group. The non-handled animals reach the same level of secretion, but do so more slowly and then maintain a high level for a longer period (Levine, 1962). The immediate response of the handled rats is considered to be adaptable, whereas the slower response which is then maintained at a high level for a long period, hinders the adaptivity of the non-handled animals. These rats had gastric ulcers and a greater susceptibility to disease; their adrenal glands could no longer cope and this brought about their death. The rats that were handled when young had a weaker adrenal-cortex response than non-handled rats when they were adult and confronted by new situations in a non-restrictive environment (Levine et al., 1967).

However, Ader (1975) underlined the fact that if the stimulations received in childhood do change the emotivity and adrenal-cortex responses of the adult, there is nothing to prove that there is a cause and effect relationship between these two parameters.

We thus know that the experiences (as used by Schneirla, 1965) undergone during childhood influence the adrenal and behavioural responses that the adult mammal has to give to his environment. However, to our knowledge, there has been no systematic study of the influence of ethological factors (specific stimuli, dominance relationships) both on the ontogeny of social behaviour and of adrenal-cortex physiology of the young mammal living freely among his kind. It follows that during ontogeny we do not really know how to differentiate the physiological and behavioural mechanisms, if they exist, which enable certain adults to immediately face up in the appropriate adaptive manner to the problems that are posed by the environment. Why, on the contrary, do other adults tolerate their environment without being able to make a response to these changes? Why do they have behavioural or physiological reactions that are considered to be harmful (non-adaptive) to their equilibrium and their survival? It is with these considerations in mind that for the last six years we have been trying to understand how the young child of one to six years organizes his physiological and behavioural responses when confronted with questions that are posed to him by various natural or cultural environments which are imposed upon him. We have not tried to evaluate the influence of the environments on the adrenal-physiology of the child after 24 hours (collection of urine over the 24 hour period). Just as Halberg (1959, 1960, 1962, 1965, 1969, 1975) in the United States and Reinberg (1969, 1971, 1974, 1976), Reinberg *et al*. (1964, 1973) and Ghata *et al*. (1969) in France have worked with human adults, we have tried to understand how physiological responses (excretion of adrenal-cortex hormonal derivatives) in children during a 24 hour-day (circadian rhythms) are related to exogenous (social and ecological) factors and to endogenous (disease) events.

Methodology

Ethology has provided us with principles and methods for studying the ontogeny of communication behaviour of young children who were left or placed in free activities with their peer mates in day care centres (children from 14 to 36 months) and in kindergartens (children from 3 to 6 years). The analysis of behavioural sequences and the creation of competitive situations (for further details, see Montagner *et al*., 1973–1976; Montagner, 1978) enabled us to show several behavioural profiles we described in part 1 (p. 207) and analysed in greater detail in *L'Enfant et la Communication* (Montagner, 1978).

Urine samples of children from 2 to 3 years are collected from Monday to Friday at 0700 hours and 1900 or 2000 hours by the parents in the home environment and at 0900 and 1100, 1500 and 1700 hours by the assistants in the day care centre. These children take a nap every day from 1130 hours (lunch ends between 1100 and 1115) to 1500 hours. The urine of 73 children was analysed. Urine samples of children from 3 to 5 years are collected on Monday, Tuesday, Thursday and Friday at 0700 and 1900 or 2000 hours by the parents in the home environment and at 0900 and 1100, 1400 and 1600 hours by the teachers in the kindergarten. These children go home at 1130 and return to the kindergarten at 1345 hours. The urine of 74 children was analysed. During the week-end, except on Saturday morning for kindergarten children (most of them attend the kindergarten from 0830 to 1130), all samples are collected by the parents in the home environment. This is also the case for kindergarten children on Wednesday which in France is a holiday for kindergarten and primary school children.

The estimation of urinary 17-hydroxycorticosteroids (or 17-OHCS) was done using the Porter and Silber reaction and cortisol was measured by the method of competitive binding of radioactive cortisol with transcortin. For further details concerning these techniques, see Montagner *et al.* (1973–1976) and Montagner (1978). Data on circadian rhythms of catecholamine excretion levels will be available in 1979.

I.   Relationship between the child's behavioural profile and his adrenal physiology

We have already shown that the circadian curves of excretion of 17-OHCS tended to be regular from one day to the next in a leader profile child and to fluctuate in the dominant-aggressive child (Montagner, Henry and Cardot, 1973). We have confirmed and corroborated these results in all the child populations that we have studied over the last six years both in the child care centre and in the kindergarten (we have a lot of precise information on weight, height, past and present diseases, diet and home environment of each child).

Figures 1 and 2 represent the circadian cortisol and 17-OHCS curves of a 3 year-old leader (the curves are regular wherever the child is in the child care centre on Fridays and Mondays or at home on Saturdays and Sundays) and a dominant-aggressive girl of the same age (the curves fluctuate) for 4 consecutive days from Friday morning to Monday evening. We gathered data on 17 leaders from 2 to 3 years and on 16 dominant-aggressive children of the same age taken from four different populations from 1971 to 1975. Figure 3 shows the curves that were obtained: the level of 17-OHCS is higher and more variable throughout the day in the dominant-aggressive children than in the leaders. (Using all the samples throughout the day, there are significant differences between the mean levels of 17-OHCS of the two curves at the same times (P <0·01 Student t-test)). These mean curves cannot be really compared with the individual mean curves which are drawn in Figures 4 to 8 because the frequency of the breaking of life rhythms and the behaviour of assistants vary from year to year (see Figures 20 to 25 which show the influence of these two parameters on circadian 17-OHCS curves).

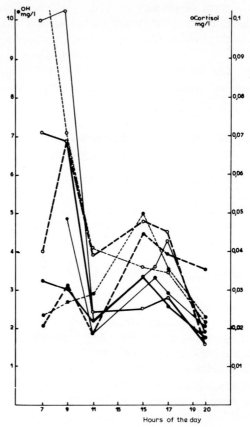

FIG. 1.   Circadian cortisol and 17-OHCS excretion curves of a boy leader from Friday 3 May (fine continuous line) to Monday 6 May 1974 (thick continuous line). The curves for Saturday and Sunday are shown with short dashes (Saturday) and thick longer dashes (Sunday). The curves have a tendency to be regular, whatever the day.

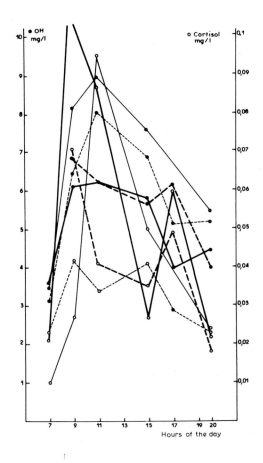

Fig. 2. Circadian cortisol and 17-OHCS curves of a dominant-aggressive girl from Friday 3 May (fine continuous line) to Monday 6 May 1974 (thick continuous line). The curves for Saturday and Sunday are shown with short dashes (Saturday) and thick longer dashes (Sunday). These curves fluctuate much more than those in Figure 1.

We tried to see if there was a correspondence between the mean circadian 17-OHCS excretion profile and the behavioural profile of the child ages 2 to 3 years. Only the mean circadian curves of children belonging to the same population can really be compared because the frequency of the breaking of life rhythms, the number of children and the behaviour of the assistants vary from year to year (see Figures 20 to 25). Figure 4 shows that the

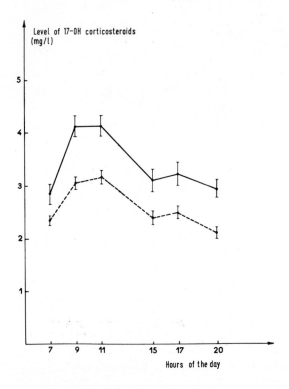

FIG. 3.   Comparison of mean circadian curves of 17 leaders and 16 dominant-aggressive children taken from the same child populations aged from 2 to 3 years from 1971 to 1975. The differences between the 2 curves are significant to P <0·01 at all times taken throughout the day. Each mean is represented with the confidence limits at the threshold level of 95%.

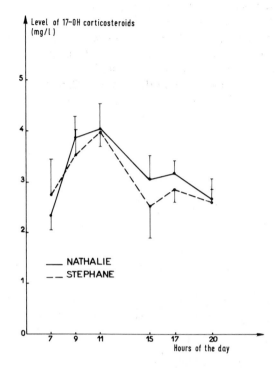

FIG. 4.   Mean circadian 17-OHCS curves of a boy leader (Stéphane) and a dominated girl with leader mechanisms (profile *d* : Nathalie) belonging to the same
child population. Both have the same behavioural sequences in a communication
situation. Both were 2 years old when the urine was collected. There are no
significant differences between mean levels of the two curves at the same times
throughout the day. Each mean is represented with its standard error, then following by one of the limits of the threshold level of 95% (the same for all
figures).

mean circadian 17-OHCS curves of a leader (Stéphane) and a
dominated child with a *d* profile (Nathalie) have approximately
the same structure. We have to keep in mind that in a communication situation these children have comparable motor patterns
(see Part I). Stéphane and Nathalie belong to the same child
population. Figure 5 shows the mean circadian curves of a
dominant-aggressive boy (Damien: profile *a*) and of a dominated-
frightened girl (Christelle: profile *e)* (see part 1, Tables 1 and 3,
pp. 221 and 226). The dominant-aggressive curve (Damien)

shows a high peak (level >6 mg/l) and a great variability around each average point. The curve of the dominated-frightened girl (Christelle) has a peak at 0900 hours with great variability of levels of 17-OHCS, then a further peak in the evening three hours after her return to the home environment. The mean levels of 17-OHCS are more variable in the cases of Damien and Christelle, especially in the morning, than in the cases of the 2 children in

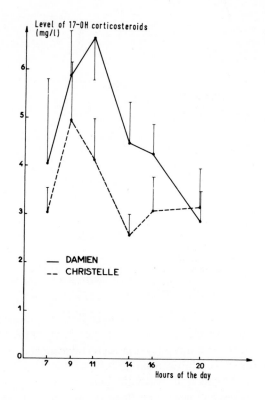

FIG. 5.   Mean circadian 17-OHCS curves of a dominant-aggressive boy (Damien) and of a dominated-frightened girl (profile e : Christelle) belonging to the same child population (see Tables 1 and 3 in part 1, pp. 221, 226). Both were 2 years old.

Figure 4 and the 3 children in Figure 6. The tendency towards aggression or fear is accompanied by a greater variability in 17-OHCS excretion. Figure 6 shows the mean circadian 17-OHCS curves of a leader 3 months previously (Claire: see part 1,

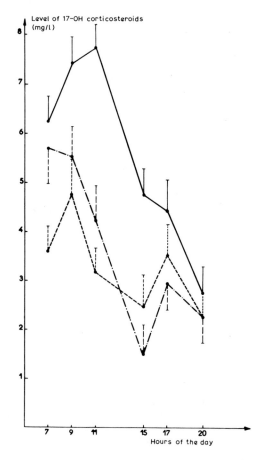

FIG. 6. Mean circadian 17-OHCS curves of a boy leader (Frédéric; - - - -), a girl leader 3 months previously (Claire:— · —: see Tables 1 and 3 in part 1, pp. 221, 226) and who became isolated like the children with a *g* profile (this happened at the same time as a severe conflict occurred between her parents), and a very isolated boy with a *g* profile (Gaël:—). Frédéric, Claire and Gaël belong to the same child population. They were 2 to 3 years old.

Tables 1 and 3, pp. 221 and 226) and who had become isolated like the children with a g profile (this happened at the same time as a severe conflict occurred between her parents), and a very isolated boy with a g profile (Gaël). Claire's curve is between the two others: it has the same structure as that of Frédéric, the leader, but it has a high level of 17-OHCS in the morning at 0700 hours like Gaël's curve (Gaël is one of the most isolated children). In Claire's behaviour we can still see communication mechanisms similar to those of the leaders, but she has a more and more marked tendency towards isolation. Damien, Christelle, Frédéric, Claire and Gaël belong to the same child population.

From one year to another, children whose behavioural structure varies very little from 2 to 3 years have identical mean circadian 17-OHCS curves (Figure 7) or curves that only slightly

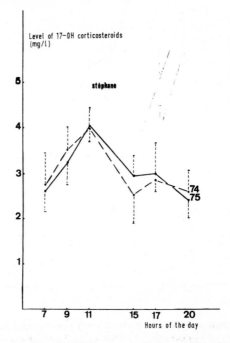

FIG. 7.   Mean circadian 17-OHCS curves of a boy leader (Stéphane) from one year to the next. Children whose behavioural structure varies very little at 2 and 3 years, as is the case here, have identical mean circadian 17-OHCS curves from one year to the next.

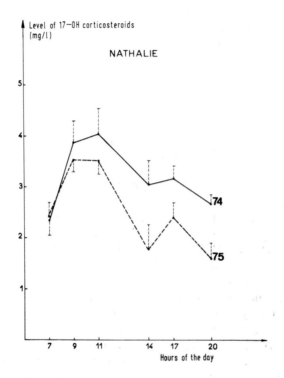

FIG. 8.   Mean circadian 17-OHCS curves of a dominated girl with leader mechanisms (Nathalie) from one year to the next. Dominated children with a *d* profile at 2 years, and who become closer to the leader profile at 3 years, have mean circadian 17-OHCS curves that only slightly differ from one year to the next.

differ (Figure 8). There are no significant differences between the mean levels of 17-OHCS of the two curves at the same times throughout the day; remember that the dominated children like Nathalie (profile *d*) have at the age of 2 years the same communication mechanisms as the leaders and come closer to this type of profile between the ages of 3 and 5 years.

However, if, in relation to the leaders (profile *b*) and to the dominated children with a *d* profile, the daily curves of the dominant-aggressive children (profile *a*) fluctuate more from one day to the other and show high levels of 17-OHCS at the circadian peak, their mean circadian curves, with each point being the mean of 10 to 16 measures for the different days, can have, as in Figure 3, the same structure: a peak in the morning, followed by a considerable drop at 1500 hours and a second lower peak at 1700 hours. The nap that the children take every day between 1130 and 1500 hours could be responsible for neutralizing mean circadian curves from very different leaders and dominant-aggressive type children even if the levels and variability of the levels are always much higher in the case of the dominant-aggressive children. With the exception of very isolated children (Gael: Figure 6) the dominated-frightened children (Christelle: Figure 5) and those whose behavioural profile has considerably changed within a few weeks (Claire: Figure 6), the structure of the mean circadian 17-OHCS curve does not always reflect the behavioural profile of the child of 2 to 3 years at the child care centre.

This is not the case for the children from 3 to 5 at the kindergarten where the children, except for a very few young ones, do not have a nap during the day†.

Figures 9 and 10 show that the average circadian curves of 17-OHCS of a 4 year old leader who is rarely or never aggressive (Figure 9) and a dominated child with leader mechanisms (profile *d*: Figure 10) have a comparable structure throughout the day with the dispersion around the mean being similar. These children are both stable and structured in their adrenal functioning and in their communication behaviour. When a child leader expresses more aggression, especially in competitive activities, he has the same curve structure, but the level is significantly higher at 0900 and 1100 hours than the previous leader (Figure 11). In the case of a dominant-aggressive child, two situations can be observed: (1) the curve is uni-modal with the 17-OHCS levels being very high (>5 or 6 mg/l) at 0900 and 1100 hours as in the child care centre (Figure 12: here in this case, the circadian peak is at 0900) and remains relatively high (> 4 mg/l) at 1400 and 1600 hours in almost all cases just as it is with the children in the child care centre. With the very aggressive-dominant children, the circadian peak can shift to about 1400 (Figure 13); (2) the curve does not show

† This section is part of M. Lombardot's thesis on this subject.

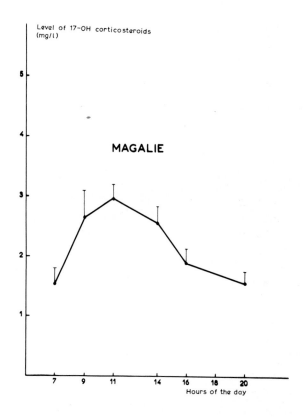

FIG. 9.   Mean circadian 17-OHCS curve of a four year old girl leader (Magalie). Leaders have mean regular unimodal curves with a low level peak which occurs most often around 1100 hours and a weak dispersion of the levels in relation to the mean level at each time throughout the day.

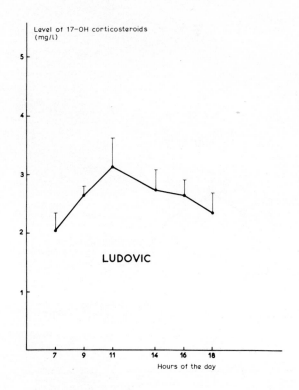

FIG. 10. Mean circadian 17-OHCS curve of a four year old dominated boy with leader mechanism (profile *d* : Ludovic). Mean circadian curves of children with this profile at 4 years often have the same structure as the leader curves.

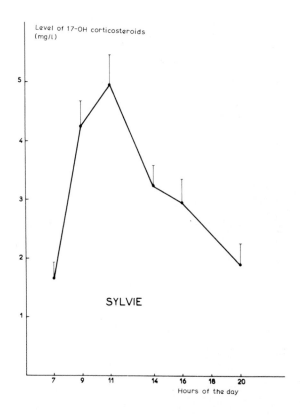

FIG. 11. Mean circadian 17-OHCS curve of another four year old girl leader (Sylvie) whose behavioural profile is the same as the previous ones, but she expresses more aggression, especially in competitive situations. She has the same structure curve, but the levels are significantly higher at 0900 and 1100 hours than in the previous children.

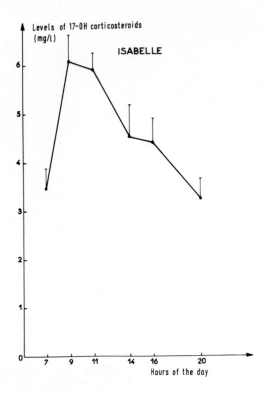

FIG. 12.   Mean circadian 17-OHCS curve of a four year old dominant-aggressive girl (Isabelle). The curve is unimodal with the 17-OHCS levels being very high at 0900 and 1100 hours as in the day care centre (see Damien's curve in Figure 5) and remains relatively high at 1400 and 1600 hours.

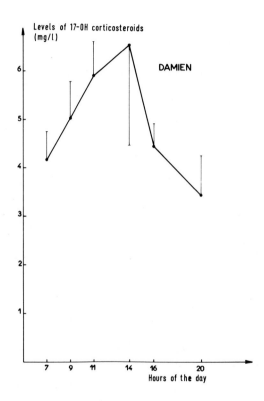

FIG. 13.   Mean circadian 17-OHCS curve of a four year old dominant-aggressive boy (Damien) who is more often aggressive than the previous dominant-aggressive girl. The circadian peak shifts to about 1400 hours.

a marked peak, but plateaus throughout the morning (0700 to 1100) or during the greater part of the day. When the plateau lasts from 0900 to 1400 or 1600 the dispersion around the mean is always very high (year 1975 for Valerie: Figure 14): the communication behaviour and the adrenal functioning of these children remain unstable and non-structured from one year to the next. The dominant children who have a fluctuating behaviour (profile c) have bi-modal curves with their circadian peaks at 0900 and 1400 hours when they return to class and at more or less high levels according to whether they tend towards a dominant-

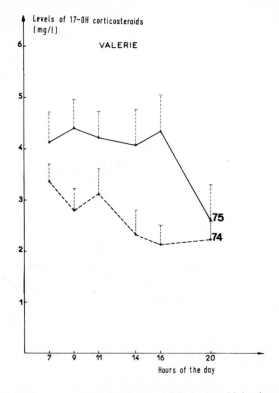

FIG. 14.   Mean circadian 17-OHCS curve of a four year old dominant-aggressive girl from one year to the next (Valérie). The curve plateaus throughout the morning (0700 to 1100 hours). When the plateau lasts from 0900 to 1400 (or 1600) hours, the dispersion around the mean is always very large (year 1975 for Valérie).

aggressive profile (Figure 15) or a leader profile (Figure 16). Just as is the case with the dominant-aggressive children, the dominated-frightened children (profile *e*) have a peak at 0900 hours, but this peak is not as high: then again there is a second rise in level at 1900 to 2000 hours which is two or three hours after returning to the home environment; the structure of the dominated-frightened curve is the same as the child with the same

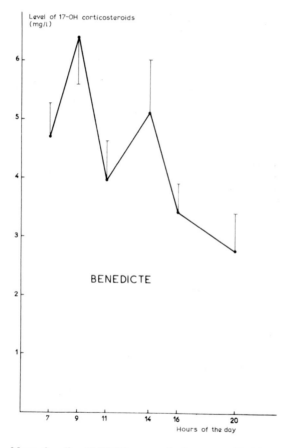

FIG. 15.   Mean circadian 17-OHCS curve of a four year old girl who has a fluctuating behaviour (profile *c* : Bénédicte). Children with this profile have bi-modal curves with their circadian peaks at 0900 and 1400 hours when they return to class and at a high level when they tend towards a dominant-aggressive profile.

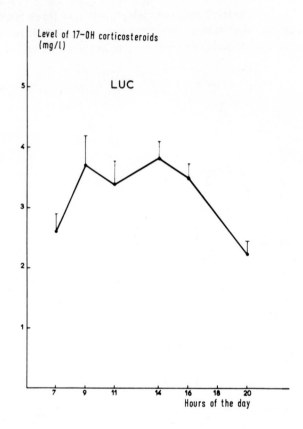

Fig. 16. Mean circadian 17-OHCS curve of a four year old boy who has a fluctuating behaviour (profile *c* : Luc). Children with this profile have bi-modal curves with their circadian peaks at 0900 and 1400 hours when they return to class and at a relatively low level when they tend towards a leader profile.

profile in the day care centre and does not change from one year to the next (Figure 17). The dominated-aggressive children (profile *f*: Figure 18) who are characterized by prolonged periods of isolation, sudden aggression and the development of a fear and escape behaviour at 3 to 4 years, have curves which form a plateau for the greater part of the day just like some of the dominant-aggressive children; then there is a rise in the evening when they return home as is the case with the dominated-frightened children. The 17-OHCS level is always very high at all

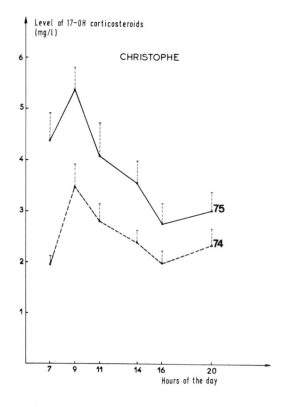

FIG. 17.   Mean circadian 17-OHCS curve of a four year old dominated-frightened boy (profile *e* : Christophe) from one year to the next. Children with this profile have a peak at 0900 hours. There is a second rise in level at 1900 or 2000 hours, which is two or three hours after returning to the home environment. The structure of the dominated-frightened curve does not change from one year to the next.

times throughout the day. The dispersion in relation to the mean is always very great. The children who stay apart from the others and do not have a defined behaviour structure (they hardly react to the soliciting of the other children, their gestuality is very poor and they receive a part of the redirected aggression of the dominant children: profile *g*) have uni-modal curves which have a very

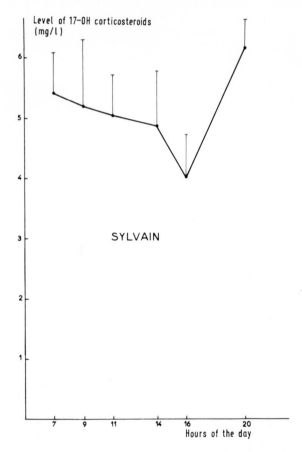

FIG. 18. Mean circadian 17-OHCS curve of a four year old dominated-aggressive boy (profile *f* : Sylvain). Children with this profile have curves which form a plateau for the most part of the day just like some dominant-aggressive children. Then there is a rise in the evening when they return home, as in the case of the dominated-frightened children.

high 17-OHCS level at the time of the circadian peak (Figure 19). The dispersion in relation to the mean is always very large.

The mean 17-OHCS circadian curve appears to reflect the behavioural structure of the young child and following on this the usual type of relationships that he has with his family and in particular with his mother.

Everything would tend to show that the children who express the most spontaneous aggression and have the most ambiguous behaviour sequences and at the same time the most inappropriate for the actual situation, have the most irregular curves which

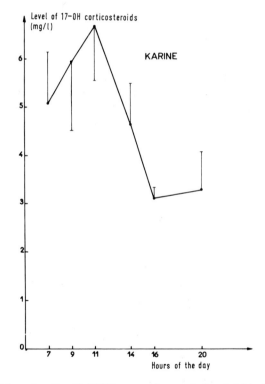

FIG. 19.   Mean circadian 17-OHCS curve of a very isolated child with a *g* profile who is four years old (Karine). Children with this profile have uni-modal curves which have a very high 17-OHCS level at the time of the circadian peak. The dispersion in relation to the mean is always very large.

often have a very high level plateau or the highest with a large dispersion around the circadian peak (this is also the case for very fluctuating children with a *c* profile and very isolated children with a *g* profile: see below). In the family these children are the most threatened, scolded and 'aggressed' (dominant-aggressive children: profile *a*) or the children who are 'pushed about' and repressed (dominated-aggressive: profile *f*). The high and very variable levels of the dominated-aggressive children in the morning and late afternoon are probably related to the pressure that these children undergo from their family: the parents of these children are rather unorganised in their daily activities or always in a hurry due to their heavy professional schedule (they are often shopkeepers, workers or teachers). The isolated and 'stifled' children who are subjected to a host of don'ts in the family environment (profile *g*) also have very high circadian peaks: at school they receive much of the redirected aggression from the more aggressive children. In the case of the dominated-frightened children (profile *e*) everything takes place as if the over-protective (or possessive) attitude of their mother (those children are very protected in the family environment) is translated by a rise in the 17-OHCS level when they return home. Excessive maternal attention would appear to bring about an adrenal response in the same direction as that which corresponds to excessive repression (case of the dominated-aggressive children) even if the rise in 17-OHCS level is not as high.

However, the children with the most appeasing and stable behaviour are also those who organize their behaviour into homogeneous sequences which are appropriate to the actual situation (leaders and dominated children with leader mechanisms). These children have mean regular uni-modal curves with a lower level peak which occurs most often around 1100 hours and a weak dispersion of the levels in relation to the mean level at each time throughout the day. These children have a mother who is appeasing and offering (see Part 1, p. 208).

The fluctuating children with bi-modal curves (profile *c*) have a mother who also fluctuates from one day to the next and from one week to another. These children are very sensitive to the variations in their environment and tend to have a peak at the beginning of each half school day 0900 and 1400 hours. According to whether the variability of the mother's behaviour is great or not the children tend either towards a leader profile or to that of dominant-aggressive profile.

II.   Other social factors and adrenal physiology†

We have already shown that on Mondays the 17-OHCS circadian curves were more often de-synchronized than on Fridays in the case of children at the child care centre (Henry, Montagner and Cardot, 1973). These results have been confirmed in four different situations: one study at a child care centre and three studies in three kindergartens (Figure 20). The breaking of the life rhythms when the kindergarten children returned to the family environment on Saturday also resulted in more frequent de-synchronizations than at the same time on the other days (Figure 20). In general any breaking in life rhythms for any family is translated in the child by a tendency towards de-synchronization (Figure 21). However, this was not the case on Wednesday, which in France is a school holiday for kindergarten children (Figure 22). On Wednesday the child is most often alone with one adult (mother, grandmother, babysitter, etc.) who is not disturbed or hindered by the activities of other adults and who does not undergo a constraining activity rhythm.

We had the opportunity to follow two child populations in two different kindergartens for two successive years. The two teachers had very different behaviour: if one had always more time available for the children (Ms F), the other was more tired and had less time, especially before holidays (Ms R). Figure 23 shows that the mean circadian curves of all the children in Ms F's class are similar before (week from 3 March 1974) and after (week from the 14 April 1974) the Easter holidays. However, the mean circadian curves of all the children in Ms R's class are different before and after the Easter holidays (Figure 24). The following year Ms F's behaviour changed following an operation for otospongiosis: the return of her auditory sensitivity made her less tolerant and more aggressive towards the children and the result was a very considerable increase in the 17-OHCS level of all the children

† This section is part of M. Benedini's thesis on this subject.

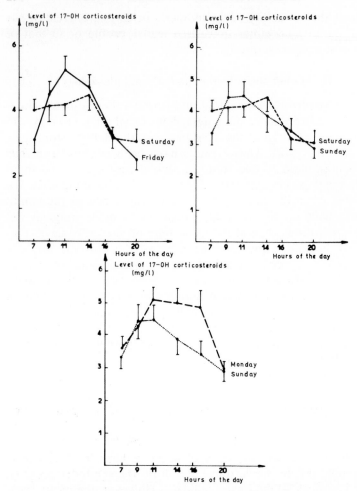

FIG. 20. Mean circadian 17-OHCS curves of 12 children belonging to the same child population in the kindergarten (children are aged from three to four years) from Friday (fine continuous line) to Monday (thick long dashes). The curves for Saturday and Sunday are shown with short dashes (Saturday) and dotted line (Sunday). Urine samples were collected 4 times throughout the day from Friday to Monday in November and December 1975. On Saturday there is a shift of the circadian peak to 1400 hours, which is 2 hours and 30 minutes after returning to home environment (on Saturday, in France, children aged from 3 to 6 years only come to the kindergarten from 0830 to 1130 hours). On Monday the 17-OHCS circadian curves have higher levels from 1100 to 1600 hours and are also more often de-synchronized than on Friday or Sunday.

from 0900 to 1600 hours (Figure 25): contrary to the previous year, there was no longer a difference in the morning between the child populations of the classes of Ms F and Ms R.

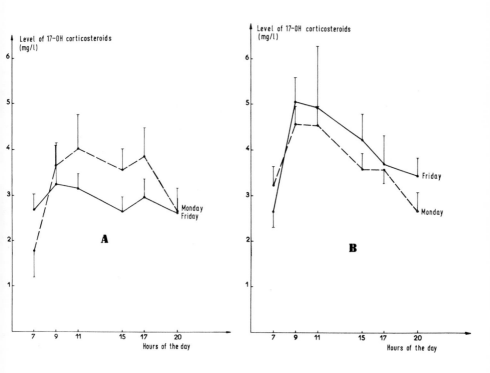

FIG. 21.   (A) Mean circadian 17-OHCS curves of 11 children belonging to the same child population in the day care centre (children aged from two to three years) on Friday 5 April (fine continuous line) and Monday 8 April 1974 (dashes). As we have already shown (Henry, Montagner and Cardot, 1973), the 17-OHCS circadian curves have higher levels and are more often de-synchronized on Monday than on Friday as long as no disturbing event occurs during the days which precede Friday.

(B) This is no longer the case when there is a break in life rhythms for the whole family in the week. Here are the mean circadian curves of the same 11 children as in (A) on Friday 3 May (fine continuous line) and Monday 6 May 1974 (dashes). One to two days after 1 May (official holiday), the break in life rhythms for any family is translated in the child by a tendency towards de-synchronization on Friday 3 May: levels of 17-OHCS in the mean circadian curve of the whole child population tend to be higher from 0900 to the end of the day on Friday 3 than on Monday 6 May.

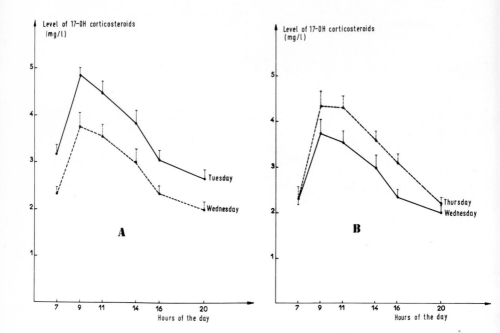

FIG. 22.   Mean circadian 17-OHCS curves of 24 children belonging to 2 kindergarten classes (they are aged from three to four years) on Tuesday (continuous
line) and Wednesday (dashes): (A), and on Wednesday (continuous line) and
Thursday (dashes): (B). Samples of urine were collected four times throughout the
same weeks in February, March and April 1975. The differences between the
levels of Tuesday and Wednesday curves are significant to $P < 0.05$ (1100, 1400
and 1600 hours) or $P < 0.01$ (0700 and 0900, 2000 hours) at all times taken throughout the day (Student t-test). But the circadian structure of both curves is similar. As
Wednesday is a school holiday for the kindergarten children in France, the child is
most often alone with one adult who is not disturbed or hindered by the activities
of other adults and who does not undergo a constraining rhythm: as a consequence,
there are only a few de-synchronizations of 17-OHCS curves following the breaking
of the life rhythm on Wednesday.

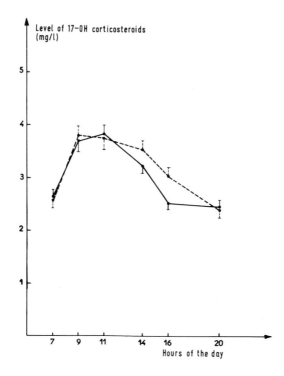

FIG. 23.   Mean circadian 17-OHCS curves of 14 children belonging to the same kindergarten class whose teacher is always appeasing and available (Ms F) before (samples of urine were collected every day during the week from 3 March 1975) and after (week from 14 April 1975) the Easter holidays. There are no significant differences between the two curves.

———— 3 March 1975;   ———— 14 April 1975

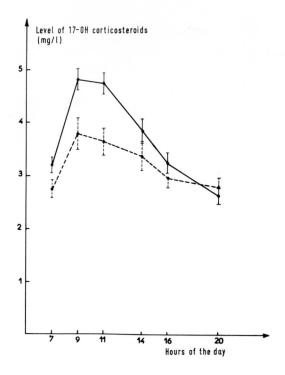

FIG. 24.   Mean circadian 17-OHCS curves of 13 children belonging to the same kindergarten class whose teacher (Ms R) is more tired and aggressive and has less time before (samples of urine were collected every day during the week from 24 February 1975) than after Easter holidays. The levels are higher from 0900 to 1600 hours before than after the holidays. Thus it would appear that the behaviour of the teacher is translated by changes in 17-OHCS levels of children's circadian curves from 0900 to 1600 hours.
—— 24 February 1975;   ———— 14 April 1975

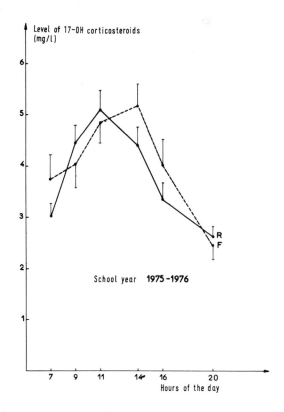

FIG. 25.   Mean circadian 17-OHCS curves of 11 children belonging to Ms F's class (continuous line) and of 14 children belonging to Ms R's class (dashes) 5 to 7 months later, after Ms F was operated on for otospongiosis. The return of her auditory sensibility made her less tolerant and more aggressive towards the children and the result was a very considerable increase in the 17-OHCS level of all children from 0900 to 1600 hours. Contrary to the previous year, there was no longer a difference between the child populations of the classes of Ms F and Ms R.

Conclusions

A simultaneous study of communication behaviour and adrenal physiology would appear to indicate the great sensitivity of the child to the family environment. We thus can see that the notion of dominance alone cannot cover the adrenal cortex responses to the social environment. If some of the dominant children (dominant-aggressive) have very high levels of 17-OHCS like the squirrel monkeys of Leshner and Candland (1972), other children (the leaders) are, on the contrary, among those who have the lowest levels. However, the relational mechanisms between the children left or placed in free activities enable us to understand better the individual differences of the child's adrenal responses throughout the day. Children who have a stable and appropriate communication behaviour also have the most stable adrenal cortex physiology. Everything would indicate that they are in harmony with their environment: these children adapt better (or show the least marked behavioural modifications) to the changes that take place in their daily life (absence or replacement of teacher, changing schools, etc.). However, the children who tend towards spontaneous aggression (dominant-aggressive and dominant-fluctuating), isolation, fear and escape (dominated-aggressive and dominated-frightened) respond to the same changes by an increase in the frequency of their aggression (dominant-aggressive) or the duration of isolation (dominated-aggressive) or the frequency of crying or seeking out the company of adults (dominated-frightened). Their responses to changes in the environment often bring about their rejection by the other children, that is unless they have not already isolated themselves and returned to their isolation. Although we do not yet have sufficient statistical data, it would appear that children whose mean circadian curve has a high 17-OHCS level at 0700 hours and then retains a high level throughout the major part of the day (some of the dominant-aggressive and dominated-aggressive children) and children whose mean circadian curve rises in the evening (dominated-frightened and dominated-aggressive children) are those who most often have the most frequent and lasting otitis, rhino-pharyngeal infections and severe sore throats. Perhaps this can be compared with the situation of mice which are not handled when they are young and which when they are adult respond to a nociceptive stimulation by retaining a high level of adrenal-cortex secretions (Levine, 1962).

In other words, the differentiation of a communication style (one's most usual manner: see Part I) seems to be accompanied by a certain circadian pattern of the adrenal-cortex gland secretions. This perhaps explains the very large behavioural–physiological vulnerability (tendency towards particular diseases) of certain individuals during an important part of their life. This also perhaps explains the great physiological vulnerability of certain individuals who have just experienced very demanding change situations where verbal or non-verbal aggression dominated.

After six years' study it would also appear that the changes in life rhythms undergone at the same time by the child and the family (Saturdays and Mondays) and the behaviour of the teacher are translated into considerable changes in 17-OHCS levels from 0900 to 1600 hours. These factors are added to the family pressure on the child and probably explain why the dominant-aggressive, dominant-fluctuating, dominated-aggressive and dominated-frightened children and children with large variations from the *g* profile express even more clearly their tendency toward aggression, fear or isolation following such changes. We will therefore have to give much thought to shaping the structures that receive children and the pedagogical attitudes of the adults who have the care of children.

References

ADER, R. (1975) Early experience and hormones: emotional behavior and adrenocortical function. In Eleftheriou and Sprott (1975), Vol. I, pp. 7–33.
ARCHER, J. E. (1969) Adrenocortical response to olfactory social stimuli in male mice. *Journal of Mammalogy*, **50**, 839–41.
BEACH, F. A. (1948) *Hormones and Behavior*. Paul B. Hoeber, New York.
BRONSON, F. H. and ELEFTHERIOU, B. E. (1964) Chronic physiological effects of fighting in mice. *General and Comparative Endocrinology*, **4**, 9–14.
BRONSON, F. H. and ELEFTHERIOU, B. E. (1965) Adrenal response to fighting in mice: separation of physical and psychological causes. *Science*, **147**, 627–28.
CHRISTIAN, J. J. (1963) The pathology of overpopulation. *Military Med.*, **128**, 571.
CHRISTIAN, J. J. (1968) The potential role of the adrenal cortex as affected by social rank and population density on experimental epidemics. *American Journal of Epidemiology*, **87**, 255.

CHRISTIAN, J. J. (1975) Hormonal control of population growth. In Eleftheriou and Sprott (1975), Vol. I, pp. 205–74.

ELEFTHERIOU, B. E. and SPROTT, R. L. (eds) (1975) Hormonal Correlates of Behavior, Vol. I and II. Plenum Press, New York.

GHATA, J., HALBERG, F., REINBERG, A. and SIFFRE, M. (1969) Rythmes circadiens désynchronisés du cycle social (17-hydroxycorticostéroïdes, température rectale, veille–sommeil) chez deux adultes sains. Ann. Endocrin. (Paris), 30, 245–60.

HALBERG, F. (1959) Physiological 24-hour periodicity: general and procedural considerations with reference to the adrenal cycle. Z. Vitamin-Hormon-u. Fermentforsch., 10, 225–96.

HALBERG, F. (1960) Temporal coordination of physiological function. Cold. Spr. Harb. Symp. Quant. Biol., 25, 289–310.

HALBERG, F. (1962) Physiological 24-hour rhythms. A determinant of response to environmental agents. In Man's Dependence on the Earthly Atmosphere (ed. K. E. Schaeffer) pp. 48–49. Macmillan, New York.

HALBERG, F. (1965) Organisms as circadian systems: temporal analysis of their physiology and pathological responses, including injury and death. In Walter Reed Army Institute of Research Symposium on Medical Aspects of Stress in the Military Climate, 1–36.

HALBERG, F. (1969) Chronobiology. Annual Reviews of Physiology, 31, 675–725.

HALBERG, F. (1975) Biological rhythms. In Biological Rhythms and Endocrine Function, (eds. L. W. Hedlung, J. M. Franz and A. D. Kenny), pp. 1–41. Plenum Press, New York and London.

HAYAMA, S. (1966) Correlation between adrenal gland weight and dominance rank in caged crab-eating monkeys. Primates, 7, 21.

HENRY, E., MONTAGNER, H. and CARDOT, N. (1973) Etude préliminaire du rythme circadien des 17-hydroxycorticostéroïdes chez les jeunes enfants d'une crèche. Comptes Rendus de l'Académie des Sciences, Paris, 276, 3453–56.

LESHNER, A. I. and CANDLAND, D. K. (1972) Endocrine effects of grouping and dominance rank in squirrel monkeys. Physiology and Behavior, 8, 441.

LEVINE, S. (1962) Plasma-free corticosteroid response to electric shock in rats stimulated in infancy. Science, 135, 795–96.

LEVINE, S. (1962) The effects of infantile experience on adult behavior. In Experimental Foundations of Clinical Psychology (ed. A. J. Bachrach), pp. 139–69. Basic Books, New York.

LEVINE, S. (1969) An endocrine theory of infantile stimulation. In Stimulation in Early Infancy (ed. A. Ambrose), pp. 45–63. Academic Press, London and New York.

LEVINE, S., HALTMEYER, G. C., KARAS, G. C. and DENENBERG, V. H. (1967) Physiological and behavioral effects of infantile stimulation. Physiology and Behavior, 2, 55–59.

LLOYD, J. A. (1975) Social behavior and hormones. In Eleftheriou and Sprott (1975), Vol. I, pp. 185–204.

MEIER, A. H. (1975) Chronoendocrinology of vertebrates. In Eleftheriou and Sprott (1975), Vol. II, pp. 469–549.

MONTAGNER, H., HENRY, E. and CARDOT, N. (1973) Sur quelques variations du rythme circadien des 17-hydroxycorticostéroïdes urinaires chez les jeunes enfants en fonction de leur profil comportemental. Comptes Rendus de l'Académie des Sciences, Paris, 277, 101–104.

MONTAGNER, H. (1974) Communication non-verbale et discrimination olfactive chez les jeunes enfants: approche éthologique. In L'Unité de l'Homme, pp. 246–70. Editions du Seuil, Paris.

MONTAGNER, H., ARNAUD, M., JEANDROZ, M., RENNER, N., ROSIER, M., HENRY, E., HENRY, J.Ch., HERBSTMEYER, M., HUMBERT, Y., KARSENTY, Ch. and CHAVANNE, J. (1974) Les activités ludiques du jeune enfant: jeu ou ontogenèse. Vers l'Education Nouvelle Numéro hors-série, 15–44, Paris.

MONTAGNER, H., ARNAUD, M., BONY, M., CARDOT, N., CHAVANNE, J., FROIDEVAUX, J., HENRY, E., HENRY, J.Ch., HERBSTEMEYER, M., HUMBERT, Y., JEANDROZ, M., KARSENTY, Ch., RENNER, N. and ROSIER, M. (1974) Phénomènes de hiérarchie entre les enfants d'une crèche-approche étho-physiologique. Film 16 mm distributed by le Service du Film de Recherche Scientifique, 96 Bd. Raspail, Paris 6e.

MONTAGNER, H. and HENRY, J.Ch. (1975) Vers une biologie du comportement de l'enfant. Revue des Questions Scientifiques (Brussels), 146, 481–529.

MONTAGNER, H., BENEDINI, M., BOLZONI, D., BONY, M., BURNOD, J., HENRY, E., HENRY, J.Ch., HUMBERT, Y., LOMBARDOT, M., MOYSE, A., NICOLAS, R. M. and ROSIER, M. (1976) Mécanismes de la communication non-verbale chez les jeunes enfants. Film 16 mm distributed by le Service du Film de Recherche Scientifique, 96 Bd. Raspail. Paris 6e.

MONTAGNER, H. (1978) L'enfant et la communication. Stock, Paris.

REINBERG, A. (1969) Biorythmes et chronobiologie. Presse Médicale (Paris), 77, 877–78.

REINBERG, A. (1971) Les rythmes biologiques. La Recherche (Paris), 2, 241–50.

REINBERG, A. (1974) Aspects of circannual rhythms in man. In Circannual Clocks (ed. E. T. Pengelley). AAAS meeting on circannual rhythms, San Francisco Feb. 1974, pp. 423–505. Academic Press, New York.

REINBERG, A. (1974) Chronopharmacology in man. In Chronobiological aspects of endocrinology (ed. J. Aschoff, F. Ceresa and F. Halberg). Chronobiologia, I (Suppl. 1), 157–85.

REINBERG, A. (1976) Advances in human chronopharmacology. Chronobiologia, 3, 151–66.

REINBERG, A., CHAUMONT, A.-J., LAPORTE, A., CHAMBON, P., VINCENDON, G., SKOULIOS, G., BOCHARD, M., NICOLAI, A., ABULKER, C. and DUPONT, J. (1973) Changes in circadian temporal structure (including sleep) of 20 shift-workers (8-h shift weekly rotation), International Journal of Chronobiology, 1, 352–53.

REINBERG, A. and GHATA, J. (1964) Biological rhythms, Walker, New York.

ROPARTZ, P. E. 1968. Etude du déterminisme olfactif de l'effet de groupe chez la souris mâle. Revue du Comportement Animal, 2, 35–77.

ROPARTZ, P. E. (1968) Quelques aspects des échanges d'information par messages odorants dans le comportement social des souris mâles. Expérimentation animale, 1, 171–91.

SASSENRATH, E. N. (1970) Increased adrenal responsiveness to social stress in rhesus monkeys. Hormones and Behaviour, 1, 283–98.

SCHNEIRLA, T. C. (1965) Aspects of stimulation and organization in approach/withdrawal processes underlying vertebrate behavioral development. In Advances in the study of behavior (ed. D. S. Lehrman, R. A. Hinde and E. Shaw), Vol. I, pp. 1–74. Academic Press, New York.

SHEARD, M. H. (1975) Endocrines and neuropsychiatric disorders. In Eleftheriou and Sprott (1975), Vol. I, pp. 341–68.

PHYLOGENETICALLY OLD PSYCHOPHYSIOLOGICAL REACTION PATTERNS IN RELATION TO POOR HEALTH

T. THEORELL

Seraphimer Hospital, Karolinska Institute,
Stockholm, Sweden

IN modern society, psychic tension frequently builds up during long work days characterized by monotony, time pressure and lack of control of the job situation (Gardell, 1971; Johansson and Lundberg, 1978). This tension is seldom allowed to be released physically. It has been hypothesized that phylogenetically old psycho-physiological reactions—with the physiological function of preparing the organism for powerful muscular action—which are triggered as a response to modern stressors may facilitate the development of "stress diseases" (Wolf and Goodell, 1968; Levi, 1972; Carruthers, 1974). Evidence will be given to support the view that certain psychosomatic illnesses of visceral organs, here exemplified by myocardial infarction before retirement age (= early MI) and ulcer or long-lasting gastritis, arise due to long-lasting psychosocial strain inducing phylogenetically old psychophysiological reactions. Other illnesses, such as neurosis, may arise in subjects who are less apt to use psychophysiological reactions to endure tension.

Early MI

Myocardial infarction in most developed countries has an incidence of about 5 new cases per year per 1000 men at risk of 40–60 years of age. After the age of 60 higher rates are found (Keys, 1972). Before the age of 60, the condition is rare among women (Bengtsson, 1973). Below 40 it is rare in both sexes. Because of the high mortality (approximately one third of the patients in the acute stage die before arriving at a hospital) and because of the fact that partial invalidism is a common consequence, this illness

267

is important from society's point of view. It has been established that more urbanized countries have a higher incidence of premature MI than less urbanized ones (Keys, 1972).

Large prospective epidemiological studies have established certain "risk factors" which are associated with risk of developing an early MI. The most important of these are elevated blood pressure (systolic and diastolic), elevated serum lipids and excessive cigarette smoking (Keys, 1972). Rosenman et al. (1975) have demonstrated that in 40–59 year old Californian men, a typical "ideal" Western behaviour pattern labelled A was associated with increased risk of early MI. This behaviour pattern was associated with risk regardless of other risk factors. Thus, using a combination of conventional risk factors it was possible to point out a defined "high risk group" that had 10–15 times higher risk than a defined "low risk" group. By using classification of behaviour pattern it was possible to add precision to the prediction. Thus, type A behaviour subjects in the "high risk" group had 20–30 times higher risk than non-type A behaviour subjects in the "low risk" group. "Type A behaviour" is characterized as excessive and aggressive competitiveness, extraordinary job involvement and constant rushing against dead-lines. Rosenman and his collaborators have used a structured interview in order to classify their subjects as As or non-As, respectively. In the classification, emphasis is put on the way the subjects respond (constant rushing) as well as to the content of the answers. Type A behaviour may be regarded as a behaviour which is reinforced by modern society. In countries with a high incidence of early MI, type A behaviour is reinforced to an extreme degree in the child literature (Appels, 1972). It has been pointed out that the young MI victim compared to a non-victim has frequently been obsessed by his work at the expense of other activities in life long before illness onset (Bonami and Rimé, 1972). Lack of appreciation from superiors may facilitate the development of early MI (Medalie et al., 1973).

The role of heredity in the pathogenesis of premature MI has been studied by using twin samples (Lundman, 1966; Liljefors, 1970; Liljefors and Rahe, 1970; de Faire, 1974; Flodérus, 1974). The impression gained from these studies is that heredity plays an important role in the development of signs and symptoms of coronary atherosclerosis (Biörck, 1975). Furthermore, it has been demonstrated, using Zyzanski's and Jenkins' (1970) three type A behaviour dimensions, that one of these, hard-driving competitiveness (H), is influenced significantly by heredity whereas the two other ones, speed and impatience (S) and job involvement (J) are not influenced by heredity (Matthews and Krantz, 1976). The question could be raised whether hereditary factors are important also in the mediation of psychophysiological activation. In order to study this question, a study was performed of a series of twins.

Thirty 54–75 year old (mean 64 years) male monozygotic (17) and dizygotic (13) pairs of twins concordant and discordant with regard to signs of ischaemic heart disease were exposed to a psychiatric interview with a duration of 15–20 minutes. The interview was performed in order to induce in the subject thoughts about conflicts that he had experienced during his life. The first segment comprised questions about childhood; the character of the parents, types of punishment used in the family and conflicts with siblings were explored. The second part comprised questions about the subject's work career; he was asked to describe his jobs, whether he felt that he had been appreciated by superiors and whether he had had conflicts with colleagues and superiors. The third part, finally, comprised questions about family life; conflicts with and illnesses in family members were explored. Cardiovascular parameters, changes in heart rate, force of contraction as reflected in the ballistocardiogram (Smith, 1973), pulse volume as reflected in digital plethysmography and blood pressure were recorded before and at three silent intermissions after each segment of the interview. Serum growth hormone as an index of endocrinological activation was measured before and 10 minutes after the interview.

Table 1(a) shows the monozygotic and dizygotic intra-pair correlations, respectively, for heart rate and blood pressure during three observations at rest and during three intermissions of the interview. In the dizygotic series no significant correlations were observed. In the monozygotic series, however, the intra-pair correlations for heart rate were significant both at rest and during interview. The intra-pair correlations for systolic and diastolic blood pressure on the other hand were non-significant at rest but significant during interview.

TABLE 1 (*a*).   Intra-pair correlations for blood pressure and heart rate during rest and during three intermissions in a psychiatric interview.

	Rest 1	Rest 2	Rest 3	Int. 1	Int. 2	Int. 3
Monozygotic series (17 pairs)						
HR	0·59*	0·67**	0·62**	0·66**	0·60*	0·65**
Systolic BP	0·34	0·34	0·48*	0·43	0·61**	0·68**
Diastolic BP	0·34	0·47	0·53*	0·52*	0·60*	0·59*
Dizygotic series (13 pairs)						
HR	−0·18	−0·12	−0·12	−0·14	−0·07	0·01
Systolic BP	−0·05	−0·11	0·06	−0·04	−0·08	−0·15
Diastolic BP	−0·17	−0·28	−0·36	−0·41	−0·31	−0·12

TABLE 1 (*b*).   Relative changes (absolute level during interview divided by absolute level at rest $\times$ 100) in circulatory variables from rest to three intermissions in a psychiatric interview (all subjects, $n = 60$).

	Int. 1	Int. 2	Int. 3
HR	101 ± 0·5	103 ± 0·8**	101 ± 0·8
Systolic BP	107 ± 0·7***	108 ± 0·8***	109 ± 0·8***
Diastolic BP	104 ± 0·8***	105 ± 0·7***	105 ± 0·7***
Plethysmogram	119 ± 7·6*	107 ± 8·2	117 ± 8·7
Force of contraction	108 ± 2·9**	104 ± 2·7	107 ± 3·0*

P <0·05   **P* <0·01   ***P* < 0·001

Table 1(*b*) shows the relative changes in circulatory parameters. It is evident that nearly all subjects experienced elevated blood pressure and that this was induced by increased stroke volume rather than by increased heart rate or peripheral vasoconstriction.

Table 2 shows the intra-pair correlations of growth hormone levels. Significant correlations were again demonstrated in the monozygotic but not in the dizygotic series of pairs. Thus, the monozygotic intra-pair correlation for growth hormone levels after psychiatric interview was significant ($r = 0.66$, $P < 0.01$). The corresponding correlation at rest was non-significant. The mean rise in all the studied subjects was highly significant ($P < 0.001$).

TABLE 2.   Intra-pair correlations of growth hormone serum levels (logarithm of absolute level)

	MZ (18 pairs)	DZ (13 pairs)
Rest	0·30	−0·24
10 min after interview	0·66**	−0·21

$P < 0.01$

The phylogenetic significance of an increased level of serum growth hormone is very complex but may lie in the role of growth hormone in increasing the levels of free fatty acids (Adamsson, 1975). Thus, when other potential energy supplies, such as glucose, are lacking or "not working" in a demanding situation, growth hormone has the role of bringing up the levels of unesterified fatty acids as an alternative source of fuel. In this experiment, the natural increase in blood glucose had been inhibited by an intravenous glucose load which had been performed about 90 minutes before the interview started. This may have "demasked" the growth hormone elevations as a psychophysiological activatory response in some subjects.

The advantage in using two series of twins, a monozygotic and a dizygotic one, is that in all pairs, the two members shared childhood circumstances to an unusual extent, regardless of zygosity. Furthermore, in the monozygotic pairs, 100% of the genes are identical whereas in the dizygotic pairs 50% of the genes are shared.

In the present series of twins, the two members of the majority of pairs had been brought up together. It could be argued that a monozygotic twin pair may have had more psychosocial experiences in common during childhood than a dizygotic pair and that part of the difference in blood pressure and heart rate concordance in the monozygotic versus dizygotic series may be explained as learned behaviour. A major effect of this seems unlikely and could hardly account for all the difference.

Thus, the data presented give evidence that part of the psychophysiological activation which took place during interview was inherited biologically. However, a rough estimation from the data presented yields the information that at least half the variance in blood pressure level during interview must be accounted for by non-hereditary factors.

Peptic ulcer and severe gastritis

These are considered "psychosomatic" in most reviews (Wolf, 1965). Animal studies have shown that genetic differences may to some extent determine who will respond to a psychosocial stressor with ulcer development and who will not (Ader, 1970). Hydrochloric acid secretion from the mucosa of the ventricle is an essential component in the pathogenesis of these conditions. Wolf (1965) as well as Engel and Reichsman (1956) have described the interplay between emotions and gastric function in human subjects whose gastric mucosa could be inspected visually through a fistula. Feelings of irritability and hostility were associated with increased hydrochloric acid secretion whereas depression and hopelessness were associated with inhibition of the hydrochloric acid secretion. Hydrochloric acid secretion is partly regulated by the vagus nerve and partly by the hormone gastrin. The gastrin secretion is influenced by the degree of biological activation and varies through day and night (Moore and Wolfe, 1973).

Epidemiology of Early MI and Ulcer

In a study of male middle-aged building-construction workers living in the greater Stockholm area, a psychosocial questionnaire was administered. This comprised questions about life changes during the past year, psychological self-descriptive variables and childhood factors (Theorell *et al.,* 1975). With the use of official death and hospital registers as well as official registers of work absenteeism, episodes of long-lasting illness (at least 30 consecutive days) were recorded for the first year of follow-up. Among those without symptoms of serious heart disease or related illness at the start, the incidence of a new myocardial infarction was 0·44%/year. The incidence of "ulcer or long-lasting gastritis" was about three times and the incidence of "neurosis" twice that of early MI. Those with long-lasting degenerative diseases of the spine and joints formed a large group, the incidence being about

10 times higher than that of MI. All the diagnostic samples were derived from those in the studied population who had not stayed away from work during the preceding year because of related illness.

Table 3 (a–d) shows psychosocial factors significantly

TABLE 3.

(a) Psychosocial factors predictive of excess risk of myocardial infarction ($n = 32$)

Increased responsibility in work previous year*
Hostility in queues*
Living in rented apartment*
Living in small apartment ($<$ 2 rooms)*

(b) Psychosocial factors predictive of excess risk of ulcer or long-lasting gastritis ($n = 54$)

Hostility with slow persons***
Hostility in queues**
Being a late child in a large family (7+)**
Previous marriage*

(c) Psychosocial factors predictive of excess risk of degenerative joint disease ($n = 188$)

Spouse seriously ill previous year**
Change in sexual habits previous year*
Decreased physical activity previous year*
Inability to relax*
Dissatisfaction with home life*
Subjectively poor financial state*
Previous marriage*
Living in rented apartment*
Low formal education*

(d) Psychosocial factors predictive of excess risk of neurosis ($n = 32$)

Unemployment for at least 30 consecutive days previous year***
"Other" change at work previous year*
Close friend seriously ill previous year*
Change in sexual habits previous year*
Dissatisfaction with home life**
Subjectively poor financial state*
Long-lasting somatic illness previous year**
Single marital status**
Being childless*

* P <0·05; ** P < 0·01; *** P < 0·001.

† "Neurosis" is here defined as follows: anxiety syndromes, asthenia without obvious organic illness and neurotic-depressive reactions causing work absenteeism for at least 30 consecutive days.

associated with risk of myocardial infarction, ulcer or long-lasting gastritis and "neurosis" during the first year of follow-up. Table 4 shows which somatic variables were predictive.

TABLE 4.   Univariate risk analysis (follow-up of building-construction workers)

	Myocardial infarction	Ulcer	Neurosis
Excessive tobacco smoking	*	**	*
Elevated systolic blood pressure	*	**	0
Relative overweight	***	0	0
Small height	**	0	0
Elevated heart rate at rest	0	0	*

0   = N.S.
*   = $P < 0.05$
** = $P < 0.01$
*** = $P < 0.001$

The MI and ulcer-gastritis groups reported themselves to be hostile significantly more often than expected. This was not the case with the degenerative joint disease group and the neurosis group (Theorell et al., 1975). In the analysis of conventional "risk factors", both the MI and ulcer-gastritis groups had a significant excess of cigarette smoking and hypertension. The early MI group was furthermore characterized by on average short height and relative overweight.

The degenerative joint disease group was not analysed in the somatic part of the study. The neurosis group did not have a significantly elevated blood pressure. In the neurosis group, excessive tobacco use was observed. Serum lipids were not analysed in this study (Theorell et al., 1976).

Of interest was the observation that the neurosis group and the degenerative joint disease group both lacked self-reported hostility to any significant extent. Furthermore, in both these groups subjects claimed more often than expected that they had had problems with their family or friends during the preceding year. This was not the case with the MI and ulcer-gastritis groups.

Each one of the studied single psychosocial variables had a small predictive power in itself. Therefore, a factor analysis was performed with the use of all the studied variables. In order to eliminate bias caused by obvious illness symptoms during the year preceding the study, only those subjects were included in the factor analysis who had had no long-lasting illness during the preceding year. The aim was to find clusters of variables which were statistically and logically associated with one another. Three such clusters were found, "unsatisfactory family conditions", "work load" and "changes in family structure". The last two clusters were composed of variables indicating mainly "life events" during the preceding year in the work and family conditions, respectively.

In the two-year follow-up 51 new cases of MI occurred among all the 5187 studied subjects. 37% of these subjects had reported at least one of the items in the "work load" cluster. The age-adjusted expected rate was 23% ($P < 0.01$). In the group of subjects with a *documented absence of previous symptoms* of coronary heart disease the corresponding prevalence was 48% compared with an expected 25% ($P < 0.01$). Thus, by combining work factors into one index we were able to increase the predictive power of psychosocial work factors considerably. The other two clusters were unrelated to risk of MI. None was related to ulcer-gastritis risk whereas "unsatisfactory family conditions" were related to risk of degenerative joint disease. Neurosis was not studied with this technique (Theorell and Flodérus-Myrhed, 1977).

In conclusion, the studies of building-construction workers indicated that a constellation of hostility, hypertension and cigarette smoking was related to risk of MI and ulcer-gastritis but less so to degenerative joint disease and neurosis. In Sweden, the latter groups are considered less certain as organic "illnesses" than the former ones, and it is widely recognized that "low back pain" may be an unverifiable excuse for staying away from work. An interpretation may thus be that the latter groups "escape" under the pressures of modern technology whereas the former groups take up the challenges using phylogenetically old psychophysiological reactions to manage the stressors. This has been referred to as "Sisyphus personality" in relation to premature coronary heart disease (Wolf, 1969). In the building-construction workers study, work factors were demonstrated to be more important for MI risk than for the risk of developing other illnesses. The ulcer and MI groups were similar to one another with regard to feelings of hostility. The average patient with a psychosomatic illness has been characterized as a person who lacks ability to express emotions in words. Instead, emotional pressures may be expressed mainly in bodily reactions (Sifneos, 1974).

References

ADAMSSON, U. (1975) Insulin-like and diabetogenic actions of human growth hormone in man. Academic thesis, Karolinska Institute, Stockholm.

ADER, R. (1970) Effects of early experience and differential housing on susceptibility to gastric erosious in lesion-susceptible animals. *Psychosomatic Medicine*, **23**, 569–80.

APPELS, A. (1972) Het hartinfarct een cultuurziekte? *Tijdschrift voor Sociale Geneeskunde*, **50**, 446–48.

BENGTSSON, C. (1973) *Ischaemic heart disease in women*. Academic thesis, Göteborg.

BONAMI, M. and RIMÉ, B. (1972) Approche exploratoire de la personalité pre-coronarienne par analyse standardisée de données projectives thématiques. *Journal of Psychosomatic Research*, **16**, 103–13.

BIÖRCK, G. (1975) *Contrasting Concepts of Ischaemic Heart Disease*. Almqvist & Wiksell Int., Stockholm.

CARRUTHERS, M. (1974) *The Western Way of Death*. Davis–Poynter, London.

ENGEL, G. L. and REICHSMAN, F. Spontaneous and experimentally induced depressions in an infant with a gastric fistula. *Journal of the American Psychoanalytic Association*.

DE FAIRE, U. (1974) Ischaemic heart disease in death discordant twins. A study on 205 male and female pairs. *Acta Medica Scandinavica*, **568**.

FLODÉRUS, B. (1974) Psycho-social factors in relation to coronary heart disease and associated risk factors. *Nordisk Hygienisk Tidskrift*, Supplement, **6**.

GARDELL, B. (1971) Alienation and mental health in the modern industrial environment. In *Society, Stress and Disease* (ed. L. Levy). Vol. I, *The Psychosocial Environment and Psychosomatic Diseases*, 148–80, Oxford University Press, London.

JOHANSSON, G. and LUNDBERG, U. (1978) Psychophysiological aspects of stress and adaptation in technological societies. This volume. pp. 285–303.

KEYS, A. (1972) Predicting coronary heart disease. In *Preventive Cardiology* (ed. G. Tibblin, A. Keys, and L. Werkö). Almqvist and Wiksell, Stockholm.

LEVI, L. (1972) Stress and distress in response to psychosocial stimuli. *Acta Medica Scandinavica*, Supplement, **528**.

LILJEFORS, I. (1970) Coronary heart disease in male twins. *Acta Medica Scandinavica*, Supplement, **511**.

LILJEFORS, I. and RAHE, R. H. (1970) An identical twin study of psychosocial factors in coronary heart disease in Sweden. *Psychosomatic Medicine*, **32**, 523–42.

LUNDMAN, T. (1966) Smoking in relation to coronary heart disease and lung function in twins. A co-twin control study. *Acta Medica Scandinavica*, Supplement, **455**.

MATTHEWS, K. A. and KRANTZ, D. S. (1976) Resemblances of twins and their parents in pattern A behavior. *Psychosomatic Medicine* **38**, 140–44.

MEDALIE, J. H., KAHN, H. A., NEUFELD, H. N. *et al.* (1973) Myocardial infarction over a five-year period. I. Prevalence, incidence and mortality experience. *Journal of Chronic Diseases*, **26**, 63–84.

MOORE, J. G. and WOLFE, M. (1973) The relation of plasma gastrin to the circadian rhythm of gastric acid secretion in man. *Digestion*, **9**, 97.

ROSENMAN, R. H., BRAND, R. J. and JENKINS, C. D. *et al.* (1975) Coronary heart disease in the Western Collaborative group study: Final follow-up experience of 8½ years. *Journal of the American Medical Association*, **233**, 872–77.

SIFNEOS, P. E. (1974) A reconsideration of psychodynamic mechanisms in psychosomatic symptom formation in view of recent clinical observations. *Psychotherapy and Psychosomatics*, **24**, 151–55.

SMITH, N. T. (1973) Ballistography. Chapter 2 in *Noninvasive Cardiology* (ed. A. M. Wessler). Grune and Stratton, New York.

THEORELL, T., ASKERGREN, A., OLSSON, A. and ÅKERSTEDT, T. (1976) On risk factors for premature myocardial infarction in middle-aged building-construction workers. *Scandinavian Journal of Social Medicine*, **4**, 61–66.

THEORELL, T. and FLODÉRUS-MYRHED, B. (1977) "Work load" and risk of myocardial infarction—a prospective psychosocial analysis. *International Journal of Epidemiology* (in the press).

THEORELL, T., LIND, E. and FLODÉRUS, B. (1975) The relationship of disturbing life changes and emotions to the early development of myocardial infarction and some other serious illnesses. *International Journal of Epidemiology*, **4**, 281–93.

WOLF, S. (1965) *The Stomach*. Oxford University Press, Oxford.

WOLF, S. (1969) Psychosocial forces in myocardial infarction and sudden death. *Circulation*, **4**, Suppl. 4, 74–83.

WOLF, S. and GOODELL, H. (eds.) (1968) *Harold G. Wolff's Stress and Disease*. Charles C. Thomas, Springfield, Ill.

ZYZANSKI, S. J. and JENKINS, C. D. (1970) Basic dimensions within the coronary-prone behaviour pattern. *Journal of Chronic Diseases*, **22**, 781–92.

ANTIDOTES TO STRESS

MALCOLM CARRUTHERS

Director of Clinical Laboratory Services,
The Maudsley Hospital and The Institute of
Psychiatry, Denmark Hill, London S.E.5

IN contrast to the theme of this book, what I shall mainly describe here is a failure to adapt to changes in human behaviour. This failure of space-age man to live in conformity with his Stone Age biochemistry and physiology is, I believe, at the root of much present-day illness, particularly cardiovascular disease, which could be described as the twentieth-century killer, as well as the first of other conditions which are more generally recognized to be psychosomatic in origin.

The growth of theories relating emotion to physical illness has been retarded by the requirement of modern scientific medicine for firm objective evidence. Only recently have physiological and biochemical techniques developed to the point where they can provide such evidence without grossly disturbing the situation which it is intended to examine. From static devices almost entirely confined to the laboratory in their use, via a generation of more portable but unreliable radiotelemetric devices, we have developed portable recording instruments, one of the best examples of which is the Oxford Medilog. This small pocket tape-recorder can be considered as a complete portable physiological laboratory. On a single C120 cassette of tape it can record the electrocardiogram, blood pressure, electroencephalogram and body temperature simultaneously over a 24 hour period. This very versatile instrument has been used in a wide range of research settings, an example being an intercontinental study of the effects of long distance air travel on both air crew and passengers (Carruthers, Arguelles and Mosovich, 1976). Electrocardiographic recordings obtained from the three pilots during the flight showed the expected heart rate peaks during landing and take-off from the various airports along the route from Buenos Aires to London, with mean rates of about 90 beats per min throughout their periods at the controls. Their high levels of adrenaline excretion was also reflected in the ST–T changes seen in these traces but absent at rest. (ST–T changes are alteration in the electrocardiographic traces, which are labelled thus:

and represent the muscle potential generated by the contracting heart muscle.) Electroencephalographic recordings also obtained on five members of the flight deck crew showed occasional tendency to mass synchronization and micro-sleep patterns indicative of fatigue and drowsiness.

The same study also used new techniques in measuring biochemical responses to stress involving the use of hormonal stress indices such as catecholamines, and cortisol together with changes in various metabolites such as lipids and glucose in capillary samples obtained by finger-prick throughout the flight. This combination of physiological and biochemical techniques gives a far more complete picture of the individual's reaction to a given situation, but requires a degree of collaboration between physiologist, biochemist and social anthropologist which is rarely available.

Previous research on the effects of emotion has been largely directed towards differentiating responses to situations which provoke either aggression or anxiety. The former category of reaction was of special interest in relation to the growing body of evidence that people who show a specific overt pattern of behaviour characterized by fierce, competitive, hard-driving, time- and deadline-conscious features, the so-called type-A pattern, were some three to four times more liable to develop coronary heart disease than individuals showing the reverse more relaxed type-B pattern (Friedman and Rosenman, 1974). Working with Dr. Peter Taggart, we initially chose racing-driving as a test bed on which to examine human responses to this extremely competitive aggression-provoking occupation (Taggart and Carruthers, 1971). Over an average half-hour period of the race, there was a marked rise in the plasma catecholamines, predominantly noradrenaline, which in turn mobilised free fatty acids from the body's adipose tissue stores. The immediate post-race peak of free fatty acids was succeeded an hour later by a rise in triglyceride levels, due to lack of utilisation of the free fatty acids under the mentally active and physically inert conditions of the race. Similar responses were seen in traffic drivers (Carruthers, Taggart and Somerville, 1973) and evident in people engaged in the hostile anti-social activity of public speaking (Somerville, Taggart and Carruthers, 1973).

By contrast, situations which promote anxiety such as the extreme condition of parachute jumping and the more everyday situation of dental surgery (Taggart, Hedworth-Whitty, Carruthers and Gordon, 1976) provoked the purely adrenaline response. This caused a rise in heart rate and a wide variety of spectacular abnormalities of the electrocardiogram, most of which could be restored to normal by beta-blockade. However, in relation to the long term causation of coronary heart disease, it would appear that the high noradrenaline situations accompanied by the lipid-raising and blood-pressure-increasing properties of noradrenaline, were likely to be more important unless the heart was already severely damaged and liable to the arrhythmias induced by adrenaline. These high noradrenaline states are induced by competitive behaviour, car driving, cigarette smoking, coffee drinking and cold conditions. This idea not only links together the commonly seen aggressive pattern of behaviour (type A) which clinically appears to predispose the individual to coronary heart disease more than sustained anxiety responses, but also leads on to the idea that noradrenaline release in relation to pleasure centres in the hypothalamus may be the common chemical pathway to pleasure in these diverse but popular situations.

The availability of methods for objectively assessing the effects of stress has not only made these theories more acceptable, but has highlighted ways in which these influences can be counteracted. Just as in the physiological area the effects of emotion can be demonstrated to the individual by means of bio-feedback systems, including galvanic skin resistance meters, pulse rate meters, muscle electrodes and detectors of alpha-wave activity, so it is possible to demonstrate the biochemical effects of stress by a system which could be called 'chemo-feedback'. This biochemical profile includes cholesterol, triglyceride, uric acid, blood glucose and fibrinogen. With an additional reading of blood pressure, an accurate prediction of risk of coronary heart disease over the next five years can be obtained using a simple circular slide rule device known as a Logarisk Calculator (Carruthers, 1975).

From consideration of the chain of events triggered by emotion (Figure 1) there are many logical points of intervention at which the various antidotes to stress are applicable. Firstly there is the area of what could be described as stress management. Where possible it involves the recognition and avoidance of non-essential forms of stress or tackling them in a different fashion. Improved techniques of communication as described by Eric Berne in his books *Games People Play* and *What do you say after you've said hello?*, are of great assistance in this process of improving communications and lessening misunderstandings. The automobile appears to provoke profoundly aggressive responses in many people and limitations of its use, or switching to alternative forms of transport may be helpful unless of course such alternatives are overcrowded as in the case of the trains described by Johansson and Lundberg (this volume, p. 285).

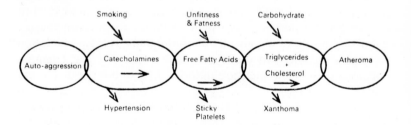

Fig. 1.   Suggested chain of events causing atheroma

Switching off the stress response and switching on the relaxation response, even if for relatively short periods of the day, is another valuable measure. Though the results of transcendental meditation have been rather disappointing, simple techniques of Hatha yoga involving 20 minutes' relaxation a day have proved effective in lowering both blood pressure and lipid levels in hypertensive and normotensive subjects, and as a further benefit appear to help those who are giving up smoking.

Some people, however, find that when they attempt these relaxation techniques underlying anxiety and other disturbing psychological symptoms come bubbling to the surface. There is a wide range of psychotherapeutic techniques which are becoming increasingly popular and more widely used for the treatment of these underlying problems. These include the ones popularised under the heading of primal therapy by Dr Arthur Janov in several books, including his recent paperback *The Feeling Child*. Also a wider range of techniques involving desensitisation by regression to early life events, which come under the heading of 'primal integration', are being applied by a Dr William Schwartly both in Canada and in Great Britain.

Rather than these more drastic remedies many people, particularly those showing the hard-driving coronary prone type-A behaviour pattern, prefer to balance a high level of mental activity with a reasonable level of physical activity. The benefits of a minimal dose of the right type of safe, dynamic rather than static, vigorous but not violent exercise have been detailed in my book *F/40: Fitness on Forty Minutes a Week* (Carruthers and Murray, 1976). This is not exactly a new idea, as Plato wrote over 2000 years ago that 'those who engage in mathematics or other strenuous intellectual pursuits, should also take regular exercise', and we have not been able to better this advice to this day.

Finally, for those who are unable or unwilling to modify any of the above features of their life style, beta-blockers, which can be regarded as drugs which block the peripheral effects of stress, are proving very effective for treatment of a wide range of both physical disorders such as cardiovascular disease and hypertension, and mental disorders such as anxiety and even schizophrenia. This is a further reason why theories that emotional stress may cause or at least contribute to a variety of physical conditions is achieving great acceptance, though it has its detrimental side in that in the search for new chemical antidotes to stress, such as the beta-blocking drugs, some of the more natural remedies have been overlooked or forgotten. It is important to look at the full range of methods which are available for helping space-age man in conformity with his Stone Age biochemical and physiological responses.

References

BERNE, E. (1975) *Games People Play*. Corgi Books, London.
BERNE, E. (1975) *What Do You Say After You Say Hello?* Corgi Books, London.
CARRUTHERS, M. (1975) Logarisk: an aid to advising the coronary candidate. *Journal of the Royal College of General Practitioners*, **25**, 251–53.
CARRUTHERS, M. (1976) Modification of the noradrenaline related effects of smoking by beta-blockade. *Psychological Medicine*, **6**, 251–56.
CARRUTHERS, M. (1977) Biochemical responses to urban environmental stress. *Man in Urban Environments* (ed. G. A. Harrison and J. Gibson, Oxford University Press. pp. 189–95
CARRUTHERS, M., ARGUELLES, A. E. and MOSOVICH, A. (1976) Man in transit: biochemical and physiological changes during intercontinental flights. *Lancet*, **1**, 977–81.
CARRUTHERS, M. and MURRAY A. (1976) *F/40: Fitness on Forty Minutes a Week*, Futura Books, London.
CARRUTHERS, M., TAGGART, P. and SOMERVILLE, W. (1973) Some effects of beta-blockade on the lipid responses to certain acute emotions. In *New Perspectives in Beta Bockade* (ed. D. M. Birley, J. H. Friar, R. K. Rondel and S. H. Taylor), pp. 307–11.
FRIEDMAN, M. and ROSENMAN, R. H. (1974) *Type A Behaviour and your Heart*, Wildwood House, London.
JANOV, A. (1973) *The Feeling Child*. Simon and Schuster, New York.
PATEL, C. (1976) Reductions of some cholesterol and blood pressure in hypertensive patients by behaviour modification. *Journal of the Royal College of General Practitioners*, **26**, 211–13.
SOMERVILLE, W., TAGGART, P. and CARRUTHERS, M. (1973) Cardiovascular responses to public speaking and their modification by oxprenolol. In *New Perspectives in Beta Blockade* (ed. D. M. Birley *et al.*), 275–86.
TAGGART, P. and CARRUTHERS, M. (1971) Endogenous hyperlipidaemia induced by stress of racing driving. *Lancet*, **1**, 363–66.
TAGGART, P., HEDWORTH-WHITTY, R., CARRUTHERS, M. and GORDON, P. D. (1976) Observations on electrocardiogram and plasma catecholamines during dental procedures: the forgotten vagus. *British Medical Journal*, **2**, 787–89.

PSYCHOPHYSIOLOGICAL ASPECTS OF STRESS AND ADAPTATION IN TECHNOLOGICAL SOCIETIES†

GUNN JOHANSSON and ULF LUNDBERG‡
Department of Psychology, University of Stockholm

Introduction

MAN's capacity for biological and mental adjustment has been an important prerequisite for existence in vastly different environments and for the development of a technologically advanced society. During an era of technological optimism this adaptability has been regarded as an asset which made it possible to send men to the bottom of the seas, to the top of the world, and even into space. Such remarkable enterprises have been undertaken by highly selected groups of men whose abilities in this and other respects were exceptional. At the same time technological and cultural changes have had a profound impact on the everyday conditions of much larger groups. It has been assumed that repeated readjustment to such changes may exact the price of impaired health and well-being (Frankenhaeuser, 1974). An unimpeded development in this direction might force man to approach his limits of adaptability.

Some of the data on which such assumptions have been based were provided by psychophysiological stress research studying adjustment to psychosocial environments characteristic of industrialized societies. This paper will present a few such environ-

† Financial support was obtained from the Swedish Council for Social Science Research, the Swedish Medical Research Council (Project No. 997), and the Swedish Work Environment Fund.
‡ The authors are equally responsible for all parts of the paper.
285

mental conditions and illustrate their consequences for the individual, using data from field and laboratory studies. Both behavioural and physiological reactions to psychosocial stressors will be presented. The data were collected as part of two long-term projects, one headed by Dr Marianne Frankenhaeuser, the other undertaken by her in collaboration with Dr Bertil Gardell (Frankenhaeuser and Gardell, 1976).

Behavioural and Endocrine Adjustment to Stressors

An important dependent variable in the studies to be reported is the sympathetic adrenal medullary activity as reflected in the urinary output of catecholamines. This variable will be regarded as an indicator of general arousal (Johansson, 1973; Pátkai, 1970), reflecting the acute mental and physical load to which the individual is exposed (Frankenhaeuser, 1975).

Since the beginning of this century it has been known that adrenaline secretion is of vital importance for the mobilization of physical energy in emergency situations. Cannon (1915) showed that adrenaline serves as an emergency hormone by stimulating cardiac activity, dilating the arterioles of the skeletal muscle, immobilizing the gut, stimulating glycogenolysis etc. These and other effects of heightened adrenal-medullary activity facilitate adjustment to demands in the physical environment. A second hormone, noradrenaline, which is also released from the adrenal medulla, was identified later (cf. Euler, 1956). The actions of the two hormones are usually qualitatively similar, although their relative potency varies (for further details concerning the biology, physiology, and neuropsychopharmacology of the catecholamines, see e.g., Blaschko and Muscholl, 1972; Friedhoff, 1975).

The secretion of catecholamines has also been shown to facilitate adjustment to demands in the psychosocial environment (e.g., Johansson, 1973). Positive relations have been demonstrated between mental performance and concurrent rate of adrenaline output (for reviews see Frankenhaeuser, 1971; 1975) and similar relationships have been found with performance in standardized tests of achievement and intelligence (Lambert, Johansson, Frankenhaeuser and Klackenberg-Larsson, 1969;

Johansson, Frankenhaeuser and Magnusson, 1973). In brief, situations requiring adjustment to psychosocial demands usually lead to an increased output of adrenaline and noradrenaline. This reaction tends to be associated with behaviourally successful adjustment. It seems, for instance, as if, by mobilizing reserve capacity, the organism can compensate for factors such as fatigue which would otherwise impair performance levels (Johansson, Frankenhaeuser and Magnusson, 1973).

Although the release of catecholamines is a phylogenetically old mechanism for adjustment to environmental demands, it still appears to have beneficial effects in a short perspective. It is assumed, however, that frequent or prolonged adrenal medullary activity may exert an extra load on several physiological functions in a way that may be harmful to the individual (Frankenhaeuser, 1972; Levi, 1972). The rate at which catecholamine levels return to baseline after acute arousal may be of importance for such long-term effects (Johansson and Frankenhaeuser, 1973; Johansson, 1976). So far, little empirical evidence is available to test the validity of this assumption (Theorell, 1978).

The use of sympathetic-adrenal medullary activity as a measure of general arousal has several advantages in the study of effects of psychosocial factors. The urinary output of catecholamines may be measured in field settings without interference with the activity of the subjects. The urinary analysis gives integrated measures reflecting an average level over periods of about one hour or more. Certain regulations concerning consumption of alcohol, tobacco and drugs have to be followed by the subjects but usually do not present major problems. The measures presented below were obtained with a fluorimetric method of analysis, based on the trihydroxyindole reaction and adapted for automatic analysis of catecholamines (Euler and Lishajko, 1961; Andersson, Hovmöller, Karlsson and Svensson, 1974).

An important factor in the genesis of physiological stress reactions is the individual's cognitive appraisal of the situation or stimulus structure (Lazarus, 1966; Frankenhaeuser, 1975). As for the adrenal medullary system it is quite clear that its activity involves and intimately integrates autonomous and central nervous system activity (cf. Mason, 1972), although the exact mechanisms for this interaction are not yet fully understood. The important role played by cortical activity is illustrated by the fact that passive anticipation of unpleasant events may evoke intense physiological arousal (e.g., Frankenhaeuser and Rissler, 1970; Niemelä, 1973; Gal and Lazarus, 1975). Another example lies in the fact that personal control over aversive stimulation, such as noise, tends to modify stress responses. The intensity of the stress reaction may increase or decrease depending on the psychological meaning of the control response for the individual (Averill, 1973). Empirical studies (e.g., DeGood, 1975; Lundberg and Frankenhaeuser, 1976) suggest that the stress-reducing effect of personal control is stronger for individuals who generally perceive themselves as being in control of life events.

It is a common observation that an individual's perception of a stressful situation is more closely related to his physiological reactions than are the physical characteristics of the same situation. Therefore, the intensity of subjective reactions has been investigated systematically in the studies reported here, using quantitative methods with self-reports on graphic scales (see e.g., Singer, Lundberg and Frankenhaeuser, 1978).

Work in Highly Mechanized Industries

Technological development has greatly changed the content of industrial work. Mechanization of production processes has had a major impact in this respect. Physical stress has been reduced or abolished by the elimination of heavy tasks. At the same time, the planning and regulation of work routines have been taken over by machinery. In order to achieve efficient, profitable production methods, the manufacturing process has been split up into tiny segments where each person is easily replaceable since he is responsible for one segment only and needs little training for his task. In many industries the workers can no longer choose their tools, methods of work, or pace of work.

Sociological and occupational health research has provided descriptions of relations between degree of mechanization and behavioural adjustment. Using a scale of mechanization (cf. Bright, 1958) ranging from a low level (represented by crafts), through mechanized jobs of an assembly-line type, to highly automated industries, where the worker is physically separated from the complex process he is surveying with built-in feedback systems (paper-mills, oil refineries, etc.), it is possible to demonstrate that the highly mechanized, repetitive, and machine-paced jobs are associated with exceptionally low work satisfaction and general life satisfaction (Gardell, 1971; Caplan, Cobb, French, Van Harrison and Pinneau, 1975). It is only recently that physiological reactions to this type of work have been investigated.

In a study of sawmill workers (Johansson, Aronsson and Lindström, in press; Frankenhaeuser and Gardell, 1976) an attempt was made to combine psychosocial, physiological, and health data in order to acquire a comprehensive picture of the impact of repetitive mechanized work on psychophysiological adjustment and health. The particular sawmill was chosen because it offered a possibility to study cyclic, repetitive and machine-paced jobs as well as jobs allowing personal discretion in the same plant. A group performing repetitive and machine-paced work, the "high-risk group", was compared to a control group performing work under less constricted conditions. The two groups, which were equal with respect to background conditions such as age, education, job experience, housing, leisure activities, etc., were studied between 0600 hours and 1500 hours on two separate days: during a work shift and during non-work activities at home. Urine samples for the analysis of adrenaline and noradrenaline were collected on four occasions during each of the two days. On each occasion the workers also made self-ratings reflecting their own experience of the situations. All measures obtained during work were transformed into a percentage of the corresponding control measure obtained during free hours.

Figure 1 shows the hormone excretion of the two groups during four periods of the work day. The risk group excreted significantly larger amounts of adrenaline than the control group. The control group level reached a maximum of about 150% in the morning and slowly decreased towards the end of the day. The risk group, on the other hand, started off at a level twice as high as their baseline. After a temporary decrease, their adrenaline level increased continuously until it reached its maximum at the end of the work shift. The noradrenaline excretion was fairly

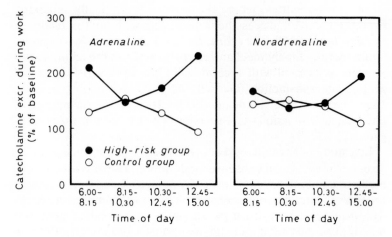

FIG. 1. Average excretion of adrenaline (left-hand diagram) and noradrenaline (right-hand diagram) during an 8-h work shift in two groups of sawmill workers: a high-risk group and a control group. Measures obtained at work have been expressed as per cent of baseline levels. (Reprinted with permission of the publisher and authors: Frankenhaeuser, M. and Gardell, B. (1976 *Journal of Human Stress*, **2**, 35–46.)

similar in the two groups, but the characteristic increase of the risk group level was obtained for this catecholamine, too.

The risk group levels of hormone output were higher than those usually found in laboratory experiments involving moderate mental stressors. The continuous increase at the end of the work shift is particularly striking since it means that these workers leave their work in a state of heightened arousal. This observation is in agreement with statements by the workers during interviews. Many of the risk group members claimed that they need an hour or two after work to slow down and to get adjusted to normal conditions so that they can interact with their family. The afternoon increase of adrenaline output may be regarded as a warning signal indicating a forced mobilization of the individual's reserve capacity (Frankenhaeuser and Gardell, 1976).

The self-ratings showed that workers in the risk group felt considerably more rushed and irritated than the control group.

Health data for the two groups were available from a self-report questionnaire. There was a clear tendency for the high-risk group to show more symptoms than their fellow workers in the control group. Headaches and slight nervous disorders, such as nervous tension and sleep disturbances, were reported by 35% of high-risk workers whereas the control group did not suffer from such disturbances. Disorders of the joints, of the low back, and in the circulatory system were also more frequent in the high-risk group than in the control group.

These results represent consequences of a very complex reality, and within each of the groups there were slight variations with regard to the psychosocial job content, e.g. in the degree of monotony, constriction, and work pace. The design of field studies of this kind does not, of course, permit definite conclusions about the influence of single environmental factors. However, by rearrangement of the data it is possible to get some information concerning factors which systematically contribute to the difference in hormone level between the risk group and the control group. An analysis of correlations between hormone levels and single environmental factors was carried out for the entire group of 24 workers. In this way it was possible to identify a number of factors which tend to be more closely related than others to the observed stress reactions.

The first of these factors was the duration of single work cycles, a measure which indicates the degree of repetitiveness. Figure 2 shows that there is a systematic relationship between repetitiveness, adrenaline secretion, and subjective well-being.

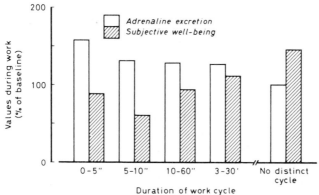

FIG. 2. Adrenaline excretion and self-rated well-being in sub-groups with work cycles of different duration.

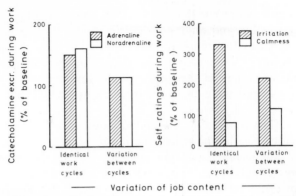

FIG. 3. Excretion of adrenaline and noradrenaline (left-hand diagram) and self-rated irritation and calmness (right-hand diagram) in sub-groups differing with regard to the variation of job content.

The shortest work cycles were associated with the highest adrenaline levels and the poorest subjective well-being. For workers whose jobs did not fall into distinct cycles, adrenaline levels during work remained at the off-work control level, and they were in a more pleasant mood at work than their fellow workers. In this diagram, as in a few others appearing below, the abscissa represents groups of participants ranging in size between 5 and 14.

Another job characteristic indicative of monotony is the degree of similarity of content between work cycles. Figure 3 shows the relation of this factor to hormone excretion and to self-rated irritation and calmness. The left graph shows that workers who performed a task involving identical work cycles excreted more adrenaline and noradrenaline than workers performing jobs with some variation between cycles. The right graph shows that identical cycles were associated with higher levels of irritation and lower levels of calmness.

The third factor indicating monotony was the degree of variation between tasks. Figure 4 demonstrates how workers performing the most repetitive tasks excrete more adrenaline and noradrenaline than fellow workers who perform more than one task. The diagram also shows that self-rated calmness as well as subjective well-being increases with task variation.

Besides monotony, the degree to which the worker was

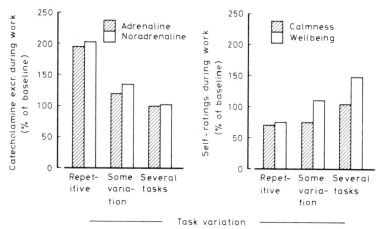

FIG. 4.   Excretion of adrenaline and noradrenaline (left-hand diagram) and self-rated calmness and well-being (right-hand diagram) in sub-groups differing with regard to repetitiveness in the work process.

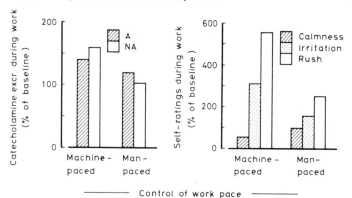

FIG. 5.   Excretion of adrenaline (A) and noradrenaline (NA) and self-rated calmness, irritation, and rush in a group with predominantly machine-paced work and a group allowed personal control over work pace.

allowed to influence his work pace seemed to be of great importance for the stress reactions. Figure 5 shows differences in stress reactions between the workers who could exert some control over their work pace and those who had no such possibility. Thus, machine-paced work was associated with higher levels of adrenaline and noradrenaline. Machine-pacing also produced more feelings of rush and irritation than man-paced work.

Other factors, like the degree of social isolation, demands for attention, and responsibility for material and product, did not show systematic co-variation with physiological and mental stress reactions.

Urban Commuting

In addition to stressful conditions at work, a great many people in urban societies have to spend a relatively long time commuting under crowded and noisy conditions between their suburban homes and their central-city jobs. The stress which arises from day-to-day commuting by public transport has recently been investigated in Sweden (Singer, Lundberg and Frankenhaeuser, 1978; Lundberg, 1976).

Train commuters who had been travelling on the same line for at least six months reported their subjective experiences during morning trips to Stockholm, and the excretion of adrenaline and noradrenaline was assessed from urine samples collected from the passengers at the station. The investigations were carried out on the Stockholm-Nynäshamn line, where people who commute between the first and the last station have to spend about 2·5 hours a day on the train. The trains on this line are relatively comfortable, with seats usually available for all the passengers.

The first investigation with train commuters was carried out in 1973. Two groups of about 15 passengers in each were studied on their morning trips to Stockholm, one group boarding the train at its first stop (Nynäshamn), the other about midway on its route (Västerhaninge). The subjects were requested to give self-reports regarding their subjective experiences on the train at different stations, and from each subject urine samples were collected after night rest and after one morning trip to Stockholm. The urine samples were analysed for adrenaline and noradrenaline.

The number of passengers as well as the perceived degree of crowdedness increased progressively as the train approached Stockholm, which means that, on average, the crowdedness on the train was greater for the subjects from Västerhaninge (shorter trip). The various feelings of discomfort also grew more intense as the train approached Stockholm, while perceived comfort decreased (Figure 6). The excretion rate of adrenaline on the

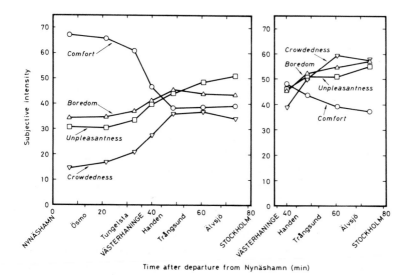

Time after departure from Nynäshamn (min)

FIG. 6. Self-reported comfort, boredom, unpleasantness and crowdedness at seven stations for passengers from Nynäshamn and at four stations for passengers from Västerhaninge.

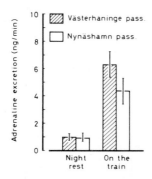

FIG. 7. Means and standard errors of adrenaline excretion on the train and at night rest for passengers from Nynäshamn and Västerhaninge.

train was found to be higher for the subjects from Västerhaninge (shorter trip), while there was no noticeable difference between the two groups during night rest (Figure 7).

The results indicate that the conditions on the train were more important for the stress experienced than the duration or length of the trip. An important effect of increased crowdedness was that it reduced the possibility of choosing seats and company on the train.

During the oil crisis in the beginning of 1974, Sweden had a short period of petrol rationing, which encouraged people to use public transport. This situation made it possible to investigate the same group of passengers under different levels of crowding. The first part of the investigation (Trip 1) was carried out before the rationing period and the second part (Trip 2) shortly after. The number of passengers on the Stockholm–Nynäshamn line increased about 10% during this period. The investigation was carried out with subjects from the two groups used in the first investigation, i.e., passengers travelling from Västerhaninge and Nynäshamn, respectively, using the same procedure as before. However, in this case physiological control values were obtained from urine samples collected while the subjects relaxed at home on a Sunday morning.

Variation in the number of passengers on the train was closely related to self-reported crowdedness, and, as before, the various feelings of discomfort became more intense as perceived crowdedness increased. In order to investigate the relationship bet-

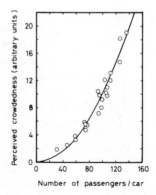

Number of passengers / car

FIG. 8. Self-reported crowdedness as a function of the number of passengers/car. A simple square function is represented by the curve drawn in the diagram. (Reproduced by permission of the publisher. Lundberg, U. (1976) *Journal of Human Stress*, **2**, No. 3, 26–32.)

ween subjective and objective crowdedness, self-reported crowdedness from the subjects was plotted against the total number of passengers/car for each station (Figure 8). This relationship was described by a simple square function represented by the curve drawn in the diagram, which indicates that if the number of passengers increases twice, perceived crowdedness increases four times, if the number of passengers increases three times, perceived crowdedness increases nine times, etc.

The catecholamine excretion during the two trips showed that both the adrenaline and the noradrenaline excretion rate was higher for the subjects from Västerhaninge (shorter trip) (Figure 9). It can also be seen that adrenaline excretion increased from Trip 1 to Trip 2 for both groups. This increase is more clearly illustrated when the subjects' adrenaline excretion during each trip is expressed in percentage of the control level obtained at home (Figure 10). The mean increase in excretion rate for both groups of subjects treated together was about 20 per cent during Trip 1, and about 60 per cent during Trip 2.

The data from the two investigations with train commuters showed that a relatively moderate increase in the number of passengers was associated with a relatively large increase in perceived crowdedness and with a significant increase in adrenaline

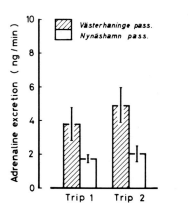
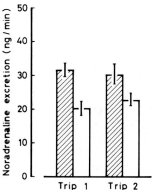

Fig. 9.   Means and standard errors of adrenaline and noradrenaline excretion on the train during Trips 1 and 2 for passengers from Nynäshamn and Västerhaninge, respectively. (Reproduced by permission from the publisher. Lundberg, U. (1976) *Journal of Human Stress*, **2**, No. 3, 26–32.)

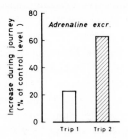

FIG. 10.   Increase from control condition in adrenaline excretion during journey for Trips 1 and 2 (mean values for the two groups of passengers treated together). (Reproduced by permission from the publisher. Lundberg, U. (1976) *Journal of Human Stress*, **2**, No. 3, 26–32.)

excretion. It is important to note that these results were obtained on a relatively comfortable train and that all the subjects had seats during the trips. The results from both the investigations indicate that the conditions on the train were more important for the stress reactions of the passengers than the duration or length of the trip. Crowding reduced personal control on the train and lack of personal control is a factor which is generally assumed to increase reactions to aversive stimulation (cf. Frankenhaeuser and Rissler, 1970; Gal and Lazarus, 1975). In the present investigations it is likely that crowding, besides reducing personal control, increased the noise level.

Discussion

The investigations reported above describe acute responses to environmental strains characteristic of a phase in man's history which has recently begun. However, they may serve to illustrate conditions which are of importance in an evolutionary perspective. The following tentative, and partly speculative reflections will touch on changes in demands for human readjustment, on changes in man's expectancies, and on interactions between such psychosocial factors and illness.

The accelerating pace of life changes caused by modern technological society has been illustrated dramatically by Toffler in his book *Future Shock* (1970). A research line, initiated by Dr. Richard Rahe and his collaborators (cf. Rahe, 1975), has focussed on the relation between life change and illness onset. The simple idea behind this line of research was that every life change, regardless of desirability, forces the individual to adjust to a new situation, which adds to the total 'wear and tear' of the organism and in some way increases the risk of illness onset. Some results have been obtained which support this idea, showing that illness rate in general is higher for people who are exposed to intense life change (Rahe, 1975). Although many researchers (e.g., Mechanic 1976; Paykel, 1976; Lundberg, Theorell and Lind, 1975) have argued that desirable and undesirable events should be separated and that individual differences and the specificity of various illnesses should be considered, the fact remains that some of the major life events seem to be related to illness onset.

Toffler assumed a continued technological development resulting in increased demands for human readjustment. Even if this assumption proves to be wrong in the long run and the present technological development is forced to end, e.g., due to a shortage of energy and/or the depletion of natural resources, the problems caused by the demand for human adaptation will not necessarily decrease. Such a development will present profound life changes to people in the industrialized countries until they have adapted to a new, more stable way of life.

It is a common observation that repeated exposure to various forms of aversive stimulation usually results in a habituation, so that physiological arousal reactions decrease with increased familiarity with a situation (e.g., Frankenhaeuser, Sterky and Järpe, 1962). It is, therefore, interesting to note that the sawmill workers, whose reaction to job stress was described above, displayed a considerably elevated on-the-job arousal even after many years on the same task. Besides the various aspects of job content which have been listed as underlying these arousal reactions and job dissatisfaction it may be worth considering another factor of a more global character. It has to do with the workers' image of themselves in a socio-cultural perspective.

Technological development has managed to eliminate many

physically heavy tasks which used to involve health hazards as well as accident risks. In addition, other physical stressors (such as starvation, poor housing, threat of natural forces) and psychosocial stressors (such as the humiliating dependency of large groups on the wealthy) have been reduced or eliminated in the industrial countries. However, these improvements in themselves have changed people's expectancies and levels of aspirations. This change has taken place not in the physical world but in the minds of men, in the cognitive structure which plays such an important role for the development or suppression of stress reactions. It is, for instance, reasonable to assume that many workers in repetitive and monotonous jobs experience a strong contrast between their fragmented, repetitive tasks and their own personal resources, between their dull, constricted life at work and their leisure time, when they are regarded as independent individuals able to take initiatives to satisfy their basic as well as their social and cultural needs.

Very little is yet known about the possible mechanisms relating psychosocial events to disease. Many researchers have assumed that catecholamines play an important role in the pathogenesis of myocardial infarction (Raab, 1970; Friedman, 1969) and it is possible that increased adrenal medullary activity has additional effects on several physiological functions (e.g., Simpson, Olewine, Jenkins, Ramsey, Zyzanski, Thomas and Hames, 1974). The relation between psychosocial work conditions, the acute activation of the adrenal medullary system during work, and the higher rate of disease observed in the high-risk sawmill workers certainly provides indirect support for the notion that psychosocial events may lead to disease, and that the catecholamines may be involved in the possible mechanisms. Psychosocial stress has also been found to influence the level of hormones regulating, e.g., the reproductory system of humans and animals (Kreutz, Rose and Jennings, 1972; Ward, 1974), and such disturbances are, of course, of significant importance from an evolutionary point of view.

The epidemiological investigations suggesting a relationship between psychosocial events and illness onset may seem to be of limited value considering the relatively weak correlations that have been reported and the lack of knowledge about the underlying mechanisms. However, in view of the great number of life changes that modern technological society creates every day, in addition to its encouragement of performance and competition, and in view of the fatal consequences of some illnesses in which psychosocial factors seem to play a role (e.g., myocardial infarction), it is obvious that we have problems of significant importance which we shall have to tackle.

References

ANDERSSON, B., HOVMÖLLER, S., KARLSSON, C. G. and SVENSSON, S. (1974) Analysis of urinary catecholamines: An improved auto-analyzer fluorescence method. *Clinica Chimica Acta*, **51**, 13–28.

AVERILL, J. R. (1973) Personal control over aversive stimuli and its relationship to stress. *Psychological Bulletin*, **80**, 286–303.

BLASCHKO, H., and MUSCHOLL, E. (eds.) (1972) Catecholamines. In *Handbook of Experimental Pharmacology*, vol. 33, Springer Verlag, Berlin.

BRIGHT, J. R. (1958) *Automation and Management*. Harvard University Press, Boston.

CANNON, W. B. (1915) *Bodily Changes in Pain, Hunger, Fear and Rage*. Appleton, New York.

CAPLAN, R. D., COBB, S., FRENCH, J. R. P. Jr., VAN HARRISON, R. and PINNEAU, S. R. Jr. (1975) *Job Demands and Worker Health*. National Institute for Occupational Safety and Health, HEW Publication No. (NIOSH), 75–160, Washington.

DE GOOD, D. E. (1975) Cognitive control factors in vascular stress responses. *Psychophysiology*, **12**, 399–401.

EULER, U.S. v. (1956) *Noradrenaline: Chemistry, Physiology, Pharmacology and Clinical Aspects*. Charles C. Thomas, Springfield.

EULER, U. S. v., and LISHAJKO, F. (1961) Improved technique for the fluorimetric estimation of catecholamines. *Acta Physiologica Scandinavica*, **51**, 348–55.

FRANKENHAEUSER, M. (1971) Behaviour and circulating catecholamines. *Brain Research*, **31**, 241–62.

FRANKENHAEUSER, M. (1972) Biochemical events, stress and adjustment. *Reports from the Psychological Laboratories*, University of Stockholm, No. 368.

FRANKENHAEUSER, M. (1974) Man in technological society: stress, adaptation, and tolerance limits. *Reports from the Psychological Laboratories*, University of Stockholm, Suppl. 26.

FRANKENHAEUSER, M. (1975) Sympathetic-adrenomedullary activity, behaviour and the psychosocial environment. Chapter 4 In *Research in Psychophysiology* (eds. P. H. Venables and J. J. Christie). Wiley, New York, London and Sydney.

FRANKENHAEUSER, M. and GARDELL, B. (1976) Underload and overload in working life. A multidisciplinary approach. *Journal of Human Stress*, **2**, 35–46.

FRANKENHAEUSER, M. and RISSLER, A. (1970) Catecholamine output during relaxation and anticipation. *Perceptual and Motor Skills*, **30**, 745–46.

FRANKENHAEUSER, M., STERKY, K. and JÄRPE, G. (1962) Psychophysiological relations in habituation to gravitational stress. *Perceptual and Motor Skills*, **15**, 63–72.

FRIEDHOFF, A. (ed.) (1975) *Catecholamines and Behaviour*, **1**, *Basic Neurobiology*, **2**, *Neuropsychopharmacology*. Plenum Press, New York.

FRIEDMAN, M. (1969) *Pathogenesis of Coronary Artery Disease*. McGraw-Hill, London.

GAL, R. and LAZARUS, R. S. (1975) The role of activity in anticipating and confronting stressful situations. *Journal of Human Stress*, **1**, 4–20.

GARDELL, B. (1971) Alienation and mental health in the modern industrial environment. In *Society, Stress and Disease*, **1**, *The Psychosocial Environment and Psychosomatic Diseases* (ed. L. Levi). Oxford University Press, London.

JOHANSSON, G. (1973) Activation, adjustment, and sympathetic-adrenal medullary activity. Field and laboratory studies of adults and children. *Reports from the Psychological Laboratories*, University of Stockholm, Suppl. 21.

JOHANSSON, G. (1976) Subjective well-being and temporal patterns of sympathetic-adrenal medullary activity. *Biological Psychology*, **4**, 157–72.

JOHANSSON, G. and FRANKENHAEUSER, M. (1973) Temporal factors in sympatho-adrenomedullary activity following acute behavioural activation. *Biological Psychology*, **1**, 63–73.

JOHANSSON, G., FRANKENHAEUSER, M. and MAGNUSSON, D. (1973) Catecholamine excretion of school children as related to performance and adjustment. *Scandinavian Journal of Psychology*, **14**, 20–28.

JOHANSSON, G., ARONSSON, G. and LINDSTRÖM, B. O. (1978) Social psychological and neuroendocrine stress reactions in highly mechanized work. *Ergonomics* (in press).

KREUTZ, L. E., ROSE, R. M. and JENNINGS, J. R. (1972) Suppression of plasma testosterone levels and psychological stress. *Archives of General Psychiatry*, **26**, 479–82.

LAMBERT, W. W., JOHANSSON, G., FRANKENHAEUSER, M. and KLACKENBERG-LARSSON, I. (1969) Catecholamine excretion in young children and their parents as related to behaviour. *Scandinavian Journal of Psychology*, **10**, 306–18.

LAZARUS, R. S. (1966) *Psychological Stress and the Coping Process*. McGraw-Hill, New York.

LEVI, L. (ed.) (1972) Stress and distress in response to psychosocial stimuli. *Acta Medica Scandinavica*, **191**, Suppl. 528.

LUNDBERG, U. (1976) Urban commuting: Crowdedness and catecholamine excretion. *Journal of Human Stress*, **2**, 26–34.

LUNDBERG, U. and FRANKENHAEUSER, M. (1976) Psychophysiological reactions to noise as modified by personal control over stimulus intensity. *Reports from the Department of Psychology*, University of Stockholm, No. 471.

LUNDBERG, U., THEORELL, T. and LIND, E. (1975) Life changes and myocardial infarction: individual differences in life-change scaling. *Journal of Psychosomatic Research*, **19**, 27–32.

MASON, J. W. (1972) Physiological foundations. In *Handbook of Psychophysiology* (eds. N. S. Greenfield and R. A. Sternbach). Holt, Rinehart and Winston, New York.

MECHANIC, D. (1976) Stress, illness, and illness behaviour. *Journal of Human Stress*, 2, 2–6.

NIEMELÄ, P. (1973) Coping processes in the anticipation of stress. *Reports from the Psychological Laboratories*, University of Stockholm, Suppl. 20.

PÁTKAI, P. (1970) Relations between catecholamine release and psychological functions. *Reports from the Psychological Laboratories*, University of Stockholm, Suppl. 2.

PAYKEL, E. S. (1976) Life stress, depression and suicide. *Journal of Human Stress*, 2, 3–14.

RAAB, W. (1970) *Preventive Myocardiology: Fundamentals and Targets*. American Lecture Series, Springfield.

RAHE, R. H. (1975) Epidemiological studies of life change and illness. *International Journal of Psychiatry in Medicine*, 6, 133–46.

SIMPSON, M. T., OLEWINE, D. A., JENKINS, C. D., RAMSEY, F. H., ZYZANSKI, S. J. THOMAS, G. and HAMES, C. G. (1974) Exercise-induced catecholamines and platelet aggregation in the coronary-prone behaviour pattern. *Psychosomatic Medicine*, 36, 467–87.

SINGER, J. E., LUNDBERG, U., and FRANKENHAEUSER, M. (1978) Stress on the train: A study of urban commuting. In *Advances in Environmental Research* (in press.)

THEORELL, T. (1978) Phylogenetically old psychophysiological reaction patterns in relation to poor health. This volume, pp. 267–277.

TOFFLER, A. (1970) *Future Shock*. Random House, New York.

WARD, I. (1974) Sexual behaviour differentation: prenatal hormonal and environmental control. In *Sex Differences in Behaviour* (eds. R. Friedman, R. Richart and R. Vande Wiele). Wiley, New York.

AUTHOR INDEX

SUBJECT INDEX